TECHNICAL WRITING

Purpose, Process, and Form

TECHNICAL WRITING

Purpose, Process, and Form

Thomas L. Warren
Oklahoma State University

Wadsworth Publishing Company
Belmont, California
A Division of Wadsworth, Inc.

English Editor: Cedric W. Crocker
Production: Del Mar Associates
Designer: John Odam
Copy Editor: Jackie Estrada
Technical Illustrators: Kim Fraley, Pam Posey
Cover: John Odam

Printed in the United States of America

1 2 3 4 5 6 7 8 9 10—89 88 87 86 85

ISBN 0-534-04155-8

Library of Congress Cataloging in Publication Data

Warren, Thomas L.
    Technical writing: purpose, process, and form

    Includes index.
    1. English language—Rhetoric.   2. English language—
Technical English.   3. Technical writing.   I. Title.
PE1475.W25   1985   808'.0666   84-11819
ISBN 0-534-04155-8

In writing this book I have had one audience in mind: students who are training for a career that calls for technical proficiency. Because you are taking a course in technical writing, I assume that you are one of those students. You may be training for a career in engineering, nursing, biology, accounting, business, medicine, or some other technical area. Or you may be preparing for one of the countless new specialties that arise every day in a society animated by technological innovation.

I assume further that the training you are getting in your other college courses will prepare you to master the technical demands of the career you have chosen. By the time you leave college, you will be superbly equipped to take your place among fellow professionals.

To achieve real success in your career, however, you must be able *to communicate what you know*. You must be able to use your technical knowledge to explore a problem and suggest ways of solving it. You must be able to assemble information, analyze it, and report your findings in a manner that will lead to more efficient procedures, better ways of doing things. My aim in this book is to help you do just that.

Throughout this book, I urge you to ask yourself two questions whenever you set out to communicate technical information in writing:

1.   What does my reader need to know?
2.   How can I help my reader to understand what I write?

Those questions appear in various guises in every chapter of the book. Ultimately, their answers lie in theories of communication, cognition, and information. This book is not about those theories, however. It is about how to communicate technical information effectively and efficiently.

You will find very little in the chapters ahead about outlines and formats. But you will find a great deal about the *process* of generating reports and other forms of technical writing. That process begins with an analysis of your reader and ends only with the preparation and submission of your final report.

The organization of the book parallels the actual steps you will follow in preparing a report. The first three chapters—on communication, style, and the writing process—provide a context for the chapters to come. Then you will move through the steps themselves: analyzing the problem, making a proposal, collecting data, organizing data, and writing the report. At every stage, I invite you to *perform* the steps you are reading about. One of the best ways to learn a new skill is to practice it.

The last four chapters—on other reporting forms, oral presentations, correspondence, and the use of visuals—will round out your skills as an accomplished communicator of technical information.

Your other courses have made you aware of the central role of process in technical performance. I hope this book will give you an awareness of the central role of process in communicating what you know.

any people have helped me make this book by contributing suggestions, encouragement, and patience. My experience in teaching and writing about technical writing has brought me into contact with a remarkable group of people at my own university and at other universities and colleges. They have been extraordinarily generous in sharing what they know. Others, from business, industry, and government, have told me about their experiences—good and bad—in the writing they have done. My special thanks go to Jim Anderson, a friend of long standing who helped me through my first efforts at teaching technical writing almost twenty years ago; to Don Cunningham, who opened his store of information and the pages of *The Technical Writing Teacher* to me; to Tom Pearsall, who encouraged me at every step; to John Walter and Herman Estrin, who were willing to take a neophyte teacher under their aegis; and to the many others whose ideas and conversations have helped shape this book. Among my good friends in business, industry, and government are Gerald Cohen, at IBM; Dick Wiegand, of the Sunstrand Corporation; Dan Hausher, with the Tulsa Army Corps of Engineers; and Lionel Howard, at Bell Labs.

Getting the book into print required monumental efforts on the part of some exceptional people: John Block led me to the wise decision to publish with Wadsworth; Kevin Howat, a splendid editor who sometimes lavished praise and sometimes withheld it, always judiciously, supported the project for more years than either of us will admit; Everett Sims made certain that the style and content made readable and intellectual good sense; Louise Thomas typed and typed and typed without question or hesitation; and the production group at Del Mar Associates put it all together.

Among the reviewers who helped shape the book through their incisive criticisms and useful suggestions are Dorothy Bankston, Louisiana State University; Don Richard Cox, The

University of Tennessee; Ruth E. Falor, The Ohio State University; Pamela Miller, Pennsylvania State University; Jack Selzer, Pennsylvania State University; Douglas Smith, California Polytechnic State University, San Luis Obispo; and Thomas Spaulding Willard, The University of Arizona.

Finally, a special friend, whose warmth and understanding made this experience one that I will never forget, needs more than words of thanks for what she has given. Marylee, my wife, knows and will always know the debt I owe her no matter what I say here.

Contents

TECHNICAL WRITING

Purpose, Process, and Form

1

The Communication Situation

All through your time in college, instructors have been asking you to tell them what you have learned in your classes. They ask you to demonstrate what you know by answering questions on tests, or they ask you to share information through oral or written reports. The purpose of these communications—for that is what they are—is twofold:

1. To demonstrate what you know to persons who can verify your work (usually, your instructors).
2. To provide information to persons who do not have it (usually, your classmates).

In collecting, analyzing, and organizing information for either purpose, you follow the same basic process.

Later on, when you are working at a job, your supervisors will ask you to provide information about your work because they need to know what you are doing. They may want to review your performance, or they may need certain information that only you possess. In a job situation, however, you cannot assume that your readers will check the correctness of your information (as your instructor does), and you must realize that they may pass your information along to others.

In most organizations your rate of advancement will be directly affected by your ability to keep others informed about your work. Table 1-1 indicates the great value companies place on the ability of their employees to write and talk to others both inside and outside the organization. Notice that skill in communicating information is essential whether you intend to be an engineer or a salesperson. Each of these companies hires people for a wide range of specialized activities. The company specializing in engine research and manufacture, for example, hires specialists in data processing, marketing, accounting, economics, advertising, publications, and photography as well as engineers in agricultural, chemical, mechanical, and electrical

Table 1-1. On-the-Job Communication Skills

Company's Product/Service	Communication Skills Identified by the Company
Aluminum products	Written and oral skills; "may be good technician but if one can't communicate, won't move up to supervisor/management job." Communication ability criterion for hiring.
Hospital and medical products	Reports presented orally and in writing.
Engine research and manufacture, replacement parts (multinational corporation)	Business writing, speech writing, proposals; 90 percent of time communicating. Assume entry person can express self; "writing is the image."
Public utility	Engineers do not know how to communicate. More spelling and technical writing needed. Top management meet younger employees through communication/report situations.
Agricultural and industrial equipment	Engineers need technical writing for lab reports and evaluations. Knowledge of graphic arts and visual aids. All must organize thoughts in formal, logical manner using proper tenses, third person, basic sentence structure—in language of the reader.
Various kinds of controls and valves	Write reports, proposals, entire story of the product. (50 percent have engineering degrees or experience in engineering and technical writing.) Ability to communicate a criterion for promotion.
Chemicals, fibers, films, industrial equipment, agricultural supplies (diversified industrial company)	Communication skills a recommended additional course; basic writing; lots of written and oral reports to management; need to communicate clearly, concisely, and completely.
Communication equipment, electronics, consumer products	"Moving up the ladder of success depends on communication skills."
Food processing and wholesaling	Desire to do well at a job and ability to communicate well with the customers and co-workers are the most important attributes of job candidates.
Corn products and starches, puddings, syrups, juices	For salespersons: "Trip reports, capital expenditures submitted on paper. Need communication skills for written and oral competency."
Insurance	"All must write well, salesmen need more speech." Entry level jobs: memos/letter writing, claims, policyholder complaints. Supervisors need oral skills and report writing.

Table 1-1. (continued)

Company's Product/Service	Communication Skills Identified by the Company
Insurance	*"The level of communication is very low." Individual with communication ability can go far. "Communication skills really pay off."*
Machine tools, precision parts	*"Sell self through writing and speech. Require speech and technical writing." For management: reports, memos, and letters.*
Alloys, metals, batteries, electronic products, chemicals	*"Clear, logical, concise, to-the-point communication in a form the receiver can understand is necessary. Word choice important. Adapt to audience."*

Source: *Adapted from Lilian O. Feinberg, et al.* Communication Placement Research Project. Information to Help Iowa State University Students Find Employment. *Ames, IA: ISU Research Foundation, Inc., 1975.*

specialties. In every case, the company stresses that "writing is the image."

Right now, in this course and in other courses, you have an opportunity to practice and develop your communication skills. Even though you will seldom be supplying new information to your instructors (who usually know the answers), you can strengthen your skills in identifying a problem, devising a method to investigate and solve it, applying that method, and reporting your results.

The purpose of this book is to help you communicate better while you are in college and later on, when you have a job. This first chapter introduces you to the subject of communication—its definition, application, formats—and to the writing process. Later chapters will treat the various steps in the process that you will normally follow when you communicate information: analyzing the assignment, clarifying the problem, developing a proposal, collecting and organizing data, and writing and revising the report.

Defining Communication

Assume that I have some information you want. I can convey that information to you in writing or orally. That, basically, is what communication is. Figure 1-1 shows one possible model for the process in a simplified diagram. The diagram is itself a form of communication (a visual aid) that enables me to transfer information to you. Notice that the model shows the mes-

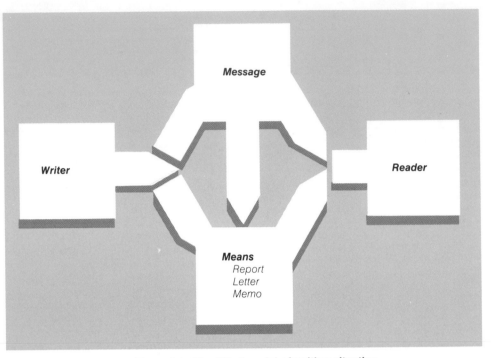

Figure 1-1. Simplified model of writing situation.

sage moving undisturbed and undistorted from the writer to the reader. If that were always the case, we would never have to worry that readers might misunderstand the message. But people do sometimes misunderstand what we write—no matter how hard we try to be clear. How does that misunderstanding come about?

Using what you have just read as an example, can you

1. paraphrase or summarize the information about communication?
2. agree that learning to communicate effectively is essential to job advancement because organizations believe it to be vital?
3. decide that you need to improve your communication skills?
4. outline a program to improve your communication skills?
5. carefully consider (at both the intellectual and the emotional level) the importance of communication skills based on the points above and *not* on a prejudice against working on your communication skills, or on what you think I am saying?

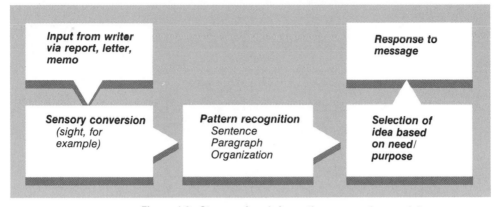

Figure 1-2. Stages of an information-processing model.
Source: Adapted from Stephen K. Reed, Cognition: Theory and Applications (Monterey, CA: Brooks/Cole Publishing Company, 1982), p. 4.

The answers to these questions suggest how well you have understood the preceding section, because the questions are arranged in order of increasing complexity.

The reader's understanding depends on two factors: how much the reader needs to know (for whatever reason) and how well the writer provides the reader with the needed information. When you misunderstand something I am trying to communicate to you, the failure is more likely to be mine than yours. I might be failing to identify your true needs, or failing to formulate the message in a manner that you can understand.

Understanding is a complex process. The reader must receive the signal (the message), transform it so that the mind can process it, recognize patterns in the message, select elements of importance, check the content, and finally respond to the message. Figure 1-2 shows this process in simplified form. Assume that you are the reader of a report. The signal enters your awareness through the sense of vision, where it is stored for a very short time (¼ second) before moving on. Presumably, you need certain information and you expect to find it in a certain form (a sentence, a paragraph, a section of the report, or in some visual form). As you scan the signal, you filter out everything that does not appear in the form you expect; if you expect the information to be presented in sentence or paragraph form, you ignore the visuals. (If you did not filter out material that is irrelevant to your need for particular information, your mind would have to process an enormous amount of superfluous information.)

Once you have filtered the material and recognized those patterns that coincide with your need, you select those items you want to understand and respond to. At this point, your mind begins to process the signal. First, it checks the signal against short-term memory. If you can understand the signal at this stage, you respond. If you cannot understand it, your mind checks it against long-term memory. If that does not lead to understanding, your mind responds by prompting you to ask questions, to seek clarification.

Consider the following memo:

Date: March 22, 1984

To: R. Johnson

From: T. Mattson

Subject: Progress Report Meeting March 21, 1984

John and Paul attended the Progress Report Meeting representing you. He read your report.

Who read your report? You cannot tell from reading the memo. Because you know that Paul is always afraid to speak before a group, you may infer that it was John who read your report. That information comes from your long-term memory, and only by drawing on it can you understand what the memo says. Or you might know that John had a bad cold and had lost his voice that day, indicating that Paul probably read the report. In any case, you are obliged to supplement the memo in some fashion before you can understand it.

The point is that when we read, a complex process goes on in our minds that enables us to understand and respond. A similar process takes place in reverse order when we set about generating a message. We have information that we want to communicate, and we put it into a form that readers can understand.

In any communication situation, however, something always seems to get in the way, causing problems and impairing understanding. The writer may use words that are unfamiliar to the reader, or the reader may be distracted and thinking of something else. Communication specialists have borrowed a term from the physical sciences—*entropy*—to describe such impediments to understanding. In communication theory, entropy is any factor that diminishes the effectiveness of communication. Entropy may arise for any number of reasons:

The writer may choose words that inaccurately represent the ideas being expressed.

The reader may not be familiar with the words being used (or may associate them with other contexts).

The medium itself may be faulty (blurred printing, for example).

The writer may commit mechanical or grammatical errors that obscure the meaning.

Because entropy disrupts the system and prevents the writer from transferring the idea, the reader must give the writer a signal of some kind. If the writer and reader are together, that signal could be a question, a puzzled look, a head shake, or some other sign indicating a breakdown in communication. If they are not together, the signal could be a phone call or a memo. This process is *feedback*. Feedback tells the writer to modify the message or the means, or to provide supplemental information to help the reader understand.

Technical Communication

Technical communication differs somewhat from other forms of communication. You have probably taken a course in composition in which you wrote themes to show that you knew how to use sentences and paragraphs, proper grammar, and the mechanics of writing. And you have demonstrated your command of course content by summarizing it in papers and on examinations. In a sense, the purpose of such writing is social; it is intended mainly to elicit a good grade from your reader—namely, the instructor.

But when you take a job, you will be developing information on your own and you will be transmitting it to a reader who has a genuine need for it and who will take action in response to what you are communicating. Your reader will use that information for specific purposes—to approve or disapprove what you are doing, to decide what action to take, or to learn what you are doing in your job. The purpose of communicating technical information is practical rather than social.

In communicating technical information you will use special forms for particular purposes. For example, when you are bringing someone up to date on a project that you are responsible for, you will use a progress report; when you are setting down the results of an experiment, you will use a laboratory or research report; when you are providing background information on a particular topic, you will use an informational report; and when you are trying to persuade the reader to do something, you will use a proposal or a feasibility report.

Whatever the form you choose for your particular purpose, you can strengthen your report through the skillful handling of a wide range of special devices or techniques. For example, you might decide to use visuals—such as drawings, charts, and schematics—to clarify statistical data and complex concepts. You might devise an orderly system of headings and subheadings to help your reader turn swiftly to those sections of greatest interest. You might highlight discrete pieces of information by setting them down in numbered lists. And you can demonstrate your ingenuity—thereby adding credibility and strength to your report—by devising techniques that are uniquely appropriate to your communication.

Technical communication, in short, is the process of transferring technical information from someone who has it to someone who needs it through the use of special forms and techniques designed to enhance the reader's comprehension of and response to that information.

Effective Communication

Effective communication is communication that produces the results you want it to produce. On the job you get quick evidence of whether your communication has been effective: Has the part been delivered? Has a decision been made? Has a change been ordered? When you write a letter applying for a job, you will know that your letter is effective if you get the interview you have requested.

In your area of expertise, you are careful to run and record experiments, to perform mathematic calculations, and to collect and analyze data. Are you equally careful in preparing your written communications? Remember that your readers will make a judgment about your ability to do technical work on the basis of the care you exhibit in handling such matters as spelling, punctuation, sentence and paragraph development, organization, and all the elements *other* than the surface meaning of the words you use. If, your readers may conclude, you are careless in the way you convey technical information, might you not be equally careless in collecting and analyzing technical data? Remember that readers respond to how well you express yourself as well as to the literal content of your communication.

Compare the two letters of application in Figures 1-3 and 1-4 for effectiveness. Which writer would you hire? Which writer would be equally accurate in the laboratory and in reports?

Your promotions and raises will depend heavily on your ability to communicate, because supervisors have little to use to evaluate you other than your written communications. (Refer again to Table 1-1, especially the comments by the public utility company.) You need to develop your skills in communicating technical information just as vigorously as you develop

211 Dunn House
Oklahoma State University
Stillwater, OK 74078
February 10, 1984

Mr. George Price
Personnel Department
Johnson Rifle Company
1500 Highway 177
Blown Rock, UT 85101

Dear Mr. Price:

I read in the Stillwater News-Press that your company is
expanding operations and needs engineers for your Research and
Development Department. I believe my background and experience
qualify me for this position. Please consider this letter as a formal
application for a position with your company as a research and
development engineer.

I expect to complete my schooling at Oklahoma State University
in May 1984. I will have a B.S. degree in engineering with an
emphasis in metallurgy. During this current school year I have
worked with Dr. Warren Blakey in experiments designed to produce
a lighter and stronger alloy for use in automobile engines. Since
many of the same stresses and pressures are exerted against a rifle
barrel as are found in an automobile engine, the work with Dr.
Blakey should prove valuable should Johnson's want to develop
new alloys. I have enclosed a data sheet that shows in more detail
my background and experiences.

I believe that I can be an asset to Johnson's and would very much
like an interview to discuss the matter further. Our spring break
will be April 1-8 this year and I will be happy to come to Blown
Rock for an interview. If you have any questions, please feel free to
call me collect at (405) 555-2651 anytime after 3:00 p.m.

Sincerely,

Margaret Hamilton

Enclosure: Data Sheet

Figure 1-3. Application letter no. 1.

412 Willard Hall
Oklahoma State University
Stillwater, OK 74078
February 10, 1984

Mr. George Price
Manager, Johnson's Rifle Company
Blown Rock, UT 85101

Dear Mr. Price:

Your advertisement in the News-Press caught my eye. I am a
senior in Engineering majoring in metallurgy. I feel your company
offers the kind of challenge my training has prepared me for, and I
would like to work for you.

Dr. Blakey, of the Engineering Department, commended my work
for him in finding a new engine alloy that is lighter and stronger.
Such work will be useful if I get the job since there are parallels
with rifles.

Thank you for considering my letter, and feel free to call if you have
questions.

Sincerely,

Ruth Oliver

Figure 1-4. Application letter no. 2.

your technical skills. Some people assume that *how* you communicate is less important than *what* you communicate. Perhaps so, but your reader responds in some measure to you and to what you say from the way you say it. How much confidence would you place in a report explaining a price increase if you discovered that there was an error of 1%? Would you shrug it off as minor and unimportant because you know the general intent of the message? Probably not. What if you had spent six months working on a project only to title your report "Ten Most Affective Ways to Increase Profits"? Of course, your reader *knows* that you really mean "effective." Are you sure? Suppose the reader knows the difference between "affective" and "effective." What will the response be?

Effectiveness also depends on the way you *organize* the information you are communicating. Most readers can guess what a misspelled word means. And they can usually figure out what you meant to say even when you have used inappropriate punctuation. But a reader who is trying to puzzle out a poorly organized report wastes valuable time and may, in desperation, simply toss the report aside. The time required to comprehend and respond to a report is a key factor in the writing and reading of reports. Organizing a report by the skillful use of headings and subheadings, visuals, and listings serves to reduce reading time. And when you reduce reading time, you save your organization money, increase the effectiveness of your communication, and build a positive image in your reader's mind.

In summary, effective communication in technical writing satisfies several compelling needs:

1. Your need to report accurately and clearly the information you have developed.
2. Your need to reinforce the validity of your report by using correct spelling, punctuation, and grammar.
3. Your need to save your reader time by organizing your report effectively.

Technical Assignments

1. Have you decided on a career goal? If so, answer the following questions on the basis of what you now know about that career. If not, choose a career you have some interest in.
   a. What is the title of the first job I am likely to get?
   b. What duties will I perform?
   c. What communication skills will I need?
   Once you have answered these questions, consult one of the occupational references (such as *Dictionary of Occupational*

Titles, Occupational Index, or *Occupational Outlook Handbook*) and see how many communication skills it lists for the job. Determine which of the following duties you will be expected to perform: writing letters, talking to customers, writing reports to customers, reporting in writing or orally to a supervisor, talking on the telephone.

Frame your answers to these questions in the form of a report to your instructor. Make certain you understand the purpose of your report as well as the format your instructor wants you to use.

2. Talk with someone who hires, promotes, and supervises people who do the kind of work you want to do. Or talk with an executive in the business, industry, or governmental agency in which you would like to work. Ask how important effective communication would be in your being hired and promoted. What kinds of communicating do the employees do? Report to the class on what you learn.

3. Make a list of the written assignments you need to prepare for your classes. What form will they take? What will be the purpose of each one? Will anyone other than your instructor be reading or listening to them? Be sure to include the assignments for this class.

2

Style and the Reader

Whenever you write something, you follow a wide-ranging tradition that guides your grammar and spelling. Traditional grammar provides the guidelines for putting words together to form sentences and paragraphs. Spelling rules tell you what letters go in what sequence to form the words. If those were all the traditions to be observed, writing would not be difficult: you would simply follow the "rules" and prepare the material. Another tradition that influences your writing is generally called *style*. It has to do with the way you say something in your writing. Compare two sentences or paragraphs that discuss the same thing and note the difference in style. Or compare the writing of someone like Lewis Thomas or Loren Eisley with the material that you read in your local newspaper. The difference lies in writing style.

The tradition of grammar and spelling is codified in grammar handbooks and dictionaries. The tradition of style is not codified, since it involves choice. You could say "Make a decision" or "Decide" and mean the same thing. Both are correct in grammatical structure and spelling, yet they are different. That difference is style. Style is decision making. This chapter introduces you to the notion of style and prepares you to make decisions about your own style. It also introduces you to the concept of reader analysis.

Writing Style

Your writing style must be appropriate to the situation or the occasion, the content, and, most important, the reader. What is the occasion for your report? Is it a formal report organized according to company requirements? Is it an informal report in memo or letter form? Or is it an article intended for publication in a professional journal in your field? Whatever the occasion, you must choose a style that will be appropriate. To write a memo in a highly formal style or to write a report for the vice president in a chatty, informal style would clearly be inappropriate.

What is the content of your report? Does it contain complex research findings presented to support a major recommendation? Does it contain matter of high seriousness, requiring the restrained use of language? Or is it a more or less casual response to a relatively unimportant request from your supervisor? The content of your report has a direct bearing on the style you choose.

The reader, however, is the most significant influence on the style you select. What are the reader's expectations? Does the reader have limited capacity to process the information you are presenting? For example, what is the reader's educational background? Knowing as much as you can about your reader enables you to select an appropriate style and make your report comprehensible.

Elements of Style

Selecting an appropriate style is the writer's responsibility, just as selecting appropriate tests is the engineer's responsibility. The style you choose reflects your understanding of the occasion, the content, and the reader. No single style is appropriate to every communication situation.

Choosing a style for a report presents the writer with quite a different problem from choosing a style for an article intended for a general audience. In making stylistic decisions, the report writer is more directly influenced by the assumed reader than is the article writer. Imagine a formal report on computer applications to accounting as compared with an article in a popular news magazine on the same subject. The report writer will direct the report to a specific reader or readers within the organization, choosing a style that is appropriate to that readership. The writer of the news article will write in a different style that will be appropriate to a broader, more general audience. True, the major news magazines conduct elaborate analyses of their readers to determine their buying and reading habits. But, given the diversity of those readers—in interests, educational background, and economic status—the writer of the article cannot write for a specific reader. The writer of the report, on the other hand, knows with certainty who will be reading the report and can adapt his or her writing style to that particular audience.

In tailoring material to a particular audience, the writer controls three principal elements of style: organization, sentence structure (syntax), and word choice (diction).

ORGANIZATION There are no set rules to guide you in organizing a given report. What you choose to present first, second, and last depends on the decisions you make on the basis of your knowledge of the purpose of the report, the assumed reader, and, in some cases, the style manual issued by the company you are working for. If your sole purpose is to communicate information to the reader, with no expectation of a specific response, you will organize your report in a way that will convey that information logically and intelligibly. If your purpose is to persuade the reader to accept certain recommendations, you will organize your report in a way that will make the logic of your reasoning compelling and convincing. If your purpose is to propose a change in operating procedures, to explore the feasibility of a course of action, or to report progress on a project, you will organize your report in a way that will satisfy your purpose and produce the results you are seeking.

Your choice of organization is a stylistic decision. It affects the development of the report; the transitions you introduce between sentences, paragraphs, and sections; your sequencing of the material in either an inductive or a deductive pattern; and your choice and placement of visuals.

SENTENCE STRUCTURE (SYNTAX) The words that make up a sentence achieve meaning through the manner in which they are arranged. At the very least, sentences must conform to the rules of grammar. Subjects and verbs must agree; pronouns must have clear antecedents; introductory phrases and clauses must be clearly attached to the elements they relate to; and verb forms must reflect the action intended. Whether you place a phrase or a clause first or last in a sentence is a stylistic decision, as is your choice of a passive-voice verb or an active-voice verb. You may choose short, simple sentences or more complex sentences that contain multiple clauses and phrases.

In making such decisions, you must be mindful of your reader's need for information and his or her capacity for processing that information. Burying a major point in the middle of a sentence forces the reader to keep a number of other points in mind while reading and may obscure the point. Any structure that requires the reader to puzzle out the relationship among the components of a sentence is likely to kill interest and induce fatigue. An effective way to keep reader interest high is to vary the structure of your sentences from time to time, alternating short sentences with longer, more complex sentences.

WORD CHOICE (DICTION) As we read, the meaning of the individual words rises to the conscious mind, and the physical appearance of the words on the page tends to disappear. Meaning builds as word follows word and as the structure of the sentence reveals their relationship. When we come across some lapse in the communication—a misspelled word, for example, or an ambiguous phrase—our attention is distracted from the meaning to the error. We pause momentarily in an effort to determine what the writer meant and then resume our reading. To avoid such distractions, the skillful writer chooses words with precision and groups them in a way that cannot possibly arouse uncertainty in the mind of an attentive reader.

The English language provides an extraordinary range of choice in selecting words for any conceivable purpose. By expanding your familiarity with words in general and with those terms that are peculiar to your specialty, you will increase your power to choose just those words that convey your meaning precisely. But you must have some assurance that the words you choose will be comprehensible to your reader. The sudden appearance of an unfamiliar term, no matter how accurately it embodies your meaning, will distract your reader's attention and impair communication. Using standard terminology and introducing definitions whenever you feel they are needed will strengthen the reader's confidence and will heighten the credibility of your report.

Intangible Elements of Style

Fortunately, the principal elements of style—organization, sentence structure, and word choice—are readily identifiable. You can learn to control them through diligent attention and steady practice. Other elements, however, are more elusive and require persistent attention on the part of writers, even writers with long experience. These intangible elements of style include tone, coherence, and rhythm.

TONE Whenever you write a report, you reveal an attitude toward the report itself and toward your reader. That attitude comes through in the tone of your writing. If you are bored by the assignment or indifferent toward the content or the reader, you may betray that attitude through carelessness in your handling of organization, sentence structure, or word choice. By dwelling on details that your reader is already familiar with, your tone suggests that you are talking down to your reader. If you fail to provide enough detail, you may seem to be talking over the reader's head. In countless inadvertent ways—by using overly simple words in writing for a sophisticated reader, or by hinting that you regard the whole exercise as trivial—you may suggest that you are in some way superior to your reader.

The tone you are conveying may not be apparent to you as you write, but your reader will sense it in reading the report. In order to elicit the response you are seeking, treat both the subject and the reader seriously and professionally. Remember that the reader of a technical report is in a sense your guest, and guests are free to depart whenever they choose. A pressing need for the information you are conveying may dissuade even a reluctant reader from discarding your report, but that reader's willingness to accept your recommendations or conclusions may be severely affected by an unfortunate tone throughout the report.

COHERENCE For a report to communicate effectively, the sentences, paragraphs, and sections that make it up must hang together coherently. Include sturdy bridges to provide transitions from one idea or subject to the next. Keep in mind the meaning you want to convey and the emphasis you want to achieve, and give your reader sure guidance through the report. Coherence establishes relationships, and relationships enhance meaning and enrich understanding.

RHYTHM In poetry, we can establish rhythm by ascribing stress to certain words and phrases. In prose, however, we lack metrical devices for imposing rhythm on our writing. We must rely instead on conveying a sense of progression to the reader from sentence to sentence, paragraph to paragraph. An awkward modifier or a misplaced clause will disrupt that progression and produce a sense of disjuncture. A sentence that runs smoothly without interruptions carries the reader along at a measured, predictable pace. Readers of technical reports, who are interested in gaining information as quickly and as accurately as possible, are distracted by self-conscious attempts to vary rhythm and resent anything that draws their attention away from the meaning of the prose. A style that calls attention to itself prompts the reader to measure the value of the information against the effort required to acquire it. By all means, vary the rhythm of your prose through an occasional shift in sentence structure, but avoid artful strivings for effect. Your readers will admire you more for skillful presentation of information than they will for rhythmic variety.

Analyzing Style

The following paragraph is from a memo describing an administrative plan for the use of a word-processing workstation. The notes at the end suggest some of the stylistic problems:

The resultant plan is one where efficiency is gained through the system, regardless of the individuals involved. A writer will enter the workstation area and begin work on his draft almost immediately—

the only task he must perform is insert his document disc in the proper disc drive (the system disc is already inserted in the proper location). The writer's contact with the administrative system on a daily basis is minimal. The two restraints placed on him are signing in and out of the workstation area (mandatory), and obtaining a clean or additional disc from the administrator (if necessary). All other preparation tasks are completed for him. He doesn't even have to turn the machine on or off. Information is literally at his fingertips, because all standard material that he is allowed to use in his draft is captured on the library disc, which has been developed, inserted, and left active in the machine for him to use. And, through User Defined Keys (established in the administrative preparation stage by system planners), the writer can use one of the nine keys to perform most of the production functions he'll need to prepare his draft for review or typing.

Notes:

1. Notice the sentence length. Of the eight sentences, three are 40 or 41 words long (2, 7, and 8). The last two sentences ask the reader to process 80 words that, in the original version, filled six and a half lines of single-spaced type. The shortest sentence (5) contains 8 words. The remaining three sentences contain 17, 13, and 11 words, respectively.

2. Of these eight sentences, four are simple in structure (3, 4, 5, and 6) and four are complex (1, 2, 7, and 8). Three of the four complex sentences are the longest, suggesting that the writer wants to make certain the reader understands complicated information. But is it all that complicated?

3. At times, the writer gives the impression of talking down to the reader—at least making the reader feel that the worker will have problems with the equipment (see sentences 3, 5, 6, and 7). Also note the use of "only" in sentence 2; this last clause appears to have been an afterthought, because it was tacked on at the end.

4. The assumed readers of this memo were named at the start of the memo and, presumably, were not the writers mentioned in the paragraph. The tone establishes a superior-inferior relationship between the readers of the memo and those mentioned as writers.

5. The paragraph achieves some measure of coherence by focusing on efficiency (see sentence 1). Each sentence does, in some measure, relate to that central point.

6. The writer of the memo achieves some variety, perhaps inadvertently, by varying the length of the sentences somewhat

and by using parenthetical insertions. Moreover, each sentence, except 8, declares at the outset what will be discussed in the sentence.

While the style may not be perfect, the writer has made a conscious effort to fit the style to both the situation (reader) and the topic.

Making Stylistic Decisions

We turn now to some actual examples of how decisions on stylistic matters influence the effectiveness of your writing. Consider the following sentence:

During the past few weeks, the experimental testing station was managed by a foreman.

By changing the verb from passive to active, we get this:

During the past few weeks, a foreman managed the experimental testing station.

By substituting specifics for generalities, we add to the information the sentence conveys:

During the past three weeks, a foreman managed the Weatherford Swine Testing Station.

At this point, we might assume that we have gone far enough. But have we considered which information the reader might consider *most* important? The sentence conveys two major pieces of information:

1. The time factor: during the past few [three] weeks.
2. What happened: a foreman managed the experimental [Weatherford Swine] testing station.

Which information should we emphasize? Is the reader more interested in knowing about the time or about the action? We can rewrite the sentence in several ways:

1. During the past few [three] weeks, a foreman managed the experimental [Weatherford Swine] testing station.
2. A foreman managed the experimental [Weatherford Swine] testing station and did so for the past few [three] weeks.
3. A foreman spent the past few [three] weeks managing the experimental [Weatherford Swine] testing station.

Notice how stylistic choices produce slightly different emphases. Through style, you can achieve an emphasis that is obvious or subtle. In an individual sentence, such as the one we have used as an example, the subtleties may be small and, in reality, insignificant. But you are not dealing with one sentence in a report. You write many sentences, and the cumulative effect of the emphases contributes to what the reader understands. In the testing station example, you can choose between emphasizing who or when. Once you decide and begin to write sentences to follow that decision, the other material you include must support your emphasis and carry it forward. Your decision depends on what information your reader needs most, as well as on your own perception of the relative importance of the information.

Consider another sentence:

The inventory was analyzed and found to be short in most of the key supply items.

Because no agent is specified here, it is difficult to substitute active verbs for the passive verbs. Still, introducing the subject "they" would serve the purpose. The ordering of the information presents some interesting possibilities. Do we state the method of accumulating data first and then report the results? Or vice versa?

They analyzed the inventory and found it to be short in most of the key supply items.

or

They found the inventory to be short in most of the key items when they analyzed it.

The first version would be appropriate to a report organized according to an inductive approach; the second suggests a deductive approach. Which approach would best suit your reader's needs? Some readers want to know your method of gathering data before considering the conclusions you base on those data. For them, the credibility of your conclusions rests on the data-gathering methods you followed. Other readers are more interested in the conclusions than in the methods. For them, the data serve only as support for your conclusions. Stylistic decisions of this sort reflect your view of how the reader will approach the report in its entirety.

Yet another stylistic decision is based on the attitude you wish to convey through a sentence. For example, here is a simple declarative statement:

Impurities in the solution are removed by use of sodium nitrites.

By substituting an active verb, you can transform the sentence into a command:

Use sodium nitrites to remove impurities in the solution.

Or, by introducing a new subject, you can make it strictly informative:

You can use sodium nitrites to remove impurities from the solution.

or

The worker can use sodium nitrites to remove impurities from the solution.

Every word in a sentence functions in a structural way: subject, verb, modifier, conjunction. Words also convey information. The word "is" functions structurally in a sentence (as a linking verb) but conveys very little information itself (only a sense of time). The amount of information each word conveys depends on whether it is specific or general: "International Ball Point Pen Model 12" conveys very specific information; "device" conveys very general information. To derive meaning from words used primarily for structural purposes, the reader must process the complete structure:

The hat is red.

The = Adjective (article). Conveys some information ("the" is specific, rather than the general "*a*").

hat = Subject. Specific information (hat rather than coat).

is = Linking verb. Conveys limited meaning (additive; what comes after is added to what?).

red = Adjective. Conveys specific information (red rather than black).

Words that convey specific information require less processing by the reader than words that convey little or no information and that function only structurally. Put another way, words that convey little or no information force the reader to work harder.

The following sentence contains a number of words that convey little or no information:

1. *Unnecessarily wordy.*

2. *Redundant; means "for."*

3. *Empty phrase. Main subject follows.*

4. *Duplicates "all" later.*

5. *Unneeded prepositional phrase.*

 1   2
It is important that in order for the sales campaign to be successful,

 3   4   5
there is to be an all-around effort by all members of the sales team.

Revised, the sentence reads:

For the sales campaign to be successful, all sales team members must make a full effort.

Now we can decide which part of the sentence should come first: "For the sales campaign to be successful" or "All sales team members must make a full effort." Does the reader require more information about what we mean by *effort*? Does the sentence contain a controlling idea that we can build on in succeeding sentences?

Developing the Central Idea

As a general rule, try to begin each sentence with the central idea of the sentence. Consider the following sentences:

1. There are three factors that influence the selection of a personal computer: applications, costs, and available space.
2. Three factors influence the selection of a personal computer: applications, costs, and available space.

The second sentence, in addition to being three words shorter than the first, catches the reader's attention at the outset. A sentence that begins with the central idea conveys information more readily than a sentence that begins with a modifier or an empty phrase. A sentence that opens with "There" or "It" reveals structure but conveys no immediate information. What happens is that the reader cannot begin to comprehend the sentence until the word "factors" appears and signals the main idea of the sentence. In the second sentence, the immediate introduction of "factors" conveys information and prepares the reader to move on to the verb.

The verb "are" in the first sentence is a linking verb that carries no information by itself. By contrast, the verb "influence" in the second sentence is an active verb that conveys information and leads directly to the rest of the sentence.

The central idea of the sentence would have been buried even deeper had the writer written:

It is important to realize that there are three factors that will be influential in the personal computer decision-making process: applications, costs, and space availability.

Let's turn back to sentence 2 and use it as the basis of a logical development in response to the reader's needs:

Three factors influence the selection of a personal computer: applications, costs, and available space.

How can we develop the central idea of this sentence? We have several options:

1. Prove that the three factors actually exist.
2. Demonstrate that three and only three factors influence the selection.
3. Show that they really are influential "factors" rather than vaguely related "reasons."
4. Describe the decision-making process and show how the factors influence the decision.
5. Define personal computer.
6. Distinguish between the personal computer and other types—"mainframe" or "minicomputer," for example.
7. Expand on each of the factors: (a) define each, (b) give an example of each, (c) explain in what sense they act as "factors," and (d) explain why we have listed them in this order.

Whatever our decision, we would avoid introducing an altogether new and unrelated topic in the next sentence. Here is an example of a sentence that would *not* advance the logical development of our original sentence:

Personal computing offers many opportunities for a business to increase its services to its customers.

The Reader

To help your reader, you need to match your style to the reader's ability to understand. You'll need to know your reader's attitudes, skills, knowledge, and needs.

The Reader's Characteristics

Awareness of the reader's characteristics will enable you to choose the style and organization best suited to the purpose of the report. Those characteristics will help you to organize, plan, and write your report in a way that will enable your reader to understand it. The following sections describe some of the questions to ask yourself in identifying the reader's characteristics.

THE READER'S ATTITUDES What are the reader's attitudes about the subject? Is the reader aware of the problem that the report addresses? Does the reader agree that the problem needs to be solved? What is the reader's attitude toward you? Has any past experience led you to suspect that the reader is well disposed or ill disposed toward you? Do you have any evidence that the reader will endorse the kind of solution you are planning to propose? What is the reader's attitude toward your department? If you are addressing a reader outside the organization, what is that reader's attitude toward your organization?

Knowing your reader's attitudes will provide you with reliable guidance in deciding on the organization and the style of your report. By accommodating your report to those attitudes, you will enhance your own credibility and thereby increase the likelihood that the reader will accept your recommendations.

THE READER'S SKILLS What skills can you assume the reader possesses? What do you know about the reader's education and background? Does the reader have professional competence in the area of your report? If you are proposing that the reader take action of some sort, is the reader capable of taking that action? Does the reader have access to the resources that your recommendations require? At the most basic level, what reading skills does the reader possess?

Intimate knowledge of the reader's skills will influence the level of technical detail you include and the manner in which you present it. That knowledge will also help you decide on such matters as the level of vocabulary, the complexity of terms, and the nature of the visuals you include to support your presentation.

THE READER'S KNOWLEDGE How much does the reader already know about the subject? Does the reader have the necessary background to understand your report? How much knowledge can you take for granted, and how much background must you provide to ensure that the reader will comprehend the content of your report?

THE READER'S CRITICAL TASKS At the outset, formulate a clear idea of what responses you want the reader to make to your report:

1. *Recall.* Do you want the reader to recall all or part of your report later on? What sections in particular? Do you want it recalled in detail or in general? If you feel that the reader needs to recall only part of the report, you can reinforce that recall through the manner in which you organize your material. Readers tend to remember the first and last parts of what they read, whether it is a section of the report or the whole report. You can also strengthen recall by using language that the reader is familiar with and analogies drawn from your reader's specialty.

2. *Transfer.* Will the reader use the information you present in preparing a report for another reader? If so, what can you learn about that ultimate reader? Perhaps your information will be transferred from you (an accountant) to an engineer (your primary reader) to a comptroller. Knowing the likely uses to which your information will be put helps you make decisions on organization, style, and emphasis.

3. *Recognition.* Do you need to convince the reader that a problem actually exists? Does the reader need to recognize that the problem is related in some way to other problems in the organization, or that the problem can be solved by drawing on existing resources? Does the reader need to recognize the significance of a particular element of the report, such as the statement of the problem, your recommended solution, or the test results? Answers to these questions will help you both in organizing your report and in focusing the reader's attention on particular sections.

4. *Problem Solving.* Is the purpose of your report to provide information the reader needs to solve a problem? How does that information relate to the solution? How can you adjust the content of your report and the manner in which you present it to contribute to the solution of the problem? If, for example, the problem involves the selection of a microcomputer and a software system, you might present your recommendations immediately, along with any background information you feel the reader needs. You might then suggest the benefits that would accrue from following your recommendations. Your awareness of the problem-solving situation will guide you in choosing an appropriate style. If you know that the reader will be transferring your information to someone else in the organization, you can anticipate your reader's need for technical detail and for convincing arguments in support of your recommended course of action.

How the Material Relates to the Reader's Needs

Knowing how the material relates to the reader's needs will help you in organizing the report and in deciding on content. The reader's ability to comprehend technical detail will suggest how complex your presentation should be, what definitions and explanations to include, and what visuals to incorporate.

CONCEPTUAL DIFFICULTY What level of complexity will the reader be comfortable with? Does the reader have sufficient technical expertise, background, and experience to handle the concepts you are presenting? Should you include definitions, visuals, analogies, and applications to adjust the conceptual level of your report to the reader's level of technical understanding? What background must you provide to prepare the reader for the more technical sections? Should you include a glossary of technical terms?

In addition to vocabulary, consider the concepts that lie behind the methods you used to gather and analyze your data, and take into account the reader's ability to make conceptual associations between your data and possible applications. Match your style to the conceptual complexity of your material. Remember that long sentences are not necessarily hard to understand and that short sentences are not necessarily easy to understand. Rather, it is the conceptual density of a sentence that determines its intelligibility.

SEQUENCE OF MATERIALS The best sequence of materials depends in part on the reader's ability to process information. What order will your reader accept as the most logical? Should you begin with your recommendations and then provide supporting details? If you are presenting several alternative recommendations, should you position the one you prefer at the beginning of the list, or at the end? If you decide to compare and contrast the alternatives, should you present the comparisons first and then the contrasts, or should you compare and contrast them item by item? Choose a sequence that you feel will best suit your reader's sense of logical development.

PSYCHOLOGICAL CONTEXT In presenting your material, try to engage your reader as a total person. Beyond the rational appeal of well-ordered and logically developed information, consider the impact your material may have on the reader's feelings and emotions. Be mindful of the connotations your language may elicit. Reading takes place in a psychological as well as a rational context, and to ignore the psychological impact of a report on the reader may jeopardize the acceptance of your recommendations.

YOUR EXPECTATIONS OF THE READER What response do you want from the reader? Do you expect the reader to supplement the information you are presenting with his or her own experience, background, or expertise? How much concentrated effort do you expect during the reading process? What you can reasonably expect from the reader will influence the demands you impose on the reader as you plan and develop your report.

Writing style and reader analysis are two concepts that you will hear more about later in this book. Both are of critical importance if you want your report to communicate information effectively. Being an effective writer means more than observing the rules of grammar and spelling. It demands an awareness of style and sensitivity to your reader's needs.

Technical Assignments

1. Locate two articles on the same topic in your technical area. One article should be written for readers who know a lot about the subject; the second should be written for readers who know little about the subject. Answer the following questions for both articles:
   a. What is the purpose of the article—why was it written?
   b. Does the article contain definitions of technical terms? List the terms.
   c. Make a brief outline of the major topics in each article. How does the organization differ? How is it similar?
   d. Do you notice any differences in the sentences? Are they longer in one article than in the other? Shorter?
   e. What differences and similarities do you find in style and in the writers' understanding of their readers?

2. Revise the following sentences in accordance with the context:
   a. Context: A progress report on a research project designed to measure air turbulence (reader: project manager).

      Sentence: Flow visualization of the turbulent flow is under investigation at the present time.
   b. Context: Final report to an accountant on a personal computer for the firm's use.

      Sentence: The conclusion drawn from the study allows a recommendation to be made on the most suitable personal computer for the firm.
   c. Context: Beginning of a report on automating a letter-writing operation (reader: head of a student recruiting office).

      Sentence: The purpose of this study is to determine the feasibility of converting the current prospective student correspondence system to a word-processing system.
   d. Context: Report to supervisor proposing a change in the present way the office develops programs.

      Sentence: If done in a logical way, program development may prevent problems that were never imagined.
   e. Context: Progress report to a supervisor.

Sentences: The research and plan for the collection of more plant-wide condensate for use in boilers is completed. The system's last update was completed in June 1983; therefore, it was necessary to perform a plant-wide survey and draw flowsheets of the existing steam condensate system.

3. Select a paragraph from an article in a technical journal in your field, and suggest ways to change it so that the style reflects the reader's ability to understand. Be aware of the reader's attitudes, skills, knowledge, and critical tasks. Be prepared to justify your revision based on those factors.

4. In a recent issue of *Reader's Digest,* locate an article on a technical, scientific, or business subject. Search out the publication the article was based on. Then complete the following:

   a. Give the complete title, author, and source for each article.
   b. Give the number of pages of each.
   c. Describe the assumed readers of each.
   d. Analyze the style of each article in the following manner:
      1) Figure out the total number of words (count the number of words in three lines, divide by three, then multiply by the number of lines in the article).
      2) Determine the average sentence length (divide the number of words by the number of sentences).
      3) Determine the average paragraph length (divide the number of words by the number of paragraphs).
      4) Measure readability by using the Gunning Fog Index: $(X+Y) \times (0.4)$, where X is the average number of words per sentence in a 100-word sample, and Y is the number of three-syllable words in the sample (exclude nouns usually capitalized, combinations of short words, such as bookkeeper, and verbs made into three syllables by adding -*ed* or -*es*). The Fog Index is the approximate number of years of formal schooling required to read the passage comfortably.
      5) Note the frequency of definitions.
      6) Note the frequency of technical terms.
      7) Judge the sophistication and complexity of the visuals.
   e. What is each author's main concern?
   f. Which article contains more technical detail? Why? (Relate to style, reader, purpose.)
   g. How much background information does each author give the reader?
   h. Which article makes the greater use of direct quotations, footnotes, and bibliography?
   i. What conclusions can you draw about the influence of the assumed reader on the style of each article?

3

Before Writing

ommunication is the process of transferring information from someone who possesses it to someone who needs it. It moves the reader from a state of uncertainty to a state of certainty. In short, communication produces change. To effect that change, you must fully understand what task you are to do, how you can develop and analyze data, and how you can present those data for your reader. In this chapter we begin to examine that process.

The process of preparing a report begins with an assignment. That assignment may be routine (such as filing regular progress reports) or special (such as reporting the results of a unique test). An assignment usually means that you are being asked to solve a problem. You set about solving that problem by drawing on your technical training.

First, you analyze the problem to determine what data you will need to arrive at a solution. Using your technical skills, you then decide on a sequence of logical steps that will produce those data. Once you have the required information in hand, you analyze and organize it in a manner that will reveal the solution you have been seeking. Finally, you prepare a report and submit it to the supervisor who assigned the task.

The procedure you follow in preparing your report should be just as controlled, just as deliberate, as the procedure you follow in arriving at your solution. Figure 3-1 suggests such a procedure. The figure shows three loosely defined steps: analyzing, writing, and postwriting.* In analyzing, you assess the assignment and the situation; in writing, you prepare successive drafts of the report; and in postwriting, you and your supervisor evaluate the report. In this chapter we focus primarily on the first step.

Figure 3-1 shows four aspects to the analyzing stage:

---

*Based on the work done at the Document Design Center of the American Institute of Research, Washington, D.C.

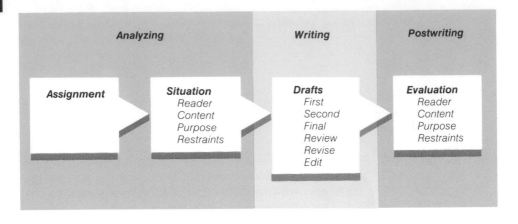

1. *Reader:* Who will your primary reader be?
2. *Content:* What information does that reader want?
3. *Purpose:* What is the purpose of your report?
4. *Restraints:* What limitations affect the assignment and the report?

The Reader

Ordinarily, the information you present in a report is not information that you need for your own purposes. It is your supervisor who needs it, perhaps in order to prepare another report for someone else. That means that you have to put yourself in your reader's place when you set about answering questions. Each report writer must be aware of and, at each stage, must make assumptions about the next reader in the chain.

So in this early stage you must concentrate on your reader's need for specific information. What does your reader want and need to know? Answer that question and you will have grasped the purpose of your report. We will consider the reader more fully in the next chapter.

Content

The content you supply in your report is the information your reader needs. Assessing that need accurately will guide you in deciding what to omit and what to include. Develop the content according to the procedures you customarily follow in your other courses.

Purpose and Function

Before you begin to collect data, establish a specific purpose: Why, ultimately, are you writing your report, and what do you want to happen as a result?

Purpose

If your report is to accomplish the purpose you have set, you must have a clear sense of that purpose from the beginning. Why is the report necessary? Why are you writing it?

If your purpose is to provide only information, you will probably decide to write memos, make phone calls, conduct interviews, or do some research in order to assemble that information and show its validity when you incorporate it into your report. If your purpose is to recommend change or suggest a course of action, you will have to marshal your data in a manner that will persuade your reader to accept your views. Once you have identified the specific purpose of your report, you can begin to gather the data you will need to prepare it.

Knowing the purpose of your report lends purpose to your data gathering by suggesting how much and what kind of data you will need. Your technical training will have prepared you to find, collect, and process the data that your purpose requires. Suppose your supervisor comes to you with a problem involving the poor condition of the company parking lot. It is full of holes and, it seems, is always being repaired. He asks, "How can we fix that parking lot and eliminate those holes?" Your first job is to analyze the assignment to make sure you understand what your supervisor wants you to do. Does the assignment give you any clues?

How—suggests a method or a procedure

Fix—suggests final goal

Parking lot—suggests the object

These clues help, but they are not enough in themselves. This assignment, like many assignments, is rather vague. So you will have to carry your analysis further:

How can we fix—suggests

1. It *can* be fixed.
2. "We" can do it or find out how to do it.

This is the sort of analysis you must undertake before you start working on the assignment. If you were to rush around talking to everyone you met about how to fix the lot, you would be wasting time gathering data you might have no need for. Instead, the sensible course of action would be to research the history of the lot, find out how many times it had been repaired before and how, determine how long those repairs lasted, identify the cause or causes of the problem, and so on.

To summarize, knowing the purpose of the report tells you not only the kind and amount of data you will need but the approach you must take to ensure that it accomplishes its purpose. If, despite rigorous analysis of the assignment, you cannot discover the purpose of your report, ask the supervisor who made the assignment.

Having determined your purpose, your next step is to establish the function of the report.

Function

Your supervisor may very well use the information you report as the basis for another report. Thus, the reporting function for one report writer becomes a data-gathering function for another. When you analyze an assignment, consider the use to which your report will be put—that is, the *function* of the report. Your supervisor may incorporate your report into another report, use it as an attachment to such a report, or just send it along with a new cover memo. The use to which your report will be put is pretty much beyond your control. But being aware of these possibilities will help you design your report in such a way that it will have the best chance to function as intended. *Purpose* is what you, the writer, know and can control; *function* is what happens to your report after it leaves you.

A report may have many functions (while having only one purpose), including some you may not be aware of as you prepare it. For example, from time to time you may have received letters that you were convinced were meant to harass you or to lecture, preach, or complain. Even though their declared intent may have been to transmit information, you saw them as having quite a different function: They didn't inform you; they *irritated* you.

When you write a report, realize that your reader may react in a way other than the way you intended. To guard against that possibility, fashion your report so that its specific purpose is unmistakable. State the purpose of your report: "The purpose of this report is to provide you with the information you need about XYZ, as you requested." Once the reader knows the purpose, you can influence the way the report func-

Table 3-1. Elements in a Report

How Report Functions To:	Language (words, tone)	Organi- zation	Content (current, complete)	Visuals	Layout	Logic
Inform	X	X	X			
Instruct	X	X	X	X	X	
Persuade	X	X				X
Request information	X				X	X
Propose	X	X	X			X

Source: *Adapted from* Simplifying Documents: A Workshop. *Washington, DC: American Institute of Research, 1979.*

tions by emphasizing various elements in it. If, for example, you believe the report will function to provide information only, you should pay special attention to the language you use, the organization, and the content. If you are requesting information, pay special attention to language and to the logic of your request. Table 3-1 shows how you can influence the function of the report through emphasizing certain elements.

LANGUAGE When you report information, you have three languages available to you: the language of words, the language of visuals, and the language of formulas. Each language is especially effective in one or more areas of communication. You must judge which language is most appropriate to your purpose.

When you use the language of words, your choice of words reflects the way you interpret your data. Most words carry at least two meanings: the *denotative* meaning, which is the meaning that most people ascribe to a word, and the *connotative* meaning, which is an associated meaning that changes from time to time, as in slang expressions.

In technical writing, it is wise to avoid words that have strong connotative meanings, especially if those meanings are negative. You may be revealing, perhaps inadvertently, your attitude toward the reader through your choice of words. Your use of the word "obviously," for example, may suggest that you regard the reader as uninformed: "Obvious as this statement is, I guess I'd better tell you what it means."

Be aware, too, that your handling of words reflects the way you think and the way you order your ideas. When you combine words into sentences, you should arrange them according to a logical sequence, as you would in framing a mathematical equation. If you are unsure of what you want to say, your sentences and paragraphs will confuse your reader and introduce entropy into the communication process. Strive to choose words that express your meaning precisely. In your own reading, how many times have you had to wrestle with words you could not understand—unfamiliar words, or familiar words used in unfamiliar ways, or new words coined for the occasion?

In short, remember that the words you choose communicate an attitude toward your reader, and that words used carelessly or imprecisely impair understanding. We will return to our discussion of language in a later chapter.

ORGANIZATION The way you organize your report has a direct influence on how effectively it communicates. If the information flows logically from point to point, with frequent clues to the organization along the way, your readers will have no trouble finding the information they need. A technical report is not a detective story in which the clues are artfully concealed, only to be paraded before the reader at the conclusion. To avoid bewildering your readers, reveal your organizational plan from the outset. In long reports, include a table of contents. In shorter reports, include a brief statement about how you have organized the material. Let your reader know what signposts to watch for while reading through the report.

The organization of a report reveals the rigor of your logic—or the lack of it. By reassuring the reader that you have marshaled your facts in logical order, you establish your credibility and have a better chance of convincing the reader to accept your point of view. We will discuss organization in greater detail in Chapters 7–9.

CONTENT The content of your report should, of course, be accurate, current, and complete. Timeliness and thoroughness require special attention. At times your reader will need extensive detail; at other times generalizations or overviews are more appropriate. Content works to support your assertions, proposals, and conclusions.

VISUALS Rendering information in visual form often makes it more readily intelligible to your reader. For example, when you are providing instructions for performing a certain activity, incorporating a flow chart will help your report function the way you intend it to. Be sure to make text references to all visuals and always discuss the visuals thoroughly in the text. Make your visuals as clear and unambiguous as the words you use. In Chapter 14 we will discuss techniques for developing effective visual presentations.

LAYOUT The way you arrange your material on the page—the layout of the report—has an immediate and direct effect on the reader. If you are setting down a series of instructions, for example, set them off from the rest of the text. If you are providing information, use numbered lists, perhaps with a symbol such as a bullet (•) before each number to give added emphasis to the items. Use extra spacing between paragraphs (double or triple) to signal to the reader that you are moving from one point to another. Avoid solid blocks of type by double spacing between paragraphs and by introducing frequent headings.

LOGIC In technical writing, as in all serious writing, your reader will expect you to follow a controlled, logical progression in the presentation of your material. In some reports, logical rigor is of particular importance. In a report designed to persuade your reader to take a certain course of action, for example, be sure to state your main point forcefully and to follow it up with supporting data that lead inescapably to the conclusion you desire. If you omit a single step in the development of your argument, the logical structure of your whole report will collapse. If you state personal opinions, identify them as such. Show that you are aware of opposing arguments and explain why your position is logically more compelling. In short, make certain that you

1. state your main point forcefully.
2. provide full supporting data.
3. lead the reader to an inescapable conclusion.
4. show that you are aware of opposing arguments.

Restraints

Every assignment has certain built-in limitations, either explicit or implicit. In the parking lot example, you would immediately recognize explicit and implicit elements that may be understood as assumptions or limitations:

Explicit.
1. Need to repair lot.

2. Holes exist.

3. Need a method to repair holes.

Implicit:
1. The holes are troublesome and dangerous.

2. The holes are wide and deep.

3. The lot can be repaired rather than completely resurfaced.

4. The problem is urgent.

5. You can recommend a solution to the problem.

These elements set the limits of the assignment, even though they may not be based on valid assumptions. If you have doubts about any of them, ask questions.

Other elements that set limits to the assignment are the desired length of the report, the type of report needed, and the amount of detail needed.

Length

Your supervisor may want a one-sentence report or a 100-page report, depending on his or her need for information. The desired length of the report and the reader's need for information serve as limitations in your analysis of the assignment. "Should we repair the holes?" suggests a short report, perhaps only "Yes, we should repair the holes because . . ." But "How can we repair the holes in the parking lot?" suggests that a more detailed, longer report is being requested. In short, the length of your report depends on your analysis of the assignment and of the reader's needs.

Types of Reports

The assignment can suggest the form and type of report you are to prepare:

A. Form
    1. Oral
    2. Written
       a. memo
       b. letter
       c. fill-in-the-blank form
       d. standard report

B. Type
    1. Informal or formal
    2. Proposal
    3. Feasibility
    4. Recommendation
    5. Other types

Both the form and type of report depend on how important the report is to your supervisor, his or her need to know, the way your reader will use the information, and what you decide the report's purpose is. Your employer's policy on internal communications will also influence your analysis of the assignment, as will the likelihood that your report will be circulated outside the organization. Each form and each type of report requires its own format and organization. In Chapter 11 we will discuss these matters in detail.

Amount of Detail   The amount of detail you include in a report depends on your estimate of the reader's need. The reader of your parking lot report, for example, may need to know as much as possible about the history of the problem, previous efforts at repair, various proposed solutions to the problem, and reasons for recommending one solution over others. As you analyze the assignment, estimate how much detail the reader is likely to need and on what topics (the surface strength of various paving materials, for example). An accurate estimate will tell you how much information you will need to incorporate in your report.

Other Restraints   A restraint, therefore, is any element, explicit or implicit, that sets limits on the performance of a task. In report writing, four restraints are common:

1. The purpose and the function of the report.
2. The reader's need for information beyond the scope of the report.
3. The review and distribution systems within the organization.
4. The lines of communication and responsibility in the organization.

Awareness of these four restraints will help you communicate the information your reader needs.

PURPOSE AND FUNCTION We have already discussed purpose and function, so this section will serve as a review. The *purpose* of a report is what you want that report to do. Some typical purposes are to inform, to recommend, to instruct, and to persuade. Every report should have a single, overall purpose that will help you in your planning.

The *function* of a report is the use the reader makes of the report, such as to become informed or to make a decision. Even when you establish a single purpose for a report, you may discover that the final report serves multiple functions. In analyzing the writing assignment, make certain you coordinate the purpose and the function of the report.

READER'S NEED FOR ADDITIONAL INFORMATION Occasionally, the reader of a report needs information that is too extensive or too complicated to be included in the report itself. In such cases, refer the reader to previous reports, articles, or reference books in which that information can be conveniently found. If you feel that the information must be included in your report despite its bulk, present it in an appendix, in an enclosure, or as a separate, supplementary report. In any case, notify the reader at the outset where the additional information can be found. If it accompanies your report, announce that fact on the title page or in the transmittal document. If the reader must consult reference works in order to find the information, provide full details on what those works are and where they are located.

REVIEW AND DISTRIBUTION SYSTEMS Every organization of any size has a chain of communication. When you submit a memo, letter, or report, you may be expected to send copies to various people throughout the organization who need to know what you are doing or who may need to take action in response to your information. How will those readers use your report? What is their need to know? You cannot write a report to fit all their needs, but you can be aware of them and, if necessary, add relevant material in an appendix. Others in the organization may need to review your report before it goes to someone inside or outside your organization. The more you know about those reviewers and their attitudes, the better you can prepare your report.

The review process (to be discussed later in this chapter) contributes to the restraints you experience when you analyze the assignment, select the content, and write the report. Familiarity with the review process enables you to plan systematic reviews as work progresses. For example, you might invite your supervisor to review the initial statement of the problem you are working on or even your preliminary outline of the report. If you are working on a major project, you might arrange to supplement your progress reports with oral reports in which you inform your supervisor of your progress on the technical phases of the project and on the main outlines of the report itself. Or you might ask the team that is reviewing your technical progress to review your report as it takes shape.

THE ORGANIZATIONAL SYSTEM A final restraint is imposed by the organization's policies governing the preparation and handling of reports. Some organizations issue their own style manuals setting forth standards and procedures to regularize the reporting process. Such manuals may cover only the most basic elements, such as how reports are to be organized, what headings and subheadings are to be used, and what types of reports are to be used for various purposes. Others go into greater detail, specifying grammar, punctuation, usage, even spelling. Style manuals range from a few pages to several hundred pages in length.

If your organization has a style manual of its own, you can consult it to determine how the organization wants its reports prepared. If not, you can turn to your reviewers for comments on your outline and early drafts.

Impact

After all the effort you spend analyzing an assignment, assembling information, and preparing a report, you have a right to expect that your report will have some impact on your readers, if not immediately then some time in the foreseeable future. In analyzing an assignment, try to make a realistic judgment of how strong that impact is likely to be and how you can measure it after submitting your report. The head of a large engineering section once discovered that the members of his staff knew they were doing a good job only if no one was yelling at them. The corollary in report writing seems to be that if a report is submitted and does not come back, it must have had a satisfactory impact. When you submit proposals, feasibility reports, or recommendations, the acceptance of your report is probably the best evidence that your report has had a satisfactory impact.

During your analysis of an assignment, knowledge of your organization's feedback channels and review process will help you judge the impact your report is likely to produce.

Feedback

By carefully analyzing an assignment at the outset, you can anticipate whether or not your report, once submitted, will prompt negative feedback. For example, how can you avoid imposing an unnecessary burden on the reader? If you make your report complete and comprehensive, your reader will have no need to consult other reports in order to supplement the information your report provides.

To engender positive feedback, try to accommodate every question your reader is likely to need an answer to. Appraise your reader's need to know and plan to satisfy that need as you analyze the assignment. Positive feedback comes in the form of compliments, praise, or acceptance.

Through careful analysis early on, you can eliminate or reduce the likelihood that your report will elicit negative feedback, and, more important, you can strengthen the likelihood that it will prompt positive feedback.

Review

A report of any consequence ordinarily goes through a review process in which someone reads and approves the report before passing it along. Your parking lot report would probably go to your supervisor, who would review it before incorporating the information into another report that would go to another supervisor for review and incorporation.

The main purpose of a review is to check for accuracy of content. In a sense, you yourself conduct the first review even before submitting a report. After all, the validity of your conclusions or recommendations depends on the accuracy of the report's content and affects your credibility as a professional.

Many reviewers look for other qualities beyond the accuracy of content. In one organization, for example, reviewers evaluate a report's organization, clarity, internal consistency, consistency with the organization's policies, relevance to the assignment, and writing style.

Review usually occurs at each level in the communication chain. In the organization mentioned above, the immediate supervisors are responsible for review. As a report moves up through the organization, the reviews grow less detailed, but they continue to concentrate on the accuracy of content and the validity of conclusions or recommendations. At every level of review, one concern is paramount: Is the report constructive? That is, even if it conveys negative findings, does it offer some positive response to those findings? If the report is critical, are the criticisms explicit, thoughtful, and well supported?

In your early analysis of an assignment, always be mindful of the review process that is followed by the organization in which you are working. Ask yourself these questions:

1. Who will make the reviews? What is their position in the communication chain?
2. When will the review process begin?
3. At what stage will the review process begin—with a rough draft? outline? finished report?
4. What will the reviewers be looking for—content only? style? format? function of the report for someone else?
5. How will disagreements over the report be resolved,

should they arise? Have you had any disagreements with the reviewers before? How were they settled?

Technical Assignments

1. Prepare a list of five topics you would like to investigate.
    a. If you were to write a report on each topic, what would be the purpose of each report?
    b. For each report, identify the principal reader and in one or two sentences state what that reader would want to know.
    c. Which of the areas listed in Table 3-1 would you emphasize in each report?

2. The review system in an organization functions somewhat like the review procedures in a class. In a short report, compare the procedures for two of your classes.

3. Ask a professor in your major field if there is a preferred style manual for that field. If there is, prepare a short report giving the title of the manual, the place where a copy can be found, and a summary of its contents. If there is no such manual, use a recent issue of a journal in your field for instructions on submitting manuscripts. These instructions usually appear near the front of the journal and are in small type.

4. Evaluate the following assignments based on the time you spend and the number of drafts you write:

Assignment	Amounts of Time You Usually Have Available	Number of Drafts You Usually Write
Lab report		
Term paper or Project		
Letter home		
Short paper		
This assignment		

What conclusions can you draw from the table? Write a short report (about 500 words) in which you discuss these conclusions and suggest ways in which you can increase the efficiency of your work. Do you spend too much time on some assignments and not enough on others? Can you correlate your efforts to achieve error-free papers with the grades you receive?

Analyzing the Problem

ome forms, such as letters and memos, are effective means of communicating specific information to a specific reader when the information is not very complex or when the reader's need is limited. Often, however, the information is more complex or the reader's need to know is more far reaching. For example, the reader may need the technical data you have collected, a fuller explanation of your reasoning process, or visual aids to clarify relationships. In such cases the letter or memo is too constricting a format. So we use the report instead. The report provides a more flexible format and gives us freedom to include more extensive and more complex information. The process, however, is essentially the same as the process for writing a memo or letter. It has five main steps: analyzing the problem; designing a solution or solutions; testing the solution; collecting, analyzing, and organizing the data; and, finally, writing, editing, and revising the report.

In the chapters that follow, we will suggest ways to accomplish each step in this process, so that when you write a report it will communicate clearly and concisely the information the reader needs to know. The first step is analyzing the problem.

In the course of your college career, many of the problems you have tackled have been assigned by your instructors: problems in math, accounting, engineering, biology, chemistry, or English. The instructor gives you a problem and you set about solving it. No doubt you have also had an opportunity to solve some problems that you yourself have devised.

When you leave school and take a job, you will often identify problems that you must somehow solve on your own in order to get on with your work. More likely, however, your supervisor will be the one who presents you with a problem and asks you to work out a solution. You will be told to assemble certain information and report it to the supervisor, who, in turn, may pass it along to his or her supervisor and to others in the organization. This chapter, and the ones that follow, will prepare you to communicate that information fully and effectively.

Understanding the Problem

Suppose your supervisor comes to you one morning and hands you a memo requesting certain specific information that the organization needs in order to clear up a problem that is causing delays or unnecessary expense. You may be working in a testing or a quality-control section, or in auditing or nursing. What your section does has a direct impact on how successful the organization is in meeting its objectives in profit or service. The information you generate may travel throughout the entire organization, affecting the performance of countless other sections. Clearly that information must be useful and accurate if it is to be read and understood by others. To achieve that goal, you must first understand the problem you are to solve.

We achieve understanding at many levels, principally through the use of language. But there are many languages other than the language of words. As we have seen, there is the language of formulas (in mathematics, chemistry, linguistics, logic), and there is the language of visuals. When you face a problem, select the language or languages that seem best suited to advance your understanding of the problem. In this chapter we will focus on the language of words, since that is the language in which problems are usually expressed.

Often the problem comes in the form of a question: What is the best way to do ...? How can we eliminate ...? Why did sales fall last quarter? Why is efficiency in our department the lowest in the company?

The very existence of a problem poses a question. Let's take a problem (expressed as a question) that you may very well face as you move along in this course: How can I generate a problem on my own that will help me analyze problems I will face later on? Although this is a contrived example, designed to suggest how a student might go about creating a problem for course purposes, it closely resembles what you may experience in an on-the-job situation. As we examine a specific example, follow the process carefully. Even though you may not be majoring in accounting, try to relate the example to your own major.

Christa's Problem

Christa is taking a technical writing course because it is required for an accounting degree. She learns that she will have to prepare a rather long (2500–3000 word) report on a problem in her major. She is to make the problem very specific, limiting it to a particular application, thereby simulating what she will have to do once she graduates and goes to work in an accounting firm. She decides to start in a logical manner to find a problem she can use.

First, she lists as many ideas as she can in random order without regard to their quality. Then, she organizes her notes in some logical sequence so that she can eventually identify a problem to use for her report. Her notes look like this:

> Must be in accounting.
>
> Must be in auditing.
>
> Interested in grocery business (family in wholesale grocery business).
>
> Also interested in computers (very limited knowledge).
>
> Write program for warehouse?
>
> Apply computer to warehouse?
>
> Use computer for auditing?
>
> Make computer available to retailer?
>
> Develop internal audit system? warehouse? chain? actual store?
>
> Store across the street:
>> small
>> family-owned
>> uses old bookkeeping system
>> appears to be in trouble
>> high turnover of personnel
>> slow turnover of merchandise
>> looks like poor cash flow
>
> Some ways to improve cash flow:
>> use of computer
>> different system of inventory control
>> closer control of billing and payment procedures
>> increase profits without raising prices

Christa now decides to review her list and group similar ideas. Her new list looks like this:

> I'm interested in accounting.
>
> I'm interested in auditing.
>
> I'm interested, mildly, in computers.
>
> My project will involve the grocery business.
>
> Can you use a computer to do internal auditing in the grocery business?

Use of computer in warehouse? chain? local store?
Andy's Grocery?

I'm working as an auditor for a large grocery warehouse
and am connected with the department that offers help
to small grocery stores.

Major problem most small grocery stores have is
cash flow.

Help Andy's Grocery improve cash flow.

At this point Christa has settled on a problem she can work
with and needs only to state it:

What is the best way for Andy's Grocery to increase its cash flow?

Now Christa can begin to solve the problem, write a report,
and complete her class assignment.

Once the process has led to the formulation of a question,
Christa is ready to analyze the problem to make certain she
understands what it entails. No doubt you know people who,
when called on to answer a question, have answered, not the
question that was being asked, but what they *thought* was being
asked. When you write a report, always state the problem so
that the reader knows what it is and also knows that *you* know
what it is. (This statement usually comes in the first section of
the report, as you will see later.)

To analyze the problem, Christa first writes out the question, then looks at each word to determine what it suggests:

What	*is*	*the best way*
Method. Describe.	Linking verb.	Criteria. Need to list. Define "best."

for Andy's Grocery	*to increase*	*its cash flow?*
Client. Source of information.	Process. Describe. Instructions. Secondary criteria. Goal. Define "increase."	Focus. Goal. Object to work on. Process. Describe.

She realizes that she will need to devise a method by which
Andy's can reach a specific goal, and she will need to establish
criteria whereby she can measure whether Andy's is achieving
that goal. To do so, she will have to take the following steps:

1. Describe a process.
2. Prepare a set of instructions.
3. List criteria to use when evaluating possible solutions.

4. Define terms for her reader.
5. Identify her reader so that her report will be clear and meaningful.

With this part of the analysis done, she can begin to develop a solution. She realizes that she needs answers to all sorts of questions:

Why is the problem important to both Andy's Grocery and Christa's employer?

What information will she need, such as the store's current cash flow, its current financial status, the goals and objectives the store's owner has in mind, current sales volume, current merchandising principles, and so on?

What are some tentative solutions to the problem?

What methods will she use to choose likely solutions and test them?

What results can she anticipate?

What recommendations can she make?

How will the recommendations be used?

How will the recommendations be tested?

What direct benefits will come after the recommendations have been implemented?

Follow-up?

Relation to criteria of "best" and "increase"?

Christa finds that one question leads to many others, but that in answering them she is developing solutions and gathering information that she can use in her report.

Here is a summary of the process Christa has been following:

1. *List topics.*
    a. Major field of interest.
    b. Within major field, narrowed interest.
    c. Within narrowed interest, specific interest.
    d. Kinds of problems I like to solve.
    e. Outside information I could use.
    f. Specific application of solution.
2. *State content and application in question form.*

3. *Analyze question.*
    a. Words that suggest process.
    b. Words that suggest instructions.
    c. Words that suggest criteria.
    d. Words that suggest sources of information.
    e. Words that suggest reader.
    f. Other key words.

4. *List specific questions to consider.*
    a. What is the problem?
    b. Why is the problem important?
    c. What possible solutions exist?
    d. What methods will I use to test these solutions?
    e. What results do I expect?
    f. What recommendations can I make?
    g. What benefits do I expect from the solution?
    h. Will I recommend anything different from the solution?
    i. If yes, what?

At this point Christa is ready to turn to two other matters: sources of data and the reader's need to know. Though they are closely related, let's look at them separately.

Sources of Data   Christa is satisfied that she has analyzed the problem well and has identified its main ingredients. She now makes a list of the key words in her problem-setting question:

what

best

way

Andy's Grocery

increase

cash flow

She sees that "what" and "way" suggest some sort of procedure, especially the word "way." Both "best" and "increase" are terms that set standards and suggest quantitative definitions. "Andy's Grocery" is both her reader and a source of information, while "cash flow" is a process or goal toward which she must work. So she revises her list to look like this:

what

way

best

increase

Andy's Grocery

cash flow

The next step is to add her comments:

what, way	Procedure. Name a process.
best, increase	Abstract. Define quantitatively.
Andy's Grocery	Reader. Source of information.
cash flow	Procedure, process, goal, focus.

Now she brings all this together in a table (see Table 4-1). This table gives Christa a good idea of how to proceed. She will have to explain to Andy what she is doing and why, gain access to his records to demonstrate that a problem actually exists, and suggest a way to solve the problem by making recommendations. She will have to analyze the records carefully so that she can establish the present cash flow and determine if it is advantageous to the store. She will also have to question Andy to make sure that he will be able to understand and use the report she comes up with. In short, Christa must now turn her attention from data to the reader.

The Reader's Need to Know

Christa's reader is Andy, an older man with long experience in the grocery business. Christa prepares to interview him in order to gain his permission to use his records. One area that she needs to explore is Andy's educational background:

1. How much formal education has he had?

Table 4-1. Christa's Analysis of Statement of Problem

Key Term	Shows	Data Needed	Source/Method
what, way cash flow	Procedure Process Method	Description Definition	Finding ways to control cash flow. Library. Interviews. Textbooks. Lectures.
best increase	Quality Goal	Definition Limits	Andy's records. Own judgment. Must know present cash flow. Predict ideal cash flow.
Andy's Grocery	Reader Source	Reader analysis Current cash flow	Interview.

2. How much informal education has he had?

3. Are there other factors that will affect Andy's ability to understand her report?

Why does she need this information? The amount of explanation included in a report gives readers a clue to what the writer thinks of them and their ability to understand. Too much information bores readers and suggests that the writer regards them as uninformed; too little information frustrates readers and suggests that the writer regards them as highly knowledgeable.

Knowing how much education (both formal and informal) your readers have enables you to judge their ability to assimilate information. How many ideas can you safely incorporate in one sentence? How strong must you make the connections between those ideas? Can you expect your readers to make inferences without having everything spelled out in detail? The more you know about your readers, the better you can communicate information and the better your chances are of getting your points across.

Above all, you want to avoid making the reader feel uncomfortable while reading your report. Make certain your ideas come through loud and clear and are not blocked by static. Avoid burdening your reader by writing above or below his or her capabilities. You do not want your reader to have to read a report with a dictionary in one hand, struggling to make sense of every sentence. Nor do you want to write in primer style, using words of only one syllable.

Your most compelling purpose in writing a report is to enable your reader to understand the points you are making. Christa wants Andy to agree that he has a problem with his store, that the problem is with cash flow, and that her recommendations will help him solve that problem. She does not want to burden him with language, visuals, and mathematics that are irrelevant and beyond his understanding. After all, he doesn't *have* to read Christa's report. If he is uncomfortable with it, he will put it aside. The same considerations apply equally well to report writing and report reading in business, industry, and government.

And so Christa needs to interview Andy before she sets about writing her report. She begins by asking him what accounting system he is using and whether he is satisfied with it. He may tell her that he pays someone else to keep his books. If so, Christa tries to find out how much Andy himself knows about accounting so that she can devise an appropriate context in which to set her report.

As Christa talks with Andy, she uses a variety of means to convey her meaning and to draw out information. She uses gestures, varying tones of voice, feedback, and other linguistic devices. She never forgets that the interview is taking place within a specific situation. She asks questions, listens attentively to Andy's questions, makes observations, and responds to Andy's comments, all within a context.

The skillful writer of reports exhibits the same sensitivity. And that sensitivity springs from a detailed, accurate knowledge of the reader.

What if you cannot question your reader directly or do not even know the reader's name? You can still make certain assumptions as long as you know that person's position in the organization. Once again, try to surmise the assumed reader's level of education (both formal and informal). The more formal education your reader is likely to have, the more freedom you have in using fairly complicated sentences and paragraphs. The more extensive your reader's professional experience, the safer it will be for you to introduce complex technical concepts.

Generally, readers who have decision-making authority in an organization have at least one college degree, usually in business or in the technical area of the organization's product or service. Moreover, a decision maker is likely to have wide experience. Many decision makers, however, because of their administrative and managerial responsibilities, may not have exercised their professional competencies for some time. The further an engineer advances in an organization, for example, the more time he or she spends on communicating and the less on engineering. And much of that time is spent communicating about nonengineering matters. As a report writer, you need to be aware that such a reader will appreciate having certain technical terms defined, especially terms that refer to recent developments in engineering.

Christa may not be able to determine everything she needs to know about Andy. So she may have to make assumptions based on her observations and on what she knows about similar people. She may safely assume that Andy knows a lot about groceries but little about accounting. She is pretty sure that his formal education is limited but that his experience is extensive. On the basis of these assumptions, she decides that it will be wise to define any accounting terms she uses in her report and to keep her style straightforward and uncomplicated. And she knows that she will not be able to rely on Andy to supply missing pieces of information. (We will expand on these points later.) She begins to form an idea of how she will present the

Table 4-2. Andy's Understanding of Cash Flow

Item in Report	No Understanding	Some Understanding	Full Understanding
Technical terms		Very low	
Technical data	X		
Mathematics		Common arithmetic	
Visuals			
Simple			X
Medium		X	
Complex	X		
Logic and reasoning		X	

information needed to support her recommendation. In other words, she begins to plan her report as she plans to solve the problem.

Armed with all this information about her reader, Christa now begins to pinpoint the reasons for his being interested in her report:

1. Why does he *need* to read my report?

2. How important to him are each of the following (high, medium, low):
    a. Statement of the problem.
    b. Importance of the problem.
    c. How I plan to arrive at a solution.
    d. The results of my solution.
    e. The recommendations I can make.
    f. Benefits from the recommendations.

Why should Andy read Christa's report? What is his primary need to know? How much and what kind of support material will Christa need to make Andy accept her report? What will add credibility to her report?

If Christa were writing a report for someone with extensive formal education and wide experience—say, someone who holds degrees in accounting and business or an engineer who happens to own a grocery store—would she approach her problem differently? Clearly she would give her report a different emphasis, provide different details, use different terminology, employ different sentence structure. But knowing Andy as well as she does, Christa is in a position to suit the level of complexity and the amount of information to her audience.

Table 4-3. Andy's Understanding of Microcomputers and Programming

Item in Report	No Understanding	Some Understanding	Full Understanding
Technical terms	X		
Technical data	X		
Mathematics	X		
Visuals			
Simple	X		
Medium	X		
Complex	X		
Logic and reasoning		X	

She knows that if she wants to recommend that Andy acquire a microcomputer, she should not go into detail on its circuitry or on proper programming procedures. She can mention technical specifications in an appendix so that Andy will have them available when talking to computer representatives. She can refer to prepackaged programs that Andy can buy (here is a chance for Christa to draw an analogy between prepackaged programs and prepackaged foods). Knowing this, she does not have to spend a lot of time gathering technical data. She knows just how much and what kind of data she will need.

At this point Christa decides to work up some tables to help her summarize what she has learned about Andy (Tables 4-2 and 4-3).

Finally, Christa draws up a worksheet to highlight the most significant features of her analysis:

Report Topic/Subject/Title: _____

1. Why does reader want to read the report? _____

2. What is the main piece of information the reader needs to know? _____

3. What do you know about the reader?

    Formal education? _____ How much? _____

    Degrees or certificates? _____ What? _____

_____

4. What parts of the subject can you assume your reader knows about? _____

_____

5. Does your reader need to understand the theory involved in your recommendations? Yes _____ No _____ Maybe _____

6. Does your reader need to understand the applications involved in your recommendations? Yes _____ No _____ Maybe _____

7. Which should receive primary emphasis—theory or applications? _____

Christa is now ready to formalize her analysis in a preliminary proposal that will be followed by a formal proposal.

Technical Assignments

1. Select one of the topics you listed for Assignment 1 of Chapter 3.
   a. State it in question form and categorize the words of the question the way Christa did for her questions.
   b. Complete an analysis following the form on page 49.
   c. Prepare a worksheet for the topic following the sample on page 53.
2. Discuss the five topics you listed for Assignment 1 of Chapter 3 with a professor in your major field and report on each, indicating how realistic each is for you to work on.
3. Interview a professor at your school who has prepared a proposal of some kind. Report on the preliminary procedures that professor used in preparing to write the proposal.

5

Making a Proposal

n Chapter 4 we saw how Christa chose a problem, analyzed it, and began to collect data in preparation for writing a report. As she proceeded, she discovered that she
would need more information about a great many matters before she could move further. But as she developed
her plan for solving the problem, she was also developing a plan for the final report. Her next step is to prepare a
proposal in which she describes in detail how she plans to
solve the problem and requests permission to proceed with
her plan. Permission usually comes from the person who
assigned the problem (in Christa's case, her instructor).

The proposal may be extremely informal. For example,
George, a civil engineering classmate of Christa's who has decided to work on the parking lot problem from Chapter 3,
proposes to the instructor: "I want to find out how to fix the
holes in the parking lot. OK?" In asking this question, George is
doing two things: he is restating the problem, and he is requesting permission to proceed. If the response is "Yes,"
George can begin work on the problem. He might ask additional questions to get some indication of limits, time available,
and whatever else he needs in order to clarify his thinking.
Again, the exchange of information may be quite informal,
conducted by phone or face to face.

Christa's problem is a little more complex, as most problems will be once you are working in your special field. She
must request formal approval from her instructor to continue
with the project. To obtain that approval, she must write a
proposal, have it reviewed and commented on, and, finally, if it
is approved, receive permission to proceed.

A *proposal* is a document that suggests a solution to a
specific problem and that requests permission to develop that
solution. The proposal describes the solution, sets forth the
costs the solution will entail, and specifies the qualifications of
the person or the organization submitting the proposal. Most
organizations have teams of people who work together to pro
duce proposals. Although Christa's proposal will be more mod-

est than the proposals generated by large organizations, the process of preparing it will parallel the process that is common in business, industry, and government. This process involves two steps: (1) preparing and submitting an informal proposal or worksheet, and (2) preparing and submitting a formal proposal.

The Informal Proposal or Worksheet

The informal proposal or worksheet is a very rough, preliminary draft. The worksheet that Christa will use contains blanks for her to fill in and represents her preliminary thinking about the project. Once it has been approved, it will serve as an outline for her formal proposal.

The instructor acts as the first reviewer of the proposal, playing the role of the supervisor who reviews proposals and passes them on to others before granting approval. Once Christa receives preliminary approval of her project, she will develop a more formal proposal that will reflect the project's full complexity.

Again, this procedure is similar to the one you will follow in a job situation. Your supervisor will assign you a project and instruct you to develop and complete it. Suppose you are assigned to assess the quality-control implications of acquiring a new drill press. Faced with a project of this complexity, you will want to make certain that you clearly understand the assignment and what is expected of you. Thus, you will analyze the problem carefully before attempting to devise a solution, and once you have done so, you will work up a preliminary proposal and submit it for approval.

The first step in writing a proposal is to define the problem carefully. This definition of the problem reveals that you understand it thoroughly and are aware of its many aspects. It also gives your supervisor an opportunity to judge whether your understanding of the problem agrees with that of others in the organization. In identifying the problem, you may suggest that there are some related problems that may surface as you proceed. In short, the proposal gives you a chance to display the thoroughness of your analysis and your awareness of the implications of the problem.

Many assignments tend to be vague, especially those that come down through the organization from one level to another. It is up to you to identify the fundamental nature of the problem, to reduce it to its essential ingredients, and then to devise an appropriate solution. The proposal process enables you to establish whether the problem you identify is indeed the problem that the organization wants you to tackle.

Many companies conduct much of their business on the basis of proposals, especially those that provide products or services to government agencies. When an agency wants to build a new bomber or have an office painted, it issues notices inviting interested suppliers to submit proposals. This process is highly complicated, and most organizations maintain special departments that do nothing but write proposals to submit to government agencies. If you understand the proposal process, you will have little difficulty serving as a member of such a department. Even if you have to produce a proposal by yourself, familiarity with the process and with the many rules and regulations concerning the preparation of proposals for the government will enable you to write effective proposals. (You may want to consult some of the books listed in Appendix C under "Proposals.")

The time you spend on the informal proposal stage will be rewarded when you prepare your formal proposal, for as we shall see, many parts of the informal proposal will transfer directly to the formal proposal.

The Parts of a Proposal

Most proposals contain three parts: a statement of the problem and recommended solutions, the writer's (or the organization's) qualifications, and the cost of the recommended solutions.

Large organizations that request and receive proposals usually parcel out the parts to various specialized units for evaluation: the problem section to technical experts, the qualifications section to management experts, and the cost section to accountants. Each unit evaluates a part of the proposal and sends a report to someone who pulls the parts together and makes a decision about the proposal. For less complicated proposals, one reviewer evaluates all three sections. Some organizations (such as government agencies) even use a point system to evaluate proposals; the weight given to the various sections suggests the importance ascribed to each. These procedures are usually used for proposals that come from outside the organization.

When you prepare a proposal, try to find out who will evaluate it and according to what criteria. The more you know about the review process, the better you can prepare your proposal. For now, how will your instructor review your informal and formal proposals? Will anyone else review them? If so, what parts? Can you help your reviewers through your use of details, definitions, visuals?

Your proposal begins with a worksheet. It consists of a

series of topics or questions that you answer with a single word, a phrase, or a complete sentence. The information falls into five groups: preliminary matter, the project problem, how you would manage the problem, the costs, and miscellaneous factors. Because each section calls for specific information, it forces you to think through the basic questions inherent in the project.

Preliminary Matter

The opening section contains the date, the writer's name, the name of the assumed reader, the purpose of the report, and a place for the reader's approval and the date of approval. This information is essential to the writer of the proposal as well as to the reader. The very act of naming the assumed reader of the proposal reminds the writer how much and what kind of technical detail to include. Specifying the purpose reminds the writer that the proposal is meant to elicit action—approval. Providing a place for approval and the date of approval is a courtesy to the reader.

The Project Problem

The problem section describes the overall project and positions the problem within that project. It consists of six subsections: Subject of the Project, Purpose of the Project, Limitations of the Project, Statement of the Project Problem in Question Form, Definition of Key Terms, and Significance of Solving the Project Problem.

SUBJECT OF THE PROJECT What is the overall project of which the problem is a part? Does it have to do with computer applications, nutrition in animals, patient care, communications among engineers, improving profits? You can be general at this point, even identifying some aspect of your major as the subject of the project: tax accounting, preveterinary medicine, mechanical engineering, or technical writing, for example. You will narrow the general subject when you specify the purpose of the project.

PURPOSE OF THE PROJECT The purpose of all proposals is to solve a problem. What is the specific problem you are addressing? Do you want to identify the best computer for particular applications, the right nutritional mixture for newborn lambs, the most cost-effective means of caring for patients in their homes, the best instructional program for improving the report-writing skills of chemical engineers, ways to improve the profit-cost ratio in the Cleveland plant? Without a specific purpose, the project will be worthless. But all projects must be limited if they are to be manageable.

LIMITATIONS OF THE PROJECT Set realistic limitations on the project based on your evaluation of the problem. Christa, you will remember, limited her project to Andy's Grocery and the cash-flow problem; George will limit his problem to one area of the north end of the parking lot. Narrow your project problem so that you can solve it in the time available to you. And ensure that it is within your technical competence and has genuine significance for you personally. Setting realistic limitations on the project will spare you frustration later on. Once you have limited your project problem, you are ready to state it in the form of a question.

STATEMENT OF THE PROJECT PROBLEM IN QUESTION FORM Stating the project problem in question form prompts you to formulate an answer and to assemble supporting details. It also gives you a clue as to the kind of information you will be looking for. "How," for example, suggests the need to develop a method or process. "Is" usually suggests feasibility. Here are some of the possibilities:

How—method, procedure

Is—feasibility, existence of something

What—method, names something

Who—person, organization

Why—cause-effect

Can/should—do something, must do something

Where—location

When—time

Most questions contain a word or a phrase that suggests a criterion:

best

logical

most profitable

easiest

simplest

cheapest

Such terms suggest criteria against which the reader can measure your recommendations.

After putting the project problem in question form, you must identify and define the key terms you will be using in your proposal.

DEFINITION OF KEY TERMS Because the reader of your informal proposal may not be the same person as the reader of the formal report you ultimately submit, be sure you define any technical terms that may be unfamiliar. Will that reader understand "algorithm"? "hydrocarbon"? Technical terms of this sort do serve as a kind of shorthand when you communicate with others versed in your specialty. When engineers talk to each other, for example, they share a common vocabulary that saves them from having to make lengthy explanations. But when an engineer talks to an accountant in the vocabulary of engineering, communication breaks down. The same thing happens when an accountant talks to an engineer in the vocabulary of accounting. Thus, to ensure understanding, always make certain that the person you are addressing is familiar with the vocabulary you use.

SIGNIFICANCE OF SOLVING THE PROJECT PROBLEM Why bother to solve the problem at all? How will your solution alter conditions? What will happen if you do not solve the problem? Will it create other problems? These are some of the questions the reader of your proposal is likely to ask. Stating the significance of solving the project problem is thus one of the most important parts of the proposal. You must demonstrate that solving the problem is significant and that to ignore it would be unwise. If you can do that, you will probably get the approval you seek. Anticipating the questions the reader is likely to raise will help you develop a strategy for the proposal as a whole.

Be as precise as possible. State that instituting new computer applications will save money and increase efficiency. Or that improving the nutrition of newborn lambs will increase yield and shorten premarket time. Or that setting up a home-care program will shorten recovery time and reduce hospital costs.

Management

Now that you have convinced your reader that the problem you are proposing to solve is of significance, you must demonstrate that you are eminently qualified to solve it. In the second major section of the informal proposal, describe the methods you plan to use, the facilities you will employ, the sources of information you will need, and your technical qualifications.

METHODS I WILL USE TO COLLECT DATA In this section, explain how you propose to collect the data that will support your recommended solution. Here are some possibilities:

Develop and distribute a questionnaire.

Conduct interviews.

Fashion a new computer program.

Analyze samples.

Observe relevant conditions.

Consult reference works and current reports.

Be careful to avoid excessive detail. If you mention tests and procedures that are standard in your technical field, you need not go into specifics. If you suspect that your reader may not be familiar with certain laboratory procedures, however, you could say, "Lab tests designed to show. . . ." Give your reader the necessary information.

FACILITIES I WILL USE TO COLLECT AND ANALYZE DATA Specify the facilities you plan to use in collecting and analyzing your data. Collecting samples for testing is pointless if you do not have access to a laboratory. A proposal for improving home-care for patients will not be taken seriously if you fail to mention how you plan to consult hospital personnel and health-care specialists. If you propose to design a new computer program for analyzing data, indicate what computer facilities are available to you. The reader must know not only how you plan to collect data but whether you have access to facilities for processing those data.

OTHER SOURCES OF INFORMATION I WILL USE In this section identify the resource persons you will consult, such as professors in your major or professionals in the field. List reference works and, if appropriate, research reports. Name the people you plan to interview. This section will demonstrate to your reader that you have thought through the project and have identified several sources of information.

MY QUALIFICATIONS FOR SOLVING THE PROJECT PROBLEM The reader will want to know whether you can do what you say you plan to do. Do you know how to collect and analyze data? Have you had experience doing library research and conducting interviews? How much do you already know about the subject? You need not go into great detail about your qualifications, but you should at least indicate your major, your class standing, and the titles of any courses you have taken that relate directly to the project. If you have had extraordinary experience in the project area, mention it. Convince the reader of your competence.

Costs

In this third major section estimate the costs—to you personally and to the organization or company—of producing a solution to the project problem. There are many areas where you may incur expenses while working on the project. Here are some of them:

1. *Tests.* How much will it cost to use the lab equipment? Will you have to pay for it, or can you run the tests as part of another course? Can you use the college lab, or will you have to send materials off for analysis?

2. *Advice.* If you ask a professional for help, will you have to pay a consulting fee? Professors normally regard advice giving as part of their regular duties. But what if your questions require special research?

3. *Materials and equipment.* Will you need to buy or rent special equipment? What about the cost of the materials (chemicals, for example) you need to run your tests?

4. *Printing.* If you decide to use a questionnaire, what will it cost to have it duplicated? Will you incur photocopying costs while you are collecting, analyzing, organizing, and reporting your data? Will you need to submit more than one copy of your proposals and reports?

5. *Postage.* What will it cost to mail a questionnaire? to write letters requesting information? Will you pay for return postage?

6. *Services.* What services will you have to pay for—computer time? typing? Will you have to pay someone to help you collect or analyze the data?

As you can see, even a modest project can be rather expensive. In this section of your informal proposal, estimate what costs you will pay for and what costs you expect to be covered by someone else. Calculate these costs carefully, because you will need to include a budget in your formal proposal.

Miscellaneous Factors

Use the final section of your informal proposal to present significant items that do not fall into the other sections: the assumed reader of your final report, that reader's need to know, the steps you will follow in preparing the final report, and your projected timetable and completion date. These items provide your reader with essential information and help you in your own planning.

ASSUMED READER OF THE FINAL REPORT The person who reads your final report may or may not be the same person who reads your informal and formal proposals. The reader may be a person who will actually use your recommendations. That person needs certain information. How much do you need to tell the reader about the details? How complex can your visuals be? What level of mathematics can the reader understand? Will you need to include a glossary? a list of symbols? The answers to these and other questions will influence not only how you prepare the proposal but the nature of the data you collect and analyze.

REASONS READER WILL WANT TO READ REPORT Readers read reports because they need information. Usually, readers read for two reasons: to learn about problems, and to learn how to solve or avoid problems.

Normally, most assignments come to you through the organization's communication chain. Someone tells you to solve a particular problem. If you can assume that the reader knows about the problem and need only be reminded of it in the final report, do not develop an extensive history of the problem. Knowing that the assumed reader wants to know how to solve or avoid the problem (or problems) helps you plan your work better.

STEPS IN PREPARING THE FINAL REPORT When you prepare your informal proposal, you probably will have no clear notion of the steps you will take to develop your final report. But you should at least have a general idea of how you will proceed. You will want to include the following steps in this section of your informal proposal:

1. *Collecting data.* The stage at which you run tests, send questionnaires, conduct interviews, and collect data in other ways.
2. *Analyzing data.* The stage at which you analyze and organize your data in the process of developing recommendations.
3. *Organizing information.* The stage at which you bring together all the information you have assembled and get it ready to incorporate into the final report.

4. *Writing/editing/revising.* The stage at which you write the final report in several drafts, editing and revising each draft, and prepare the finished versions of any visuals you plan to include.

5. *Preparing the final copy.* The stage at which you type the report, hire a typist to type it, or run it off on a word processor. You will also need time to proofread and make extra copies.

Projected Timetable

Once you have an idea of the steps you will follow, you will be able to develop a timetable for the entire project. The following allocation of time is typical:

Collecting data	30%
Analyzing data	20%
Organizing information	10%
Writing and revising	30%
Preparing final copy	10%

Of course, your own work habits will determine the percentage of time you will spend at each stage.

Finally, you must predict, at least tentatively, when you plan to complete the entire project. Set a goal for yourself—the date by which you want to complete your final report—and then work back to see whether you have time to complete each stage. If not, adjust your time allocations or, if possible, move your completion date along to a more realistic time. Keep an eye on the calendar to ensure that your progress is in phase with your timetable.

Figure 5-1 shows George's completed informal proposal for solving the problem of repairing the holes in the parking lot. He submits this informal proposal to his instructor for preliminary approval. Once the instructor has approved it, George can use appropriate parts when interviewing various people on the best way of doing the job. Those people will see that George has thought through the problem and knows what he wants to do.

The Formal Proposal

The formal proposal evolves from the informal proposal and presents the problem, solution, management, and costs in much greater detail. It is the formal document that organizations submit in response to a request for a proposal. Thoroughness in preparing the informal proposal will enable you to prepare the formal proposal with little difficulty. In fact, you will find that the requirements for preparing a formal proposal

INFORMAL PROPOSAL

Date: January 15, 1985   Approval: _____

Name: George Nelson   Date: _____

Assumed Reader: Professor Stanton, Technical Writing Instructor

Purpose of Report: Get approval from Professor Stanton

Problem Section

  Subject of the Project: Holes in the parking lot.

  Purpose of the Project: To repair holes in parking lot.

  Limitations of the Project: Parking lot north of Morrill Hall, the
  north end of the first aisle from the west.

  Statement of the Project Problem in Question Form: How can the
  holes in the north end of the first aisle from the west in the
  parking lot north of Morrill Hall be repaired?

  Definition of Key Terms: "How" suggests a method; "repaired"
  suggests an activity.

  Significance of Solving the Project Problem: When standing water
  freezes and thaws, it damages the surface of the parking lot and
  creates potholes. These holes are dangerous to walkers, drivers,
  and riders of bicycles, mopeds, and motorcycles.

Management Section

  Methods I Will Use to Collect Data: Soil sampling around problem
  area, core drillings of existing parking lot surfaces and
  subsurfaces, and measurements of elevations; interviews.

  Facilities I Will Use to Collect and Analyze Data: The parking lot
  and the civil engineering laboratory.

  Sources of Information I Will Use: Professor Fischer in Civil
  Engineering; library; head of Physical Plant Maintenance.

  My Qualifications for Solving the Project Problem: First-semester
  senior majoring in civil engineering; courses in materials testing,
  soils, road surfaces, and surveying.

Continued on page 66

Figure 5-1. Informal proposal.

Costs

    Estimated Costs in Developing Solution to Project Problem:

    Approximately $45 for materials, copying, and typing.

Miscellaneous

    Assumed Reader of the Final Report: Head of Physical Plant

    Maintenance.

    Reasons Reader Will Want to Read the Report: To learn that a

    serious problem exists, and to learn of ways to solve the problem.

    Steps in Preparing the Final Report: Collect data; analyze data;

    organize information; write, edit, and revise final report; type and

    proofread final report.

    Timetable for Steps in Preparing the Final Report: Collect data, 4

    weeks; analyze data, 2 weeks; organize information, 1 week;

    write, edit, revise report, 3 weeks; prepare and proofread final

    copy, 1 week.

    Projected Completion Date for Final Report: May 7, 1985.

Figure 5-1. (continued)

are somewhat more flexible than they are for an informal proposal. Figure 5-2 presents a sample outline for a formal proposal.

Unlike the informal proposal, the formal proposal requires headings and subheadings designed to inform your reader and to permit ready access to sections of greatest interest. When you prepare a formal proposal, use complete sentences and well-organized paragraphs, paying particular attention to the quality of your writing. If the occasion is very formal indeed, you may decide to include a title page and a table of contents. Figure 5-3 shows a completed formal proposal.

Why Some Proposals Fail

Regrettably, some proposals fail to win approval. The most common reason is that the writer has failed to explain the problem clearly and convincingly to the reader. Faced with a

INTRODUCTION
    * Statement of the problem, including limitations.
    * Background of the problem, as appropriate.
    * The need to solve the problem, including the significance of the
      problem and of the anticipated solution (especially its
      significance to the reader). State as a question.
    * Definition of key terms, as needed.
    * The assumed reader and that reader's need to know.

BODY
    * Procedures.
      —The approach you plan to use (how you intend to solve the
        problem).
      —Where you intend to work.
      —The resources available to you, including advisers and
        consultants.
    * Task breakdown and timetable.
      —Specific tasks or steps.
      —Dates for completing each task, and completion date for final
        report.
    * Your qualifications for handling the project, including specific
      courses and work experience (include a full résumé in an
      appendix to the report).
    * Proposed outline of the major sections of the final report.

CONCLUSION
    * Summary of problem and methods for solving.
    * Request for approval from appropriate persons.

APPENDIXES
    * Working bibliography (preliminary list of the materials you are
      using and expect to use).
    * List of people, with their position or title, whom you plan to
      contact while working on the project.
    * Copy of your résumé.
    * Preliminary budget.

Figure 5-2. Sample outline for formal proposal.

June 28, 1984

Steve Combs
Executive Director
United States Wrestling Federation
405 W. Hall of Fame
Stillwater, OK 74074

Dear Mr. Combs:

With Karen Dillard leaving at the end of July and a new fiscal year coming up in September, we should evaluate the Computer Service Department.

During the peak season for new and renewable memberships by officials and coaches, the department's ability to handle its work load was severely strained. Just keeping the files current for accounts receivable and wrestling clubs accounted for twenty to twenty-five hours of computer time in a week. We enter the names of officials and coaches whenever possible, but after receiving applications for memberships, the delay between entering the data and mailing out the packets is often two to three weeks and occasionally longer. Why? One major reason is the programs we now use for maintaining and updating the files of our coaches and officials along with the files for State Chairmen, NWCA, etc.

Proposal

I propose to determine the feasibility of acquiring a new, more efficient program for the address files.

Having a more efficient program for the address files will decrease the time it takes to retrieve a file by state and name. Also, the more flexible the correction function, the less time we will spend re-entering data. A more efficient program will significantly reduce the delay between data entry and mailing of packets because we can add more addresses in less time. Files will be easier to keep current. Basically, the more efficient the program, the more efficient data entry personnel can be.

Background

These address files are relatively small, usually not containing more than 1400 or so names and addresses of coaches, officials, state chairmen, and the like. Basically, we operators enter new members, keep addresses current, keep printouts handy for staff use, and also fill requests for printouts and address labels from state officers and other interested parties from around the country.

As important as these duties are, ledger entries, accounts receivable, and club accounts take precedence over them. Therefore, time allocated for entering new addresses for the coaches' file or

Figure 5-3. Sample formal proposal.
Source: Nicole Yarborough. Used by permission.

the officials' file must be used efficiently and effectively. At present, this is not possible for two reasons: (1) typographical errors must be laboriously corrected by entering whole sections of data, i.e. name, address, and zip and phone numbers (for instance, if a phone number is entered incorrectly, we must re-enter not only the correct phone number but also the zip code and the other phone number). Often, correcting errors will take up to a minute. If you multiply ten errors per hour of data entry, ten minutes of the hour is spent correcting errors rather than entering new data. (2) Alphabetizing a file by state and names within the state, or "alphastating," takes up an incredible amount of computer time. Every time we print a file we must "alphastate." If that file is over 100 addresses, process time increases as follows: 0-100 addresses or records—3 to 5 minutes; 100-300 records—8 to 10 minutes; 300-600 records—20 to 60 minutes; 600-900 records—1 to 3 hours; over 900 records—3 to 7 hours. And these are average times—not the worst cases. Considering this very lengthy time factor, we cannot initiate "alphastating" when there is heavy use of the terminals for other data entry. As a consequence, these files lose their current status and become crowded at the bottom of the files with new names in no specified order.

Procedure

I will collect data on different types of address programs from catalogs and by interviews, comparing costs and features. My projected timetable for research and writing can be found on page 4 of this proposal. At present my ceiling for total expenditure on this project is $500.

Qualifications

Besides my experience in computer programming as a data entry operator, I am qualified to make recommendations. Having worked for this organization in this capacity, I know what features are desirable to facilitate rapid data entry.

I hope you will consider this proposal for determining the feasibility of acquiring a better address program. I believe that a more expedient program would significantly increase our productivity in the Computer Services Department.

If you have any questions or suggestions about this proposal, please let me know.

Respectfully yours,

Nicole Yarborough

Nicole Yarborough

Figure 5-3. (continued)

RÉSUMÉ

Nicole Yarborough

College and permanent address: 112 North Ramsay
Stillwater, OK   74074

Phone: Home: (405) 555-2617
                                      Work: (405) 555-5242

JOB OBJECTIVE: Computer Programmer/Business Applications

WORK EXPERIENCE: United States Wrestling Federation:
Oct. 1981 to present   Data input, BASIC programming, file
                            maintenance

EDUCATION: Bachelor of Science, Computer Science,
                            Oklahoma State University, Stillwater,
                            1982.

COURSES: COBOL: Business applications, team
                            projects.

                            FILE STRUCTURES: Language PL/1
                            Knowledge of hardware, JCL, VSAM
                            (IBM), use of external storage, discs
                            and tapes.

                            NONNUMERIC ALGORITHMS: Language
                            PL/1 sorts and searches, data structures.

SUPPORT COURSES: Social Issues in Computer Science,
                            Technical Report Writing, Speech,
                            Algebra, Trigonometry, Calculus

Placement papers available upon request from OSU Placement
Office.

Figure 5-3. (continued)

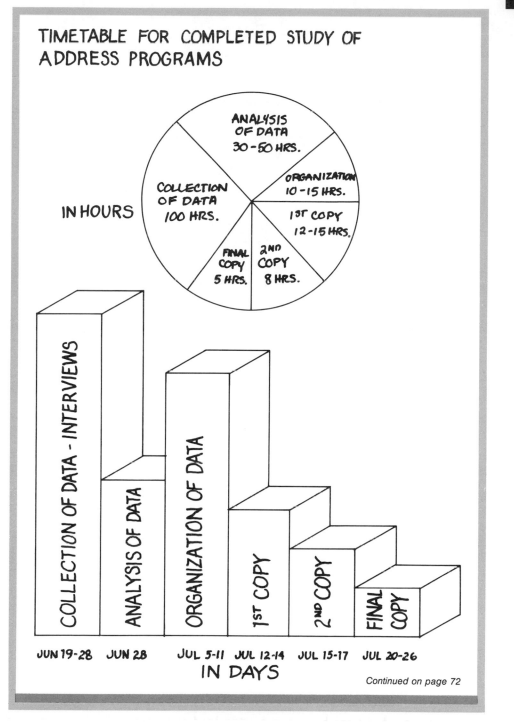

TIMETABLE FOR COMPLETED STUDY OF
ADDRESS PROGRAMS

ANALYSIS
OF DATA
30-50 HRS.

ORGANIZATION
10-15 HRS.

COLLECTION
OF DATA
100 HRS.

1ST COPY
12-15 HRS.

IN HOURS

FINAL
COPY
5 HRS.

2ND
COPY
8 HRS.

COLLECTION OF DATA - INTERVIEWS

ANALYSIS OF DATA

ORGANIZATION OF DATA

1ST COPY

2ND COPY

FINAL COPY

JUN 19-28   JUN 28   JUL 5-11   JUL 12-14   JUL 15-17   JUL 20-26

IN DAYS

Continued on page 72

Figure 5-3. (continued)

RESOURCES

Keet, Ernest E., "Eliminating the Risks of Buying Software," INFOSYSTEMS, Feb. 1978.

Goetz, Martina, "Software Package Generation," Computerworld, Oct. 6, 1980.

Calsoft, Software Catalog, Spring 1982.

Archibald, Dale, "The Making of Magnetic Media for Micros," Softtalk, Feb. 1982, pp. 161–164.

Standish, Thomas A., Data Structure Techniques. Menlo Park, CA: Addison-Wesley Publishing Co., 1980, pp. 44–122.

PERSONS:

Dr. William Eastman
Business Bldg.
OSU

Dr. Phillip Hitch
Mathematical Sciences Bldg.
OSU

Susan Price
Computer Services Department
USWF
Stillwater, OK   74074

Figure 5-3. (continued)

confusing, inadequate statement of the problem, the reader assumes that the writer did not really understand the problem to begin with. The truth may be that the writer has simply ignored the reader.

What are some other reasons for the lack of clarity in the problem section? Here are a few:

1. The writer presents only parts of the problem instead of setting forth the problem in its entirety.

2. The writer assumes that the reader knows all the details, including background details.

3. The writer gives the impression that the problem is not really a problem at all, leading the reader to assume that the writer doesn't understand what the problem is.

4. The reader, unable to understand the problem, decides that the writer's solution is unsound.

The reader wants convincing evidence that you truly understand the problem and all its implications. Provide that evidence in your statement of the problem.

Another reason for the failure of many proposals to win approval is that they are poorly planned—either in the organization of the actual proposal itself or in the presentation of the solution to the problem. Because a proposal reflects the way the writer thinks, a poorly planned proposal suggests that the writer is probably incompetent in technical matters as well. Poor planning invites rejection. And a poorly planned proposal *should* be rejected.

Never assume that your reader will somehow know what you mean. Your reader reads what is there on the page, not what was in your mind as you wrote. Actually, you cannot safely assume that the reader is really reading what is on the page, because readers tend to read what they want to read. The only safeguard against that tendency, and it is not an altogether reliable safeguard, is to write with such absolute clarity that the reader cannot fail to comprehend your meaning. Careful planning will help you achieve such clarity.

Finally, some proposals are rejected rather than approved because the writer fails to persuade the reader that he or she can truly solve the problem. The writer must demonstrate technical expertise that is adequate to the purpose. It is therefore important that you state your skills and training explicitly, that you include an up-to-date résumé displaying your background and experience, and that you demonstrate access to adequate facilities and appropriate sources of information.

Technical Assignments

1. Write an informal proposal for solving a problem in the area of your major. You might use the topic you select for Assignment 1 in Chapter 4. Treat the writing of your proposal as a process marked by careful planning and awareness of its purpose. Ask your technical writing instructor, and perhaps a professor in your major discipline, to evaluate it.

2. Prepare a formal proposal based on your informal proposal. Ask the same people to evaluate it.

3. Ask the librarian to help you locate a "Request for a Proposal" issued by a government agency. If you cannot find one, see whether there is an office at your college that handles research grants, or ask your major professor for help. Once you locate such a request, answer the following questions:

   a. What is the name of the agency requesting the proposal?
   b. When is the proposal due?
   c. What are the program objectives?
   d. Are there restrictions on who may reply? If so, what are they?
   e. Does the request provide any guidelines on how to prepare the proposal? Does it specify what sections to include? If so, how do they resemble or differ from the sections you are to include when preparing proposals in this course?
   f. Does the request mention compliance with the Civil Rights Act? OSHA requirements? confidential aspects of the proposal and the awards? security? special agency requirements?
   g. Does the request outline the review process the proposal will be subjected to? If so, summarize it.
   h. Does the request specify the form or format in which the proposal must be cast? If so, list or summarize the requirements.

4. Check the Yellow Pages for companies in your town that you think may do business by proposal. (Look under headings such as "Petroleum" and find companies that specialize in services.) Call one of them and explain that you would like to interview someone at the company who writes proposals. Make an appointment, conduct the interview, and report to the class on how that company prepares proposals. Before you conduct the interview, consider how you are going to use what you discover:

   a. To whom will you report your information?
   b. What will they be most interested in learning about writing proposals?
   c. How much detail will they want?

5. Interview one or two professors who have submitted proposals. What was their experience?

6

Collecting Data

nce your proposal has been approved, you can begin to collect the data you will need for your report. There are three major sources of data: the library, other people, and your own observations and tests. Because you will become familiar with the techniques for observing conditions and running tests through course work in your major, this chapter focuses primarily on using libraries and on obtaining information from other people through questionnaires and interviews.

Libraries

Libraries give you access to a rich fund of information: tests, observations, analyses, and *reports*. Moreover, a library has a staff that will guide you in your search for the data you need for your particular purpose. If your library is equipped with computers, you will have a vast range of potential sources beyond the library's own holdings.

Basically, however, your main sources of information will be books, encyclopedias, articles, and government publications. In this section we will suggest ways of devising a search strategy that will lead you efficiently to the sources of the data you need.

Search Strategy

When you prepare to perform a laboratory test or a field test, you develop a search strategy beforehand to ensure that your efforts will be purposeful and efficient. You need the same sort of strategy in your search for data in the library. A good way to begin is to prepare a research worksheet. Let us take the example of Carrie.

PREPARING A RESEARCH WORKSHEET Carrie's major is elementary education, and, because she plans to be an administrator some day, she is taking a course in report writing. Her project is to investigate whether the local school system should introduce a kindergarten reading program. Figure 6-1 shows her research worksheet after she has completed it.

Her worksheet is rough, but it provides a good starting point. She makes entries for each of the possible applications, even though she knows that some of them will probably not be relevant to her purpose. This is a wise decision, because she may discover later on that her readers want more information than her principal source, the *Education Index*, provides. They may want information, for example, on legal implications, state and federal mandates, learning theory, and reading cognition. The *Education Index* will provide clues to such topics, but legal indexes and psychology abstracts open the way to additional resources. Carrie's awareness of other sources serves two purposes: it broadens her view of the project as a whole, and it helps her to narrow her list of possible sources. It also reminds her that she is not limited to a single, discipline-related source.

DETERMINING KEY TOPICS Now Carrie must identify a basic vocabulary to use in her search, because all the indexes and abstracts she will be using are organized according to topics and subtopics. After studying her worksheet, she selects "reading" and "kindergarten" as the key terms. She knows that reading is a subject that is part of a program that is part of a curriculum. But, since she has heard of "reading programs" more often than "reading curriculums," she includes "program" in her list of terms. So her list reads:

reading

program

kindergarten

When she checks the *Education Index*, she finds three useful headings: "Reading," "Teaching," and "Kindergarten." As she looks at the *Index* for one or two years, she copies out the titles and sources of articles under these headings that relate to her problem. She can also use these terms to check indexes and abstracts in other areas should she decide to extend her search.

Now she is ready to move on to the next two tasks:

1. Locating, reading, and taking notes on the articles listed in the *Education Index*.
2. Searching out other sources of information in the library.

1. State topic/project/problem in question form: *Should the school board introduce a reading program for the kindergarten?*

2. List the key terms (especially nouns and verbs): *Should, school board, introduce, reading program, Kindergarten*

3. Into what major field or discipline does the project fall?
   Education

4. A. Principal index: *Education Index*

   B. Principal abstracts:

   C. Secondary indexes:

   D. Secondary abstracts:

5. Other sources. In the space below, write the possible applications of the discipline/project area.

Discipline/ Project Area	Possible Applications
Accounting	*Cost accounting; budgets*
Agriculture	*Rural vs. urban school systems*
Biology	*Physical capabilities; anatomy, physiology, etc.*
Economics	*Costs to public, taxes; bond issues; future savings*
Education	*Long- and short-term benefits*
Engineering	*Space problems/solutions; physical facilities*
History	*Past examples of problem and proposed solutions*
Law	*Legal implications; state and federal regulations*
Literature	*Available research; reading programs*
Psychology	*Learning theory; reading comprehension; impact on child; motivation*
Science	*?*
Technology	*Equipment; computer-assisted instruction*
Sociology	*Social impact; long-range implications; cultural-economic factors*
Philosophy	*Moral, ethical questions; traditional attitudes*

Figure 6-1. Research worksheet.

Carrie went directly to the *Education Index* because she was familiar with it from having written term papers for other classes. But what if she had been uncertain about what indexes were available and what journals would have the most valuable articles on her subject? In that event, the first sources to check would be

1. Eugene P. Sheehy, compiler. *Guide to Reference Books*, 9th edition, published in 1976.

2. *Ulrich's International Periodical Directory*, 16th edition, published in 1975.

Most libraries keep these publications readily available.

Two other sources of information are computer searches and government documents.

COMPUTER SEARCHES Many libraries now provide computer-search facilities, and a few university libraries maintain computers on campus. In either case, the procedure to follow parallels Carrie's procedure in consulting the *Education Index*:

1. Identify the discipline.

2. List the key terms in the problem.

3. Organize the terms into major and supporting headings.

One widely available collection of information on education is contained in the ERIC system (ERIC is an acronym for *Education Research Information Center*). It contains a wealth of references, including speeches made at conventions, papers published in conference proceedings, articles in periodicals, and books. Carrie could not have used ERIC very effectively until she had narrowed down the terms that she would look up. With ERIC (and with many other computer data bases), you can consult an accompanying reference book that lists the terms that are most likely to lead you to the information you are searching for. This book is the ERIC *Thesaurus*. Figure 6-2 shows a sample listing from the *Thesaurus*.

You may also seek help from a librarian who is familiar with the procedure for choosing the most appropriate terms for a computer search. The librarian will probably ask you to fill out a form similar to the one shown in Figure 6-3. In the "keyword" section you will list the terms you decide are most directly related to your problem.

HINTS FOR THESAURUS USE

1. Read the Introduction carefully.
2. "Translate" your topic into subject index terms (Descriptors)
3. Look up the Descriptors.
4. Read the Scope Notes.
5. Look at the terms under your Descriptors.
6. Make a list of the other terms that could have been used for the same concept.
7. Look up those terms and repeat steps 4-6.

DESCRIPTOR
as it appears in
Alphabetical Descriptor
Display

ADD DATE
date term was
added to the Thesaurus

LEARNING LABORATORIES

POSTINGS NOTE
number of times term
was used in indexing
CIJE and RIE

CIJE: 206   RIE:296

Jul. 1966   **DESCRIPTOR**
GC 920 ◄—**GROUP CODE**

SN

SCOPE NOTE

Facilities with programed or
autoinstructional materials and
the equipment required for their ◄——— usage definition
display—used primarily for
independent study or
individualized instruction (note: ◄——— prior indexing note
prior to mar80, the instruction
"learning centers, use learning
laboratories" was carried in the
thesaurus)

USED FOR ———► UF

Autoinstructional Laboratories
(1967 1980)

former descriptor
used from 1967 to 1980

NARROWER TERM ——► NT

Language Laboratories

BROADER TERM

BT

Educational Facilities
Laboratories

RELATED TERM

RT

Audiovisual Centers
Autoinstructional Aids
Dial Access Information Systems
Educational Media
Electronic Classrooms
Independent Study
Individualized Instruction
Learning Resources Centers
Programed Instruction
Reading Centers
Skills Centers

Figure 6-2. Sample listing from the ERIC Thesaurus of Descriptors.
Source: Oryx Press, 2214 N. Central, Phoenix, AZ. Reprinted with permission.

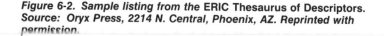

OKLAHOMA STATE UNIVERSITY
LIBRARY
SEARCH REQUEST

PLEASE COMPLETE THIS FORM AS FULLY AS POSSIBLE PRIOR TO
GIVING IT TO A REFERENCE LIBRARIAN. CARE TAKEN NOW WILL
SHORTEN THE COMPUTER TIME AND GREATLY IMPROVE THE
CHANCES FOR A SUCCESSFUL SEARCH.

NAME _____ DATE _____

DEPARTMENT ADDRESS _____ PHONE _____

HOME ADDRESS _____ PHONE _____

STATUS: _____ Faculty   _____ Graduate Student

SEARCH TOPIC: Describe precisely and clearly the subject/topic you
want searched. Examples: "The effects of any mutation on the eye color
of the fruit fly (Drosophila melanogaster)." "Development and use of
educational games to teach communications skills to married couples."

KEYWORDS: List terms or phrases that describe your topic. Give
synonyms, symbols, abbreviations, spelling variations, and special uses.
Thesauri of key-word descriptors are available for some data bases. Ask
the reference librarian about the availability of thesauri in your subject
area.

KEYWORD/PHRASE	KEYWORD/PHRASE	KEYWORD/PHRASE
SYNONYMS, etc.	SYNONYMS, etc.	SYNONYMS, etc.

ABSTRACTS NEEDED (if present in file searched) Yes _____ No _____

Figure 6-3. Computer search request form.
Source: Oklahoma State University Library. Used with permission.

SEARCH COST: We cannot predict in advance the cost of a search. As a guide to the searcher, please indicate the approximate amount you would be willing to pay for the requested search. $ _____

    NOTE: The fee you will be charged is for the search conducted at your request. It is possible that no relevant citations will be found.

METHOD OF PAYMENT: Complete one of the following: (Charges are made to OSU departmental or grant accounts only.)

Cash _____ Check _____
Department Account Name and Number _____
Grant Account Name and Number _____
Requester's Signature and OSU I.D. No. _____

INFORMATION BELOW TO BE COMPLETED
BY LIBRARY PERSONNEL

Librarian Receiving Request _____ Date _____

Search conducted by _____ Date _____

Search consultant(s) _____

Time Consumed: Interview _____ Formulation _____ On-Line _____

Billing _____ Critique _____ Administrative (35%) _____ Total _____

(Requester Present: Yes ___ No ___)

Date	DataBase/ Vendor/ Session no.	Log-on	Log-off	Search time	On-Line Cost	Print Charges	Telecom Cost	Subtotal
___	___	___	___	___	___	___	___	___
___	___	___	___	___	___	___	___	___
___	___	___	___	___	___	___	___	___
___	___	___	___	___	___	___	___	___
___	___	___	___	___	___	___	___	___
___	___	___	___	___	___	___	___	___
___	___	___	___	___	___	___	___	___
___	___	___	___	___	___	___	___	___

SDI entered: Vendor ___ Label ___
SDI released: Vendor ___ Label ___
Permanent Save Searches entered: Vendor ___ Label ___
Permanent Save Searches released: Vendor ___ Label ___
Billing: Inv. _____ Form of Payment ___ Date ___
Cash paid: Deposited _____

Figure 6-3. (continued)

If Carrie consulted ERIC and decided that she wanted even more information, she could ask the librarian to check additional computer sources. Libraries with "on line" facilities can use the telephone to draw on scores of computer data bases in other locations. Such libraries provide guides that explain the procedures, the data bases available, and the disciplines and subjects covered.

Because computer searches can be expensive, be careful when you use them, and find out beforehand how much they will cost. Charges for such services usually include

1. a charge for the librarian's time.
2. a rental charge for use of the terminal.
3. a charge for each answer the computer provides.
4. the cost of having the answers printed out.
5. a charge for having a list of sources and brief abstracts printed out either while you wait or mailed to you later on.

Remember to include these costs in your proposal if you plan to run any computer searches.

GOVERNMENT DOCUMENTS The United States government publishes a vast amount of material on a wide variety of subjects, and there are some 1400 libraries in the United States that make government publications available to the public. Some of them receive a copy of everything the government publishes— as many as 70,000 pieces of material a year, ranging from one-page information sheets to multivolume reports. The material appears either in actual documents and books or on microfilm or microfiche. In addition, many libraries receive documents from the United Nations and various state agencies. Since the U.S. government engages in every sort of activity—business, industry, education, environmental protection, and so forth— you will find that it publishes up-to-date, expertly prepared material on just about any topic you choose to explore. This section will help you locate that material.

First, two considerations to keep in mind:

1. Most libraries catalog government documents separately from their other holdings, so you may need help in locating them.
2. The government uses a different system of classification from the system used by most libraries (either the Dewey Decimal System or the Library of Congress

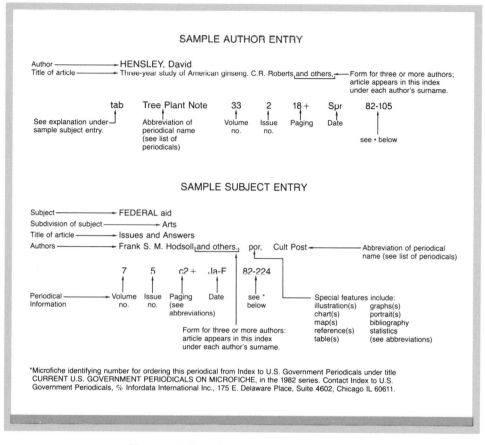

Figure 6-4. Sample entries for the Index to U.S. Government Periodicals. (Reprinted with permission.)

System). So again, you may need help in locating the appropriate indexes and catalogs.

Two principal guides to government publications are *The Index to U.S. Government Periodicals* and *The Monthly Catalog of U.S. Government Publications.*

The *Index* (see Figure 6-4) is similar to the *Reader's Guide to Periodical Literature* and other indexes to periodicals. It lists the contents of some 200 periodicals published by the government. The entries are by subject and by author. The "authors" are actually the government agencies that sponsor the respective publications; that in itself is a convenience when you are searching for information on a specific topic. However, the *Index* is rather difficult to use when you are looking for material that is highly technical. (See Appendix B for the titles of specialized indexes to technical information.)

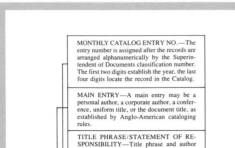

MONTHLY CATALOG ENTRY NO.—The entry number is assigned after the records are arranged alphanumerically by the Superintendent of Documents classification number. The first two digits establish the year, the last four digits locate the record in the Catalog.

MAIN ENTRY—A main entry may be a personal author, a corporate author, a conference, uniform title, or the document title, as established by Anglo-American cataloging rules.

TITLE PHRASE/STATEMENT OF RESPONSIBILITY—Title phrase and author statement are recorded from the title page, cover, or first page of the publication cataloged. Material in brackets is supplied from other sources.

SUPT OF DOCS CLASS NO.—This is the number assigned by the GPO Library to identify the document cataloged.

EDITION—The edition is recorded from information in the document.

SERIES STATEMENT—This appears in parentheses and includes the phrase identifying the document as one of a series.

NOTES—Notes include miscellaneous information about the physical makeup of a publication or about the information contained in it.

SAMPLE ENTRY

83–0123

A 1.9:2271

Creighton, C.S. (Charles S.), 1926–
 Control of catepillars on cabbage / [prepared by Science and Education Administration.]—
 1981 ed. [Washington, D.C.?] : U.S. Dept. of Agriculture, Science and Education Administration : For sale by the Supt. of Docs., U.S. G.P.O., 1980.
 23 p. : ill. ; 23 cm.—(Farmers' bulletin (United States. Dept. of Agriculture) ; no. 2271)
 "This bulletin supersedes Farmers' bulletin no. 2099, Control of caterpillars on commercial cabbage." Item 9 (microfiche)
 S/N 001–000–04185–1 $1.50
 1. Cabbage—Diseases and pests—United States. 2. Caterpillars—Control—United States. I. United States. Science and Education Administration. II. Title. III. Series : Farmers' bulletin (United States. Dept. of Agriculture) ; no. 2271
 SB 762.U55a 1981 80–603339 334.76/0664
 OCLC 7200702

IMPRINT—The imprint contains place of publication, issuing agency, and date of issue. Includes name of distributor if different from issuing agency.

COLLATION—Collation notes pages, illustrations, and size.

SUBJECT HEADINGS (Arabic numerals)—Headings are selected from Library of Congress subject headings. Some local and NLM subjects will be used. Local subjects will be indicated by a star (✩). NLM subjects will be indicated by an asterisk (*). NAL subjects will be indicated by a dagger (†).

LIBRARY OF CONGRESS CLASS NO.—This is given when it appears in the publication or the OCLC data base.

OCLC NO.—This is the number assigned by the OCLC to identify this record in the data base.

ITEM NO.—This document was distributed to depository libraries requesting this item number (microfiche) indicates document was distributed in microfiche.

STOCK NO.—This is a Government Printing Office sales stock number. It is used only in ordering from the Superintendent of Documents.

PRICE—GPO sales price.

ADDED ENTRIES (Roman numerals)—When the Government author is not a main entry, it is included with added entries.

LIBRARY OF CONGRESS CARD NO.—Included for libraries ordering printed cards from the Library of Congress.

DEWEY CLASS NO.—Dewey class is recorded if it appears in the OCLC data base.

Figure 6-5. Sample entry for **The Monthly Catalog of U.S. Government Publications.**

The Monthly Catalog of U.S. Government Publications lists books and pamphlets rather than periodicals (see Figure 6-5). Like a card catalog, it enters information by subject and by author. It contains several indexes, including a keyword index of titles. The monthly catalogs are consolidated at the end of the year into an annual volume. Thus, for the current year refer to the monthly issues, and for past years use annual collections.

Publication of both the *Index* and the *Monthly Catalog* lags behind the publication dates of the items they list, often by as much as three months. This is understandable, given the number of documents the government issues every day.

Other specialized government publications include

1. *The American Statistics Index (ASI).* The *ASI* indexes over 400 sources of governmental statistics by subject, agency, report number, category, and title. Figure 6-6 shows a sample subject search.

2. *Congressional Information Service Index (CIS).* The *CIS* lists transcripts of hearings in the House and Senate. It is produced by the Congressional Research Service in the Library of Congress. It includes overviews of topics and reports both sides of

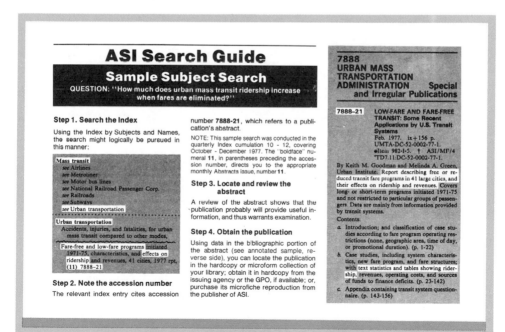

Figure 6-6. ASI sample search.
Source: Reprinted with permission of Congressional Information Service, Inc., 4520 East-West Hwy., Bethesda, MD.

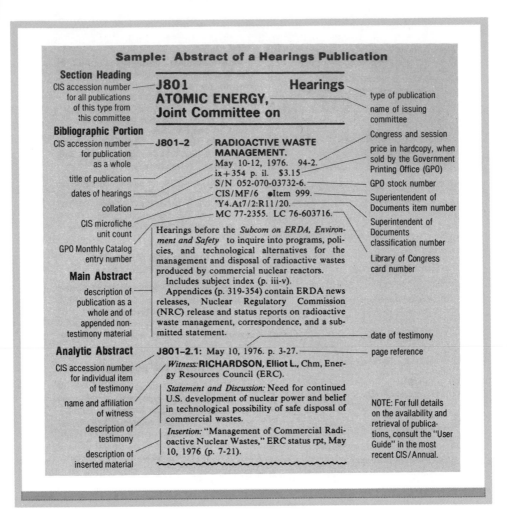

Figure 6-7. CIS/Index sample abstract.
Source: Reprinted with permission of Congressional Information Service, Inc., 4520 East-West Hwy., Bethesda, MD.

a given issue, often with opinions or recommendations. Figure 6-7 shows a sample abstract.

3. *Government Reports and Announcements Index.* This index, which is published twice a month, lists all the hundreds of thousands of government reports published each year, with an abstract of each report. An annual consolidation brings all the issues together, with listings by subject, author, agency, and contract number. All documents listed are available through the National Technical Information Service, a reprint division of the Department of Commerce. Figure 6-8 shows a sample entry.

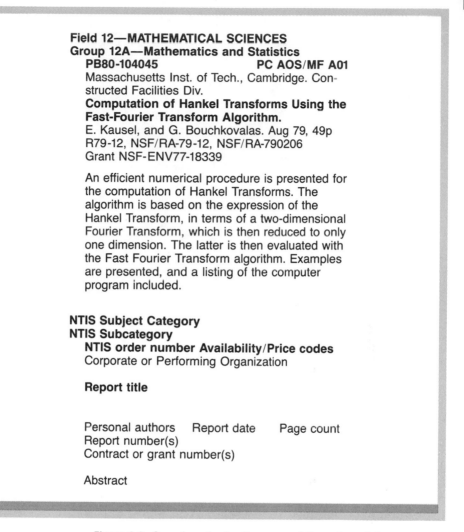

Field 12—MATHEMATICAL SCIENCES
Group 12A—Mathematics and Statistics
 PB80-104045   PC AOS/MF A01
 Massachusetts Inst. of Tech., Cambridge. Con-
 structed Facilities Div.
 **Computation of Hankel Transforms Using the
 Fast-Fourier Transform Algorithm.**
 E. Kausel, and G. Bouchkovalas. Aug 79, 49p
 R79-12, NSF/RA-79-12, NSF/RA-790206
 Grant NSF-ENV77-18339

 An efficient numerical procedure is presented for
 the computation of Hankel Transforms. The
 algorithm is based on the expression of the
 Hankel Transform, in terms of a two-dimensional
 Fourier Transform, which is then reduced to only
 one dimension. The latter is then evaluated with
 the Fast Fourier Transform algorithm. Examples
 are presented, and a listing of the computer
 program included.

 NTIS Subject Category
 NTIS Subcategory
  NTIS order number Availability/Price codes
  Corporate or Performing Organization

  Report title

 Personal authors   Report date   Page count
 Report number(s)
 Contract or grant number(s)

 Abstract

Figure 6-8. Sample entry for Government Reports and Announcements Index. (By permission of the National Technical Information
Service, publisher and distributor.)

4. *Statistical Reference Index (SRI)*. The *SRI* lists statistical reports issued by commercial publishers. See Figure 6-9.

5. *Monthly Checklist of State Publications*. This index lists publications by state and gives you the information you need in
order to obtain a publication through interlibrary loan or to
find it in your local library. Figure 6-10 shows a sample page.

6. *National Technical Information Service (NTIS)*. This branch
of the Department of Commerce provides access to a wide

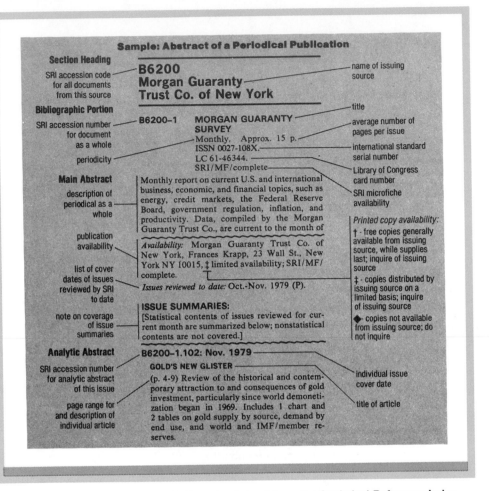

Sample: Abstract of a Periodical Publication

Section Heading

SRI accession code for all documents from this source

B6200
Morgan Guaranty Trust Co. of New York

name of issuing source

Bibliographic Portion

title

SRI accession number for document as a whole

periodicity

B6200–1   **MORGAN GUARANTY SURVEY**
Monthly.   Approx. 15 p.
ISSN 0027-108X.
LC 61-46344.
SRI/MF/complete

average number of pages per issue

international standard serial number

Library of Congress card number

SRI microfiche availability

Main Abstract

description of periodical as a whole

publication availability

list of cover dates of issues reviewed by SRI to date

note on coverage of issue summaries

Monthly report on current U.S. and international business, economic, and financial topics, such as energy, credit markets, the Federal Reserve Board, government regulation, inflation, and productivity. Data, compiled by the Morgan Guaranty Trust Co., are current to the month of

Availability: Morgan Guaranty Trust Co. of New York, Frances Krapp, 23 Wall St., New York NY 10015, ‡ limited availability; SRI/MF/ complete.

Issues reviewed to date: Oct.-Nov. 1979 (P).

ISSUE SUMMARIES:
[Statistical contents of issues reviewed for current month are summarized below; nonstatistical contents are not covered.]

Printed copy availability:
† - free copies generally available from issuing source, while supplies last; inquire of issuing source
‡ - copies distributed by issuing source on a limited basis; inquire of issuing source
◆ - copies not available from issuing source; do not inquire

Analytic Abstract

SRI accession number for analytic abstract of this issue

page range for and description of individual article

B6200–1.102: Nov. 1979

GOLD'S NEW GLISTER
(p. 4-9) Review of the historical and contemporary attraction to and consequences of gold investment, particularly since world demonetization began in 1969. Includes 1 chart and 2 tables on gold supply by source, demand by end use, and world and IMF/member reserves.

individual issue cover date

title of article

Figure 6-9. Sample abstract from the Statistical Reference Index. Source: Reprinted with permission of Congressional Information Service, Inc., 4520 East-West Hwy., Bethesda, MD.

variety of government documents. In a sense, it serves as a retail source for government publications. It offers customized computer searches, and it catalogs documents covering broad and narrow topics.

These are but a few of the many sources you can use to find information disseminated by the government. Again, a carefully planned search strategy, familiarity with various indexes, and access to trained librarians will guarantee you an abundance of information that will enrich your reports. Use these sources as you analyze your assignment and plan your search strategy. The information you assemble will enable you

ALABAMA

- 3608 -
ALCOHOLIC BEVERAGE CONTROL BOARD.   Annual
beer report.   1981/82.   Montgomery.   [6] p.
    Report year ends Sept. 30.

- 3609 -
DEPT. OF AGRICULTURE AND INDUSTRIES.   Annual
report.   99th;   1981/82.   [Montgomery]
109   p.   ill.
    Report year ends Sept. 30.   8-20448

- 3610 -
DEPT. OF EXAMINERS OF PUBLIC ACCOUNTS.
[Report of examination of] Alabama Corrections Institution Finance Authority, State of Alabama, Montgomery. 1979/81.   Montgomery.   A, 8 p.
    Report period ends Sept. 30.

- 3611 -
DEPT. OF EXAMINERS OF PUBLIC ACCOUNTS.
[Report of examination of] Alabama Soil and Water
Conservation Committee; special review: travel and
contracts, State of Alabama, Montgomery, October 1,
1979 through September 30, 1982. Montgomery
[1982]   A-F 1.

- 3612 -
DEPT. OF EXAMINERS OF PUBLIC ACCOUNTS.
[Report of examination of] Alabama Soil and Water
Conservation Committee, State of Alabama, Montgom-
ery, October 1, 1979 through September 30,
1982.   Montgomery [1982]   A-E, 20 l.

- 3613 -
DEPT. OF EXAMINERS OF PUBLIC ACCOUNTS.
[Report of examination of] Department of Conservation
and Natural Resources, State of Alabama, Montgomery.
1977/81.   Montgomery.   A-P, 86 p.
    Report period ends Sept. 30.

- 3614 -
DEPT. OF EXAMINERS OF PUBLIC ACCOUNTS.
[Report of examination of] Department of Industrial
Relations, State of Alabama,
Montgomery. 1978/81. Montgomery.   A-F, 55 p.
    Report period ends Sept. 30.

- 3615 -
DEPT. OF EXAMINERS OF PUBLIC ACCOUNTS.
[Report of examination of] revenue sharing and anti-
recession fiscal assistance funds, State of Alabama,
Montgomery, October 1, 1980 through September 30,
1981. Montgomery [1982]   A-B, 14 l.

- 3616 -
DEPT. OF EXAMINERS OF PUBLIC ACCOUNTS.
[Report of examination of] State of Alabama, Highway
Department local public works grant #04-51-20014,
Blount County, November 1, 1977 through November
15, 1979. Montgomery [1982] A-B, 13 l.

- 3617 -
DEPT. OF REVENUE.   Quadrennial Report. 1978/82.
[Prepared by Research Division. Montgomery] 109
p. ill.
    Report year ends Sept. 30.

- 3618 -
LAW INSTITUTE.   Alabama government manual. Edited
by Richard A. Thigpen and Coleman B. Ransone, Jr.
6th ed.   [University, c1982]   xvi, 504 p.
    Issued in cooperation with the University of Alaba-
ma Center for Public Law and Service
                                            82-051150

- 3619 -
LAW INSTITUTE.   Handbook for Alabama county com-
missioners.   Edited by James D. Thomas and Keith B.
Norman.   4th ed.   [University, c1982]   xviii, 149 p.
    Issued in cooperation with the Association of County
Commissions.
    On cover: Law Center, University of Alabama.
                                            82-51151

- 3620 -
LAW INSTITUTE.   Handbook for Alabama probate
judges. Edited by Keith B. Norman.   3d ed. [Universi-
ty, c1982]   xi, 126 p.
    Issued in cooperation with the Alabama Probate
Judges' Association.
    On cover: University of Alabama Center for Public
Law and Service.   82-71572

- 3621 -
LAW STATUTES, ETC.   Alabama physical therapy practice act, Code of Alabama 1975, Section 34-24-190, et
seq., as amended. [Montgomery, 1982]   9 p.

- 3622 -
OFFICE OF STATE PLANNING AND FEDERAL PRO-
GRAMS.   Alabama and NHEW Federalism.   [Mont-
gomery, 1982]   A4, B46, C32 1.
    $10.00.   83-620757

- 3623 -
OFFICE OF STATE PLANNING AND FEDERAL PRO-
GRAMS.   1982 Alabama metal working directory.
[1st rev. ed.]   Montgomery, 1982.   ix, 133 p.
    $10.00.   83-620760

- 3624 -
STATE LICENSING BOARD FOR GENERAL CONTRAC-
TORS.   Licensed contractors in the State of Alabama.
No. 49, addenda nos. 3 & 4; 1982.   Montgomery.
5, 8 p. annual.

- 3625 -
STATE PLANNING DIVISION.   Alabama county data
book, 1981 [by Elizabeth Gibbs]   Montgomery,
1981. 84 p. ill.
    $4.00.   83-620753

- 3626 -
STATE PLANNING DIVISION.   Alabama regional economic outlook 1982: twelve regional planning and development districts [by David C. Cheng, Care E. Fergu-
son, Jr., and J. Barry Mason]   Developed by Center for
Business and Economic Research, University of Alabama. Montgomery, 1982.   x, 173 p. ill.
    Cover title: Alabama economic outlook, 1982; twelve
regional models.
    $10.00   83-602755

Figure 6-10. Sample page from **Monthly Checklist of State
Publications.**

to provide your reader with a background and a context for your report—and, if you use it deftly, will help you persuade your reader to accept your recommendations. The very act of searching out information will strengthen your ability to use data-gathering techniques and procedures effectively and efficiently.

Company Libraries*

Many people work for organizations or agencies (including government agencies) that maintain their own libraries. Such a library may be nothing more than a file cabinet of reports written by members of the organization, or it may be as comprehensive as a university library. When you begin to work for an organization, check to see whether it maintains a company library, and, if so, what kinds of information it contains. One company, Martin Marietta, maintains nine information sources, ranging from a legal library to a technical information center (TIC). The TIC has over 35,000 technical volumes, more than 1,000 military manuals, some 150,000 reports, over 300 periodicals, and numerous in-plant training courses. In addition, it maintains its own computer data base and has access to more than 200 other data bases. The Martin Marietta library is larger than many college libraries, and it is available to all employees who need information to do their jobs.

The TIC furnishes a wide array of services to employees of Martin Marietta, including

1. computerized searches of government, commercial, and company literature.
2. searches of indexes and abstracts by TIC personnel.
3. interlibrary loans from state and federal government sources and from university libraries.
4. biweekly abstracts of materials on specific topics.
5. information on new publications: titles of new books; abstracts and titles of materials; summaries of articles from various sources.

The Martin Marietta Technical Information Center provides an unusually wide range of services because this company believes that well-informed employees are productive employees. Many other organizations also maintain similar centers of technical information. If the company you work for

*Material in this section is based on information supplied by Dr. Morton Meltzer, Manager, Technical Information Center, Martin Marietta, Orlando, Florida.

offers information services of this sort, be sure to take advantage of them. They will be invaluable to you in keeping up to date in your specialty.

Other People*

The second major source of data is other people, including experts in the field and people with informed opinions on a given subject. Just as the success of your search for data in the library depends on the strategy you devise, so, too, will the success of your consultations with other people. As in other phases of report writing, analyzing the problem and determining what your reader needs to know will help you select the experts who will be most helpful to you. The two principal methods of collecting data from other people are questionnaires and interviews.

Questionnaires

Whether you use questionnaires or interviews, you must formulate your questions carefully beforehand, select the group you intend to consult, administer the questions, and collect and analyze the results. To do all that, you must follow a step-by-step approach.

DEVELOP A RESEARCH DESIGN Knowing precisely what data you need will govern the research strategy you employ. Your data must meet one overriding criterion: usefulness to your reader, usually as background or support information. Consequently, you must decide at the outset

1. In what form will you collect the data? You can frame your questions so that they can be answered in one of several ways: by a number, a multiple-choice response that you can convert into a number, a short answer that you can scan for key words, or a lengthy answer from which you can glean relevant details. Depending on your strategy, construct your questions so that they will elicit the type of response you want.

2. What sections will you include in your questionnaire or your interview? What purpose will each section serve? Some sections may provide primary data, while others may provide data that will help validate your recommendations.

*Some of the material on questionnaires in this section was adapted from Douglas R. Berdie and John F. Anderson, *Questionnaires: Design and Use* (Metuchen, NJ: The Scarecrow Press, Inc., 1974).

3. What costs will you incur in distributing your questionnaire or conducting your interview?

IDENTIFY YOUR SAMPLE Identify and classify the people you want to consult in accordance with some system: by job, by experience, by education, by position. Also, make decisions on these matters:

1. How many people do you want to survey?
2. How many responses will constitute a significant number?
3. How much personal information do you want to get from each person and how will that information relate to your overall design?
4. What specific information do you want? Your respondents need to know precisely what you are asking for, why you want it, in what form, and how you intend to use it.
5. What back-up strategy will you resort to if an inadequate number of people respond?

FRAME THE QUESTIONS The skillfulness with which you frame your questions will have a direct influence on the success of your survey. If your respondents are baffled or offended by the wording, the results will be of little use. Word your questions in a way that will be appropriate to your audience and relevant to your purpose.

Structure each question to ensure that the reader will provide the information you want. Use simple, unambiguous words. Avoid overly formal words and unduly specialized terms. Remember that your respondent is doing you a favor by answering your questions, and ineptly worded questions may simply go unanswered. Avoid vague, general words ("several," "significant number of," "most," "usually," "soon"). Be sure that the words you use do not carry one meaning for you and another for your reader ("conservative," "value," "liberal"), and that they do not have emotional overtones ("best," "worst," "awful").

If you use abbreviations and acronyms that may be unfamiliar to your respondents, explain them. Make your questions fair. (The classic example of an unfair question is: "Do you still beat your wife?") Indicate whether you want a fact or an opinion. Never ask for more than one piece of information in each question. Do not tack on "or not" at the end of a question and then ask for a yes-or-no answer. Try to avoid linking one question to another by saying "If yes, then ..." Instead, make sure that each question can be answered by itself. Ask questions that are real and not hypothetical.

When you design your questionnaire or interview, decide precisely what kind of data you want, because the responses will constitute the data you get. Consider what type of answer will enable you to analyze the results efficiently and usefully. Provide space for every possible response—for "Don't know" as well as for "Yes" and "No." When you ask for multiple-choice responses, provide space for "Other." You may discover possibilities you were unaware of. Use open-ended or essay questions when you want general information, but remember that responses to such questions are hard to quantify and analyze. In laying out your questions, use a vertical arrangement:

    ____ Yes

    ____ No

    ____ Don't know

PRETEST After you have constructed your questionnaire, pretest it on a random sample from the group you plan to survey, in order to spot any hidden problems. Even if you can test it only on classmates or instructors, do so before sending it to your main group. Ask for comments from your sample respondents and then revise your questionnaire accordingly. At the very least, have your questionnaire evaluated by your technical writing instructor.

CONDUCT FIELD WORK Now you are ready to collect your data. How will you distribute your questionnaire—by mail? deliver copies by hand? leave copies in a convenient place? Determine which method will bring you the fullest response. Mailing questionnaires is costly (envelopes and postage both ways), but it gives your survey an air of professionalism. Handing out copies ensures that they will get into the hands of the right people and gives you a chance to answer any questions, but it is a time-consuming procedure. Leaving a pile of questionnaires in a convenient location may mean that you will miss many of the people you want to question, but it does make your questionnaire available to a large population. In short, choose the method of distributing your questionnaire that best suits your need for data and that is most appropriate to the group you are surveying.

Finally, how will you collect the completed questionnaires? Have them mailed back? Pick them up yourself? Whatever you decide, make certain that you give complete instructions for returning the questionnaires. Spell out those instructions at the beginning and the end of your questionnaire and in your cover letter. Include them even if you enclose a self-addressed, stamped envelope.

INCLUDE A COVER LETTER Whenever you send out a questionnaire, you should accompany it with a cover letter in which you explain your purpose and your plan for the results. Typically, such a letter contains

1. an introduction in which you briefly state your background and your reasons for sending the questionnaire.
2. a statement of the overall purpose of your research and how the questionnaire fits into that purpose.
3. an outline of how you plan to use the data.
4. an indication of how you will safeguard the respondent's identity (*anonymous:* No one, not even you, will be able to link any response to any respondent; *confidential:* You will know who prepared each response but you promise not to reveal who said what. You may decide to use a code number of some kind, but make certain the reader knows what you are doing).
5. instructions for returning the completed questionnaire, including the date by which you need it.
6. an expression of your appreciation to the reader for taking the time and trouble to complete the questionnaire. (Do not thank the reader. You thank someone only after he or she has done something for you.)
7. a reminder of when the questionnaire is to be returned.

In a headnote to the questionnaire itself, repeat in brief form the same information:

1. The purpose of the study and of the questionnaire.
2. How you will use the data.
3. How you will safeguard the respondent's identity.
4. Instructions for returning the questionnaire.

At the end of the questionnaire, you can once again express your appreciation and repeat the return instructions and the desired return date. You may, if appropriate, offer to send a copy of the results to the respondent.

ANALYZE THE RESPONSES Once you have received the completed questionnaires, you must analyze them. Is the return significant enough to make your results valid? Your analysis of the purpose of your questionnaire (what did you want to learn?) and of your survey group will determine whether the number of completed questionnaires is adequate. When you incorporate your findings in a report, you will need to indicate how many questionnaires were completed, how you interpreted the responses, and what criteria you used for validation.

Questionnaires are helpful tools for collecting data when they are prepared carefully and used effectively. Figure 6-11 provides a checklist that you can use to evaluate questionnaires.

Interviews

The procedures used in questionnaire data collection are applicable to interviews as well. The major difference, aside from the manner in which you conduct the survey, is that interviews usually generate information beyond the data you are seeking. Few people will answer "yes—no—don't know" to a question without explaining their answer. Pretesting your interview questions will prepare you for such explanations and will suggest how to evaluate them. Above all, be courteous when conducting interviews. Thank your respondents for the time and trouble they have spent on the interview. A follow-up note of thanks gives evidence of your professionalism.

Use the checklist in Figure 6-11 to evaluate your interview questions.

Observations

The third major source of information is your own observations. Here you use the methods you have learned in your other courses, including laboratory tests, on-site inspections, and observations in the field. There are other methods, but these are the most prevalent. They all entail a point of view, and they all require an orderly procedure for recording the data you observe.

One of the most efficient ways of recording data is to keep a notebook of some kind. Your notebook should contain a statement on the methods, materials, and procedures you are using, as well as a complete record of the data you collect. The

CHECKLIST

	Yes	No
1. Design		
I know what I want to learn from the questionnaire or interview.	—	—
I know how the data I collect will fit my overall data-collection plan.	—	—
I know the form I want my data to come to me in.	—	—
I know how much the questionnaire or interview will cost me.	—	—
2. Population		
I know the persons who have the data I need for my report.	—	—
I know where to find them.	—	—
I know how many responses I need to make my study significant.	—	—
I have an alternative plan in case the number of responses falls below what I need.	—	—
I have done a reader analysis on the people I will survey.	—	—
I know the needs of the respondents in order for them to answer my questions.	—	—
3. Questions		
I have worded my questions in a way that will elicit the information I need.	—	—
I have used specific words in the questions that my readers can understand.	—	—
I have stated my questions fairly.	—	—
I have asked for one piece of information in each question.	—	—
The responses listed include all possible answers.	—	—
I have listed the responses vertically.	—	—

Figure 6-11. Checklist for questionnaires and interviews.

4. Pretest

I have pretested my questionnaire.   ___ ___

I have included evaluation of the questionnaire as part   ___ ___
of the pretest.

I have refined the questionnaire based on evaluations   ___ ___
from the pretest.

I have had the questionnaire evaluated by my   ___ ___
technical-writing instructor.

5. Distribution

I have considered all methods of distributing my   ___ ___
questionnaire.

I have given complete instructions for returning the   ___ ___
questionnaire in the cover letter, at the beginning of the
questionnaire, and on the last page of the
questionnaire.

6. Analysis

I know what statistical methods to use in analyzing the   ___ ___
data.

I have established criteria for evaluating the validity of   ___ ___
each completed questionnaire.

I am prepared to explain to the reader of my final report   ___ ___
the statistical tests I have used and the criteria for
validating the questionnaires.

Figure 6-11. (continued)

notebook gives you a chronological record of your work, even when you are only sending out a questionnaire or conducting an interview.

Here are some suggestions for the efficient use of a notebook:

1. Date each entry, and perhaps even enter the times at which you began and completed an activity.

2. Use clear headings for your entries. Place major headings flush left and indent second-level heads an inch or more.

3. Number your entries or use some other mark (a dash, an asterisk, or a bullet); leave generous space between entries.

4. Remember that you will be returning to these notes later, when your memory has dimmed. Thus, you should provide as much detail as possible.

5. Make it possible for someone else to ferret out information from your notebook. Private codes are fine for personal diaries, but they have no place in your notebook.

6. Include rough sketches of schematics, outlines, line graphs, and so on. You will need them when you prepare finished visuals later on.

7. Record your failures *and* your successes. In short, record everything.

A well-kept notebook is a valuable resource when you turn to your problem-solving procedures. If you run into difficulties along the way, a review of the methods you used, neatly recorded in your notebook, may give you a clue to the source of an error. Finally, an accurate, detailed notebook may be of value to the organization you work for and will give you a record of your own work.

Technical Assignments

1. Write a brief report to your instructor in which you list the principal sources you plan to use in developing your final report. Divide the list into groups based on general sources, materials specific to your discipline, and government documents. Prepare an opening paragraph in which you identify the library you plan to use and the topic you plan to work on. Conclude the report by requesting suggestions for other sources of information.

2. Prepare a list of people you plan to interview. Draft a letter requesting an appointment. Include
   a. your project and its purpose.
   b. the interviewees' importance to the project and your need for their help.
   c. the amount of time you believe the interview will take.
   d. suggestions as to times and dates.

   Prepare a list of the questions you want to ask and include them as an enclosure. Show the letter and questions to your instructor (and consultant, if appropriate) before mailing them.

3. Prepare a series of interview questions to use in discussing your project with someone in your school. Choose someone who is well informed on the subject. Write a report on your experience. Include suggestions for the other members of the class on how to conduct a successful interview.

4. Develop a questionnaire asking students for their views on a local school issue (such as tuition and fees, the value of fraternities/sororities, intercollegiate athletics, intramural athletics, environmental protection, the military draft). Prepare a report for your instructor in which you explain the issue and its importance, the methods you plan to use to collect data, and how you plan to analyze the data.

5. Identify a company that maintains a fairly large library and write for information about the library and its holdings. Report your findings to the class.

6. List the major terms and subterms you plan to use in a search strategy.

7

Organizing Data I:
Using Patterns and Formats

e come now to the third stage in the process of collecting, analyzing, and organizing data for use in a report. In this chapter and in the next two we will concentrate on the most effective ways to organize data for ultimate presentation to your readers.

We have seen that two basic problems face the writer of a report:

1. Deciding what information the reader needs.
2. Deciding how to collect and analyze that information in a way that will satisfy the reader's needs.

To solve these two problems, the writer must plan each successive step of the process, always keeping the reader in view. First, the writer determines what the reader already knows about the subject (the shared experiences) and what additional information the reader desires (the information the writer will convey in the report). If the writer fails to keep the reader's needs in mind, communication breaks down.

A common cause of communication failure is faulty organization. Without clear signals to show the way, the reader is at a loss as to what is happening and what will happen next. Imagine trying to drive from New York to Los Angeles without a road map, especially if there were no interstate highway system to follow. The reader of a report needs a map just as much as a cross-country traveler does.

Some writers ignore the reader along the way and then, at the very end of the report, suddenly lay out their conclusions and recommendations. They write reports as if they were writing detective stories, with all the clues cleverly obscured until the climax is reached and everything is made clear. Imagine what would happen if you were denied the course syllabus, grading standards, and details of the assignments until the week of the final exam. You must have that information at the beginning of the course, not at the end. Similarly, the reader of a report needs essential information at the very outset.

Moreover, the reader wants to know how the writer views the information that has been brought together in the report. What sections are of the greatest significance? What was in the writer's mind as the information was being processed? What purpose guided the writer in collecting and analyzing the data?

Clearly, converting data into usable information requires three steps: collection, analysis, and *organization*. A common error in report writing is to describe in great detail the methods employed in collecting and analyzing the data but to say nothing at all about the rationale that underlies the organization of the report.

The Need for Organization

Imagine for a moment that you are giving a talk. If you tell your audience that you are going to make two points and you state what those points are, and if you then say that you will expand on those points in a particular context, your audience will know what to listen for. Similarly, telling your readers what sections they will encounter in your report, and the sequence in which they will encounter those sections, prepares them for what is coming. If they want, they can even skip a section or skim it to check it against what they already know.

Another reason for informing your readers about your organization is to make clear whether you are following a familiar order of presentation or are creating an original sequence that, in your opinion, is better suited to your purpose. Many companies insist that writers of reports follow a standardized sequence to make it easier for those who read reports to find just what they want in its accustomed place. Actually, such prescribed progressions are well suited to the content of most reports—trip reports, for example, or progress reports or feasibility reports. If you have ever written a laboratory report, you know that the logical sequence of sections is inherent in the nature of the report itself. And mainly for that reason, that sequence has become traditional and is expected by readers of such reports. Beyond all that, a familiar sequence saves time for managers and supervisors who are obliged to read countless reports swiftly and with full comprehension.

So what it all comes down to is organizing your data in the manner best suited to your purpose and to the purpose of the readers of your report. You array your facts much as a general arrays his troops before battle. What is the best disposition of your strengths? Why is that disposition better than others? Like the general, you order your facts in response to your past experience, the current challenge, and your objective.*

The process of organizing data into patterns of usable information is what cognitive psychologists call "chunking." Chunking occurs when the mind links groups of data together to form a pattern. Two common examples are telephone numbers and Social Security numbers. When you look up a phone number, you perceive it as two groups of numbers, one with three digits, the other with four. Social Security numbers are also chunked: three digits, two digits, four digits. Chunking imposes an order on discrete facts and helps you remember them. In a sense you are doing the same thing, though at a different level, when you chunk the data you have collected and analyzed.

As we have noted, most companies want information presented by category in a certain sequence. The categories provide large groupings for related bits of information. The groupings in telephone numbers serve as categories, too: area code, exchange, and number. The same is true of Social Security numbers and many credit card numbers.

Labels and Headings

The use of categories in organizing a report helps you as you write the report and helps your readers as they read it. To identify each category—each group of related data—you assign it a label. You might label one category "Methods and Materials"; another, "Results"; a third, "Discussion." The labels you choose are related to the nature of the information, the reader's needs, and your purpose.

Labels are usually *descriptive*—they describe, in a kind of shorthand, what the reader will find in the section that follows. Descriptive labels give only a hint of what is to come, however. They provide the reader with no real indication of the information contained in the section. Does the reader need to read the section on "Methods" in order to understand and accept the section on "Recommendations"? Probably, but not necessarily.

Informational headings do a much better job of guiding the reader through the organizing categories of a report. For one thing, they save the reader time. They reveal in an instant whether a particular section must be read or whether it can be skimmed or skipped. And they help conserve the reader's energy, holding it in reserve until the sections of the report where you set forth your conclusions and recommendations.

*This analogy is from Sir Arthur Quiller-Couch, *The Art of Writing* (New York: Capricorn Books, 1943), p. 293.

Table 7-1. Comparison of Descriptive Labels and Informational Headings

Descriptive Label	Informational Heading
Methods	Stress and Durability Tests
Results	Z-22 Plastic Lasts Twice as Long
Recommendations	Z-22 Plastic Preferable to H-10 Plastic
Discussion	Three Reasons for Modifying Standard Tests
Background	Earlier Applications of Plastic

Table 7-1 compares standard descriptive labels with the informational headings that might appear in a report on plastics. Notice how much more helpful the informational headings are.

Whereas descriptive labels appear in report after report, informational headings are unique to a single report or to a group of reports on a single project. Their freshness and precision suggest to the reader that you have given serious thought to the report and its organization.

If, however, you cannot devise informational headings that serve your purpose, by all means use descriptive labels. They are better than nothing at all.

When you communicate with someone, you are likely to have some experience in common with that person. That shared experience may be very slight (you have only a language in common) or quite extensive (you have had the same education and work experience). If you have some way of judging the extent of that shared experience, you will have a good idea of how much information you must provide to ensure that your communication will make sense. If you are uncertain about what you and your reader have in common, you will include a glossary of terms, a list of symbols, background information, even a review of the literature on the subject. Knowing that shared experience helps you develop labels and headings that help communication.

Components of the Report's Front Matter

Certain elements must be included in all reports. These parts contain information that is essential to the reader, and they appear consistently from report to report. In this section we will discuss the obligatory parts of the report's front matter. In later chapters we will discuss other parts that may vary from one report to another.

Standard Approaches

The simplest form of front matter consists of a memo with its standard headings:

Date:

To:

From:

Subject:

These labels give your readers essential information about the memo and prepare them for the main body of information that follows. That, in fact, is the purpose of the front matter in any memo, report, or proposal.

In more formal documents, standard labels announce the separate parts of the report, still with the purpose of preparing the reader for what follows. For the front matter, these parts include

the cover

the letter of transmittal

the title page

summary or abstract

the contents

list of illustrations

glossary of terms

list of symbols

About This Report

You need not include all of these elements in every report. The more formal the report and the more complex the subject, the greater your need for the full range of elements.

The Cover

The cover is the outer dress of the report. It may be a sheet of paper, a file folder, or a binder. The cover protects the report and gives it some air of formality. In choosing the type of cover you will use, consider how many people will handle the report and how bulky it is. Whatever cover you choose, label it in some manner. Figure 7-1 shows two sample labels: one for a class report and one for a report written for an organization

Title	Microcomputers in Accounting: A Proposal
Name	Edward Carling
Date/Class	April 4, 1984 ENGLISH 3323

Label for a class report

Title	Incorporating Microcomputers in the Accounting Process: A Proposal
Name/ Department	Ronald White Information Processing/Management
Identification	Report #84-6286
Date	May 22, 1986

Label for an organization report

Figure 7-1. Sample cover labels.

The Letter of Transmittal

The letter (or memo) of transmittal conveys the report from the writer to the reader. In fact, it may just be clipped to the cover of the report. The letter of transmittal announces the report, summarizes it, and lists acknowledgments (if appropriate).

ANNOUNCING THE REPORT The first paragraph of the letter of transmittal gives the reader the following information:

1. Who is transmitting the report (the writer).
2. The title of the report.
3. Authorization for the report.
4. The primary reader(s) and those to whom copies are being sent (the distribution list).

SUMMARY The second paragraph summarizes the report, briefly stating the problem and the conclusions or recommendations. This paragraph should be short and to the point.

ACKNOWLEDGMENTS If others have helped in collecting the data or preparing the report, they should be mentioned here. Also, if the reader of the letter is expected to take any specific action in regard to the report, that should be stated in this last paragraph.

When preparing a letter of transmittal, follow good letter or memo form (see Chapter 13) and indicate that the report is attached. Sign the letter. Figure 7-2 shows a sample letter of transmittal.

The Title Page

The title page gives complete information about the report: the title of the report, the name of the writer, the writer's class or department, the date, approvals, and a very brief summary of the report. Figure 7-3 shows two sample title pages.

The title of the report consists of a main title and a subtitle. The main title tells the reader

1. what the major element in the report is (what you manipulated; what the focus is).
2. what you performed the manipulations on.
3. what element or elements you measured.

The subtitle indicates the type of report: proposal, feasibility study, laboratory report, progress report, or whatever.

The brief descriptive summary on the title page states the content of the report without referring to the results, conclusions, or recommendations. In company libraries, the title page (and sometimes the abstract or summary page) is often copied and filed for quick access.

Summary or Abstract

In every report you submit, include a summary of your major points, findings, conclusions, and recommendations. Many times this is the only section your reader will actually read. Your supervisor may receive scores of reports from various departments, and your summary will suggest whether your report is one that must be read in its entirety. Moreover, copies of your report may find their way to a great number of people, some of whom may be interested in it, others not. They need to decide quickly whether their job requires them to have the

Dodge City, Kansas
December 16, 1984

Dr. Thomas L. Warren
Director, Technical Writing
Classroom Building, Room 001
Oklahoma State University
Stillwater, OK   74078

Dear Dr. Warren:

I submit two complete copies of my report titled "A Mobile
Clinic for Veterinary Farm Calls," as the final assignment for
English 3323, Intermediate Technical Writing. As you will recall,
Dr. William Boyd will receive the original.

The report discusses the needs and problems of Dr. Boyd's
large-animal veterinary practice, lists the criteria used to find a
possible solution, then describes the proposed solution: a mobile
clinic outfitted specifically for veterinary farm calls.

I wish to thank Dr. Sarah Williamson for acting as my consultant
and giving me advice and support during the research and writing
of this report.

Sincerely,

Mike Burge
English 3323

MB/mcr

This letter and the report noted (pp. 110, 112, 113, 114, and 117) are used by
permission of Mike Burge.

Figure 7-2. Sample letter of transmittal.

MICROCOMPUTERS IN ACCOUNTING
A Proposal

by
Edward Carling

April 4, 1984

ENGLISH 3323
Dr. Thomas L. Warren

Microcomputers offer public accountants a fast and
convenient way to handle client data. This report
details the advantages of using a microcomputer and
recommends specific hardware and software.

Approved By: Approved By:

_____   _____

_____   _____

Continued on page 110

Figure 7-3. Sample title pages.

A MOBILE CLINIC FOR VETERINARY FARM CALLS
A Proposal

Prepared
by
Mike Burge

for
English 3323
Intermediate Technical Writing

Abstract

This report contains a discussion of the problems
found in a large-animal veterinary practice, lists the
criteria for solving the problems, and describes a
proposed solution.

December 16, 1984

Approved by: Approved by:

_____   _____

_____   _____

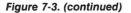

Figure 7-3. (continued)

information you are reporting. The summary enables them to make that decision.

The summary or abstract includes three main elements:

1. An overview of the problem. Here you summarize the main problem or topic of your report. If you prepared the report in response to specific assignment, say so. But do not give such details as who made the assignment, when, and why. (Include those details with the background information.) State the problem and its significance, provide a very brief background, and, perhaps, define one or two of the key terms.

2. A brief description of the methods you used to gather and analyze your data.

3. A brief statement of your conclusions or recommendations. You might arrange them in a numbered list in order to focus attention on them. Also, summarize the significance or benefits accruing from your conclusions or recommendations.

The length of your summary or abstract depends on two factors: The nature of your readers and the complexity of the subject.

THE READERS You already know who the primary and secondary readers of your report will be. But who else may have an interest in it? Many reports move throughout an organization, sometimes to the highest levels. Often, readers along the way must read and respond to hundreds of reports. And then there are the company librarians who file abstracts of reports for readers not on the distribution list. Finally, there are readers who may turn to your report months or years after you submit it. Clearly, in order to accommodate all the readers who may have an interest in your report, you would have to repeat the entire report in your summary, and that is impossible. So the best you can do is to make the summary just long enough to satisfy the majority of the readers who are likely to be interested in your report.

COMPLEXITY OF THE SUBJECT The more complex the subject, the more details on your solution, conclusions, or recommendations you will need to include in your summary.

Generally, the summary or abstract should not exceed two double-spaced pages or one single-spaced page. Figure 7-4 shows a sample abstract.

ABSTRACT

Conducting a large-animal practice is often hard, dirty, exhausting work requiring many hours of the veterinarian's time. Each practice has problems for which solutions cannot be found, and the vet who enjoys his practice anticipates and accepts these problems. But, too often, problems that can be solved are also accepted because the busy vet, though aware of the problems, cannot take the time needed to research possible solutions.

The veterinarian who practices large-animal medicine must find effective ways to use work hours efficiently. Though the normal work day is 12 to 14 hours and the doctor is on call 24 hours daily, the actual time spent treating patients is half the total number of hours worked. The remaining half of the work day is spent locating and packing professional equipment and traveling to and from farm calls. The veterinarian must conduct the practice in a variety of locations and must anticipate and prepare for each practice site and patient. A practice of high quality and productivity must have organization as an essential element.

A growing number of veterinarians have found that conducting a large-animal practice from a mobile clinic offers increased on-site patient services, more efficient use of time, well-organized storage in small spaces, and personal convenience. These veterinarians are finding that increased efficiency and productivity also increase earnings.

A 24' x 8' furnished mobile clinic can carry 2,000 lbs. of equipment and can still be towed by a standard model ¾ ton pick-up truck. The initial purchase price of a furnished clinic is less than $20,000 (actual price at this time is $19,050). Operating and maintenance costs average 15¢ per mile traveled, depending on individual vehicle and average miles per gallon of regular gasoline.

A veterinarian uses over 200 different drugs and pieces of equipment each week. The storage in a mobile clinic is capable of handling this drug and equipment load.

The clinic has two limitations: (1) it does not contain a surgery, and (2) it does not have the facilities to handle the more elaborate lab tests. The benefits do outweigh the limitations, though, making the mobile clinic an investment in increased practice quality, productivity, and profitability.

Figure 7-4. Sample informative abstract.

The Contents   The table of contents lists all the sections of the report, with major and minor headings and the number of the page on which each section begins. Its purpose is to give your reader a convenient guide to the various sections and also to demonstrate how you have organized the report. Figure 7-5 shows a typical contents page.

CONTENTS

Figure 7-5. Sample contents.

Two sets of page numbers are usually used in a contents: lower-case Roman numerals (iv, v, vi) refer to other pages in the front matter, and Arabic numbers (1, 2, 4) refer to pages in the report proper. Reference to attachments may be either letter-number combinations (A-1, A-2, B-1, B-2, and so on) or a continuation of the numbering of the report itself. Attachments should be numbered separately if they are likely to be detached from the report to be used for another purpose (perhaps for another report based on the same information).

List of Illustrations

If your report includes visuals of any kind, list them at the beginning so that your reader can locate them easily. If you include only one or two visuals, there is no need to list them on a separate page. You might enter them on the contents page following any appendix material. But if you include three or more, list them on a separate page. Figure 7-6 shows a sample list of visuals. If you include both figures and tables, use the heading "Illustrations" and list the figures first and then the tables, as in Figure 7-6.

LIST OF ILLUSTRATIONS

iii

Figure 7-6. Sample listing for figures and tables.

Glossary of Terms

A glossary is a list of definitions of terms that you have reason to believe your reader may not understand. (Chapter 9 explains how and when to write definitions.) Provide a glossary when you know for certain that your reader has had no training or experience in the subject or when you suspect that your reader may not be familiar with the latest information on the subject. If you use only two or three terms that may prove troublesome, define them in the context of your report rather than in a separate glossary. Even when you are sure that your reader will understand the terms themselves, you may want to include a glossary in order to emphasize certain concepts. Finally, the glossary serves as a list of key terms that will facilitate the filing of your report in the company library. Figure 7-7 shows a sample glossary.

GLOSSARY OF TERMS
USED IN THIS REPORT

Term	Meaning
bar	a short, round piece of steel that is driven upwards as a bottom latch pulls back; prevents the top latch from unlatching.
bottom latch	latches the internal cover/machine.
bracket	connects the handle to the internal cover.
electronic chip	miniature integrated circuit board; has predetermined functions.
handle	part used to lift the internal cover; part of the external workings of the machine.
J-K flip flop	specialized electronic chip; controls two or more input signals; holds circuit open or closed.
top latch	latches the access cover/internal cover.

Figure 7-7. Sample glossary.

```
                          LIST OF SYMBOLS
                          USED IN THIS REPORT
        Symbol                 Meaning
        Hz                     hertz (frequency)
        N                      newton (force)
        J                      joule (work, energy)
        W                      watt (power)
        V                      volt (potential difference)
```

Figure 7-8. Sample list of symbols.

Many organizations specify that the glossary be included as part of the front matter. Others prefer to have it positioned at the end of the report, as an attachment. Placing it in the front matter makes it easier for your reader to find it and emphasizes its importance. Handling it as an attachment makes it easier to remove for use elsewhere. In any case, be sure to follow the practice required by the company you are working for.

List of Symbols

A list of symbols explains what symbols you are using in the report and how you are using them. Include any abbreviations or acronyms used in your report. Figure 7-8 shows a sample list of symbols.

About This Report

The last major section of the front matter is About This Report. This section describes the major subject or topic the report covers, why the writer wrote the report, and what to expect in the report.

THE MAJOR SUBJECT OR TOPIC OF THE REPORT State the major subject here and indicate its limitations—that is, the specific aspects of the subject you are dealing with. Also, identify in a general way the readers you are addressing.

WHY YOU WROTE THE REPORT Tell your reader what prompted you to write the report (other than the fact that your supervisor told you to write it). State the particular purpose you intend it to serve and the information you mean it to convey. Is your

About This Report

   This report discusses a mobile clinic, designed for Dr. William Boyd, and outfitted to function as a farm call clinic. The report presents the need for a mobile clinic, and lists three sets of criteria that must be met in order to solve the stated problems. Further, the report offers the mobile clinic as a solution and describes the construction components of the clinic.

   Finally, the report describes the interior layout of the clinic, its feasibility as a solution, and the benefits and limitations of the design. The report offers conclusions and recommendations.

Figure 7-9. Sample About This Report section.

intention to inform or to persuade the reader to take some action, or to influence a decision? Knowing your purpose at the outset will enable your reader to use your report efficiently and economically.

WHAT THE READER IS TO EXPECT Explain how you have organized the report. What comes first? What comes next? Spare your reader surprises along the way. Identify the emphasis of the report. As always, remember your reader's need to know and work to satisfy that need by providing information clearly and concisely. Figure 7-9 shows a sample of an About This Report section.

   The main portion of the report follows immediately after the front matter. In the next chapter we will explore ways of organizing the major sections of the report in response to the reader's primary need to know.

Types of Reports

Before we end this chapter we must mention six common report types you can expect to be writing after you have joined an organization: progress, feasibility, field or trip, information, laboratory research, and proposals (see Table 7-2). The type of report you write on a given occasion will depend on the assignment, the context, the data available, and, above all, the reader's needs. These six types of reports serve different purposes and function in different ways.

Table 7-2. Six Most Common Types of Reports

Report Type	Purpose	Major Sections	Visuals	Notes
Progress report	1. Indicate progress on a project 2. Review history 3. Evaluate progress of a project	1. Project the report covers and date of last report 2. Overall goals of project 3. Major tasks needed to complete project 4. Tasks completed: a. Date b. Relationship to goals c. Work completed 5. Tasks to be done: a. Work not completed b. Projected dates c. Problems experienced or anticipated 6. Evaluation of progress	1. Timelines showing amount of time spent; projected future time frames 2. Tables giving technical data such as costs, partial results, etc. 3. Line graphs showing data from tables 4. Photographs of site	1. Issued when phase of project completed or begun 2. Called Periodic Report when written at stated intervals; usually follows form and does not vary from report to report
Feasibility report	1. Evaluate a situation or proposal 2. "Can we do what situation or proposal calls for?"	1. Project for evaluation a. Statement of problem b. Importance of problem 2. Criteria for successful solution 3. Proposed solution 4. Evaluation	1. Timelines 2. Tables of potential data, such as costs 3. Line graphs based on tables 4. Lists comparing needs and abilities	1. Thorough and extremely honest; no room to hedge 2. Need data to support conclusion that project will or will not succeed 3. Stress practicality or impracticality

Table 7-2 (continued)

Report Type	Purpose	Major Sections	Visuals	Notes

Field or trip report	1. Provide record of trips away from office
	2. Collect data at site
		1. Purpose of trip
		2. Location or site
		3. Dates and times as appropriate
		4. Observations or conversations
		  a. Data collected
		  b. Methods used to collect data
		5. Evaluations, conclusion, recommendation
			1. Maps
			2. Photographs
			3. Tables of data
			4. Line graphs of data
				1. Summarize conversations
				2. Emphasis is on what actually happened and conversations

Information report	1. Pass along information relevant to a problem	1. Statement of problem information relates to 2. Importance of information to problem 3. Sources of information 4. Summary/abstract of information	1. Visuals from sources adapted for reader 2. New visuals based on information	1. Usually reviews of literature or summaries of conversations

Laboratory or research report	1. Give results of laboratory tests or experiments
	2. Explain how tests or experiments were conducted
		1. Problem or subject
		  a. Statement
		  b. Definitions
		  c. Need for solution
		2. Theory or review of literature
		3. Materials
		4. Methods or procedures
		5. Results/data collected
		6. Discussion
		  a. Meaning of results
		  b. Need for solution
		  c. Evaluations of most significant results
		7. Conclusions, recommendations, evaluations
			1. Tables of data
			2. Line graphs
			3. Schematics, flow charts
				1. Must be accurate and thorough
				2. Thoroughly discuss visuals
				3. Emphasis
				  a. On methods (for future duplication)
				  b. On results (for decisions and information)

Continued on page 120

Table 7-2 (continued)

Report Type	Purpose	Major Sections	Visuals	Notes

Proposal	1. Offer to solve a problem; offer solution to a problem	1. Problem
		  a. Statement
		  b. Need for solution
		  c. Definitions
		  d. Criteria for success
		2. Possible solution or solutions
		  a. Statement of expected results
		  b. Benefits/ advantages
		  c. Disadvantages
		  d. Relation to criteria
		3. Sources of data
		  a. Location
		  b. Method of collection
		  c. Analysis
		  d. Reliability
		4. Conclusions, recommendations
			1. Timelines
			2. Maps, photographs, drawings
			3. Tables of data
			4. Line graphs of data
				1. See Chapter 5 for fuller treatment

The organization you work for will probably require other types of reports as well, designed to meet its specific informational needs. The organization's style guide or procedures manual will provide you with details on each type, its purpose, the major sections to be included, the type of visuals to use, and any special features.

Technical Assignments

1. Write a report to your instructor in which you list and discuss the parts of the front matter you plan to include with your report. Justify each part in terms of your purpose and the reader's needs.

2. Go to the library and find a government report on a subject of interest to you.
   a. What format does it follow? List the major headings.
   b. Does it use subheadings? Sub-subheadings?
   c. Are the headings and subheadings informational or descriptive? Give examples.

    d. Who is the assumed reader of this report? What are the reader's informational needs?

    e. Does the report contain any of the following: cover? letter of transmittal? title page? summary or abstract? table of contents? lists of illustrations, symbols, glossary? introductory section telling the reader about the report?

3. Using a report from industry or business, repeat assignment 2.

4. Prepare drafts of each of the following for evaluation by your instructor:

    a. Letter of transmittal.

    b. Title page.

    c. Contents page.

    d. List of illustrations.

    e. Glossary of terms (if appropriate).

    f. List of symbols (if appropriate).

    g. Abstract.

    h. About This Report.

8

Organizing Data II: Types of Organization

T ry to make sense of the following numbers:

3456789101112

These 13 digits might represent a phone number: (345) 678-9101, X112. Or a project number of some kind: 34-5678-910-1112. Or a credit card number: 345-6789-10111-2. Or they might stand for a series of streets: 3rd, 4th, 5th, 6th, 7th, 8th, 9th, 10th, 11th, 12th. There is no way of divining exactly what they mean as they stand. Only when you know their source and their purpose do they take on a meaning that transforms them from numbers (data) to information. Only then can you organize them into meaningful units of information. For example, telephone numbers and all the area codes and extensions that go with them produce long series of digits. Consider

A	B	C	D	E	F	G	H	I
8 –	0 –	405 –	624 –	6142 –	405 –	624 –	3020 –	7486

Each of these nine groups of numbers divided by hyphens means something. When I am at a hotel and want to call my office, I need to use them all:

A connects the telephone in my room to a long-distance circuit.

B indicates that I want to place an operator-assisted call.

C is the area code.

D is the prefix and first digit in the circuit that connects me with the university's phone system.

E is the combination of digits that connect me with the English Department office.

F, G, H, and *I* constitute my telephone credit card number.

Few people could remember these 26 digits and their sequence unless they knew their source and purpose. I am accustomed to thinking about these numbers in groups because I know the source and purpose of each group. When I grouped them just now, they meant little to you; but when I explained their source and purpose, they began to make sense. The fact that we share the common experience of expecting telephone numbers to be grouped in this way furthered your understanding.

Grouping data is a way of organizing data. This chapter has to do with grouping data into useful information in ways that reflect the nature of the data themselves and that respond to the reader's needs.

Data-Based Organization

What do you make of the following numbers?

87

92

65

93

73

59

92

88

90

87

92

If your instructor told you to group these numbers into meaningful information, you would want to know something about the source of the data and the purpose of your forming them into groups. Some grouping has already occurred, since the list consists of eleven pairs of numbers. What further groupings could you devise?

1. You could group them in numerical sequence, either smallest to largest or largest to smallest.
2. You could group them according to their frequency of occurrence: three occurrences of 92, two of 87, and one each of the remaining six pairs.
3. You could find the average number and group the numbers above and below the average.

These numbers happen to be the grades of engineering students on a recent examination. The instructor wanted to compare the test scores of engineers with those of accountants, economists, computer scientists, and English majors. (The comparison showed nothing unusual; students are students and some prepare better than others. Success on tests is rarely a function of college major.)

Once you learn the source and purpose of the numbers, they take on meaning. They cease being mere numbers and become *information*. Similarly, readers of reports need to know the source and purpose of your data so they can understand them as information.

Readers also need to know the source and purpose of nonnumerical data. Suppose you have a test coming up in sociology and you know it will contain some questions on descriptive statistics. Unfortunately, you were absent on the day the instructor explained that subject. You need a crash course to get ready for this important test. Normally, you could turn to a friend who is majoring in statistics, but she is out of town this weekend. So you decide to search out a book you have heard about that gives a brief introduction to descriptive statistics for those who think they have no ability at all. Where will you find it? The library. But how can you find the one book you need among all the thousands of books there? You could search the shelves, but that would take more time than you have. So you turn to the card catalog, a tool that organizes nonnumerical data in a way that enables you to find your book quickly.

The catalog organizes data in three ways: by author's name, by book title, and by subject. Source and purpose, again. Because you know neither the author nor the title, you look under the subject "Descriptive Statistics." And there you find a listing for *Elementary Descriptive Statistics for Those Who Think They Can't,* by Arthur Coladarci and Theodore Coladarci.

That's the book you're after, but where can you locate it? You notice a number on the card that tells you how the library has organized its materials. With the help of a table that con verts numbers into locations, you find the book, take it back to the dorm, and prepare for the test. Knowing how the library is organized allows you to find what you are looking for.

Putting a report together in a way that enables your readers to find the information they want is *organization*. Putting the paragraphs and sentences of the report together in meaningful ways is *organization*. Grouping your data so that it has meaning for your readers is *organization*. Organization is influenced by factors as simple as punctuation and as complex as the logical sequencing of ideas.

When you first looked at the list of test scores, you might have been tempted to group them in ascending or descending order. Because one of the characteristics of a number is its magnitude, you knew that you could group the numbers according to magnitude. In other words, the *inherent characteristics* of the data made it possible for you to group them by at least two methods. Once you knew their source and purpose, other ways of grouping suggested themselves. The same possibilities exist with any set of numerical data: frequency of use, frequency of occurrence, numbers of participants, and so on. The concept of number implies both analysis and grouping.

But numbers are not the only data that imply analysis and grouping. What if an earthquake were to strike your town and knock all your LPs off the shelves? If you had arranged the records in some random fashion, you would have no difficulty putting them back. But if you had grouped them according to some principle, you would be careful to restore them according to their original organization. You might group them

by artist.

by type of music.

by record company.

by some other characteristic.

There are other possibilities: original cost, date of purchase, size, color. In short, each record has certain inherent characteristics that imply grouping.

Organizing your data is similar to organizing your records. In organizing numerical data for a report, your first thought might be to group them in some visual form—a line graph, a pie chart, or a bar graph. Nonnumerical data might also be grouped visually: describing a process suggests a flow chart; describing an area suggests a map; describing an object suggests a drawing.

Although data may fall naturally into ascending or descending order, there are other ways of organizing them, including

1. *Chronological order*. When you gather and analyze data you are following a procedure. Procedure suggests a process, and a process suggests a sequence of events that occur in time. So you might present your data according to the order in which you collected them, starting at the beginning. How did the second set of data you collected modify your perception of the

first set? Proceed sequentially until you have organized all the data in the order in which you collected them. By presenting your data in this fashion, you will emphasize for your reader the *sequence* in which you collected them and the *temporal relationships* among them. For example, in reporting the results of a visit to an organization, you could present the information you gathered in the order in which you gathered it. What did you learn first, second, and so on?

2. *Sequential order.* When you are presenting numerical data, you may want to organize them from smallest to largest or the reverse—in other words, according to their relationships. You may want to focus your reader's attention on the smallest item, on the largest, or on progressive increases or decreases. Chronological and sequential organizational patterns work well when the data are relatively simple. When, for example, you report the memory capacity of several minicomputers, you can list the capacities from smallest to largest or the reverse, depending on the emphasis you want your reader to perceive.

3. *Inductive or deductive order.* When you want to draw some generalization from your accumulated data, you may present either the data and then the generalization (inductive) or the generalization and then the data (deductive). In a report recommending the purchase of a machine, you could present your recommendation first and then the data (such as cost savings), or the data first and then your recommendation.

4. *Order of relative importance.* Which data are most important to your conclusions or recommendations? By organizing your data on the basis of their relative importance, you can build up to your conclusions or recommendations. You must include all your data in an appendix, however—even data that support conclusions or recommendations that are contrary to your own. Not only must you include them, you must label them clearly and modify your conclusions or recommendations to accommodate them.

5. *Multiple solutions.* Sometimes your data will suggest more than one solution to the problem. When that happens, present the solution you believe to be best and then give the others. If you have only one or two others and you can describe them briefly, you may decide to present the preferred solution last.

In presenting solutions, always indicate the strengths and weaknesses of each in terms of the organization's objectives.

Here are some sample outlines for presenting multiple solutions:

> Problem
> Statement of Solutions A, B, and C
>> Solution B
>>> Rejected
>>> Reasons
>> Solution C
>>> Rejected
>>> Reasons
>> Solution A
>>> Accepted
>>> Reasons

> Problem
> Statement of Solutions A, B, C, and D
> Criteria for Acceptable Solution
>> Solution A
>>> Accepted
>>> Reasons (based on criteria)
>> Solution B
>>> Rejected
>>> Reasons (based on criteria)
>> Solution C
>>> Rejected
>>> Reasons (based on criteria)
>> Solution D
>>> Rejected
>>> Reason (based on criteria)

Each of the five methods we have listed represents a valid way to arrange your data. Actually, you may decide to combine methods when you write your report, using for each section the method that seems most appropriate. You may also decide to combine these data-based plans of organization with the reader-based plans discussed next.

Reader-Based Organization

In the last section we presented ways to organize data based primarily on the nature of the data themselves. Now we turn to ways of organizing data based primarily on the needs of the reader. When you write the various sections of your report, you will no doubt combine the two approaches as the occasion warrants. Here we will focus on your reader's needs and how you can best advance reader understanding through the organization of your data.

Reader's Needs

As we saw in earlier chapters, the fundamental principles in report writing are knowing what information your reader needs and conveying that information effectively. Organizing your information is part of the delivery system you use to communicate the information your reader needs. Organization exists at two levels: grouping information through the course of the whole report, and informing your reader about how you have grouped that information. At both levels the paramount consideration is what your reader needs to know.

In order for a reader to understand what you are presenting, he or she must have some sense of organization during the reading. If you fail to demonstrate the organization you have imposed on the information, your reader is obliged to make up for your shortcomings. But if you make your organization apparent, you ease the reader's burden and stand a better chance of winning approval for your recommendations.

Knowing in advance what your reader needs to know makes it easier for you to organize your information and for your reader to read and comprehend it. One way to organize information in response to your reader's needs is to use the questions listed in the following section as guideline.

Six Questions

Readers come to a report with specific information needs and a specific purpose. You can often identify that purpose by determining their interests. Here are some interests readers typically bring to reports:

Decision making, problem solving.

Understanding general concepts.

Checking specific tests and results.

Improving performance.

By far the most compelling interest, and the one that you will most often face in writing reports, is in decision making. Decision makers need information and recommendations in order to move forward and get on with their job. They rely on reports that provide them with the complex, specialized information they need to discharge their many responsibilities. Clear, concise reports are essential to them and to the organization

Most readers ask six questions when they turn to a report:

1. What problem or subject does the report address?
2. Why is that problem or subject important to the organization?
3. What methods has the report writer used to collect the data and to develop recommendations?
4. What results did those methods produce?
5. What is the significance of those results in relation to the problem and the organization's goals?
6. What are the recommendations?

These questions follow a logical sequence. Some readers, however, motivated by their own special interests, will follow another course in their appraisal of a report. Still, these questions provide a useful starting point as you begin to organize your report.

In examining the needs of the potential readers of your report we will turn first to those readers who are primarily interested in decision making and then consider readers who are interested in understanding general concepts, checking specific test results, or improving performance. The predominant interest of a reader influences the sequence in which the six basic questions are likely to be asked.

DECISION MAKING Decision makers will constitute the main audience for your reports. Their most pressing need is for information that will enable them to advance the organization's objectives, which are usually related to a product or a service. They rely on reports for that information. If such persons could work on only one problem at a time, or if they could themselves assign a single problem to each employee, they would know immediately, just by checking the title or the writer of a report, precisely what each report covered. Such is not usually the case, however. Decision makers deal with countless problems and employees. Usually, they assign the parts of a particular problem to various employees whose role in the organization and whose technical expertise best qualify them for the job. Or they may refer a major project to a subordinate who then divides it up among several employees.

So decision makers cannot know automatically what problem or part of a problem a given report covers. What they *do* know is the significance of each problem to the organization's goals and objectives. Their most urgent need is to know what problem you are reporting on. The least important question is the significance of the problem to the organization's goals and objectives because they should already be aware of it.

The next question decision makers ask is: What do you recommend? They rarely have time to ponder and deliberate over all the possible solutions that might conceivably be applied to a problem. They rely on you to do that for them and to come up with recommendations that in your judgment are the most promising. They may choose to reject your recommendations, of course. But they need to have your recommendations organized and presented in sufficient detail for them to reach a decision and to take action. To help them do so, you should summarize the benefits that your recommendations will bring.

The next question decision makers are likely to ask is, what data did you use to develop your recommendations? Normally, you base your recommendations on the data you obtained while solving the problem. For example, the specifications of various minicomputers help form the basis for your recommendation of one system over another. The reader who must make decisions is probably not interested in the details of the analysis of those data. Rather, he or she will look at the data as they relate to your recommendation. Thus, instead of including every piece of information, you should select those data that were most influential in your own thinking when you formulated your recommendation.

Consider, too, how familiar your reader is with the data. Do you need to go into detailed explanations, or will the data speak for themselves? Will your reader prefer raw data or data that have been sifted and consolidated? Which data will give the greatest credibility to your recommendations?

Your use of the remaining questions in organizing your report depends on your estimate of what your reader needs. Does the reader need to know the methods you used in developing the data? Does the reader need to know the significance of the data? Answers to those questions will suggest the best way to sequence the sections of your report. You may, for example, decide on the following outline as the best accommodation of your reader's needs:

> Statement of the problem, including
> > Authorization
> > Background
> > Definitions of key terms

> Recommendations
>> Possible solutions to the problem
>> Principal solution to the problem
>> Recommendations
>> Benefits
> Basis for your recommendations
>> Sources of data
>> The data themselves
> Summary
> Appendix
>> Methods used to collect data
>> Analysis of data
>> Interpretations or discussions of data

Notice what has happened to the six questions listed earlier. You have selected some and ignored others, and you have altered their sequence, all in response to what you deem to be the reader's principal interests. The questions have served as a guide, but you have adapted them to suit the situation. In preparing reports for readers with interests other than decision making, your choice and sequencing of the questions will again be different.

UNDERSTANDING GENERAL CONCEPTS You will occasionally write reports on technical topics for readers whose main interest is in learning about the general concepts you are discussing. These people may be doing work quite different from yours— handling public relations, for example, or maintaining liaison with other organizations, or working in accounting. How would you use the six basic questions in organizing a report for those readers?

Here again, the first question you should try to answer is, what problem or subject does the report address? Readers of this sort have a particular need to be informed of the subject of your report and to be given definitions of key technical terms and any background information required for an understanding of the subject. Be precise, because your readers will not be familiar with the technical aspects of your work.

You will also need to provide reasons why the reader should be interested in reading your report. Why is the problem important? If you know what sort of work your reader does, suggest early in the report how the problem affects the reader's job. If you know little about what the reader does, describe how the problem relates to the organization as a whole, particularly if it is part of a larger problem. Readers who are primarily interested in general concepts need far more background information than decision makers do.

Next, present your recommendations. What solution or solutions are you proposing? Be careful not to burden your reader with technical terms and overly complex concepts. How will your recommendations affect the reader's job? Make it clear that your understanding of these implications is based on your own perspective. What implications will your recommendations have for the organization as a whole? Be general about the concepts but specific about the implications.

CHECKING SPECIFICS Readers whose principal interest is in checking tests and results are likely to be just as qualified in technical matters as you are—perhaps even more qualified. They probably have advanced degrees and long experience with the subject matter of your report. Many want to know whether your report is technically accurate. So after stating the problem, you should provide precise details about the methods you used in preparing your report.

These readers have no need for a detailed explanation of the problem or its significance. They know all that. You might want to give some background information at the outset or in an appendix, but not in the main body of the report. You might even provide a list of the reports you used in preparing to solve the problem. But these readers will be primarily interested in the results of your efforts and in the methods you used to obtain those results.

Explain your methods in specific detail. State exactly what tests you conducted, what procedures you followed, how you collected your data. Your purpose is to establish the credibility of your results, not to provide guidance for duplicating your work. Use whatever technical terms you need. Your readers will understand what you are saying as long as you say it clearly and accurately.

Readers who are primarily interested in specific details will probably have little concern for other matters. You might explain why the problem is of particular significance to the organization, perhaps suggesting why failure to solve it would be harmful to the organization as a whole and to your own department. And you might suggest that the results you obtained are directly related to solving the problem. In presenting your recommendations, try to relate them to your reader's role in the organization.

IMPROVING PERFORMANCE The last group of potential readers for your report consists essentially of your peer group. These readers are looking for information that will help them improve the way they do their jobs. So concentrate on answering

Table 8-1. Six Questions Arranged for Four Readers*

Question	Decision Making	Understanding General Concepts	Checking Specifics	Improving Performance
1. What problem or subject does the report address?	1	1	1	1
2. Why is that problem or subject important to the organization?	6	2	4	2
3. What methods have you used to collect data and develop recommendations?	4	6	2	3
4. What results did those procedures produce?	3	4	3	4
5. What is the significance of those results in relation to the problem and the organization's goals?	5	5	5	5
6. What are the recommendations?	2	3	6	6

*Numbers refer to importance of question: 1 = highest importance; 6 = lowest.

those questions that have a direct bearing on their job, their department, and the organization's goals.

The paramount question to answer in reporting to these readers is, what is the problem? They may not need to have technical terms defined or technical aspects presented in detail, but they do need to know how the problem relates to their job and why it is important. Providing them with relevant details will clarify that relationship.

Because these readers are your peers, feel free to describe the methods you used, in whatever technical detail you deem necessary. The methods you used in solving the problem of the report may help them improve their own problem-solving techniques. Ask yourself what you would want to know if someone were writing the report for you.

In presenting your recommendations, you will concentrate on ways to apply your results to the job at hand. The purpose of your report, and the reason your readers are interested in it, is to help them improve their own performance.

Table 8-1 arranges our six questions for each of the four groups of readers. Figure 8-1 gives the same information in flow chart format.

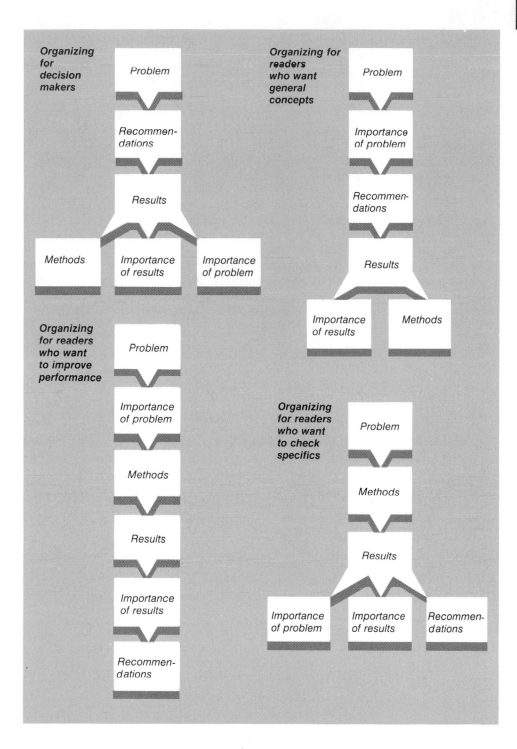

Figure 8-1. Organizational patterns for four readers.

The purpose of this six-question approach is to help you organize reports in response to your reader's need to know. Identify that need and organize your information in a manner that will best enable the reader to comprehend it and act on it.

Technical Assignments

1. Write a brief report to your instructor in which you list and discuss the organizing techniques you plan to use in a final report. Justify your decision on the basis of the reader and the subject.

2. Find the book on statistics mentioned on page 125. Describe the process you followed, including:
   a. what cards you checked in the card catalog.
   b. the book's numerical code (Library of Congress or Dewey Decimal System) and what it means.
   c. how you converted the code into a location.
   d. your success in locating the book.

3. Study your college catalog.
   a. Can you think of a better way to organize the various sections? Look especially at the sections on admission, costs, and grades.
   b. Can you suggest a better way to organize the course listings in the catalog? What assumptions did the writers make about the reader's needs?
   c. Look at earlier catalogs published by your college. Do they all follow the same organization? What basis, do you think, will the revisers of next year's catalog use to organize the data?

4. Locate a research report. How is it organized? What suggestions can you make for improving the organization?

9

Organizing Data III: Techniques

n Chapter 8, we presented two ways of organizing data: on the basis of the data themselves (data-centered) and on the basis of the reader's need (reader-centered). When you organize material for a report, you will probably use a combination of these two methods. In this chapter, we will continue to examine ways to organize data, but here we will focus on techniques to use in writing sentences, paragraphs, and sections and in constructing the report as a whole. The techniques you decide to use (and you will use several in each report) must always relate to the overall purpose of the report and to the purposes of each section, paragraph, and sentence.

Declaring the organizational pattern you plan to follow and then arranging your material according to that pattern will enable the reader to process your information efficiently and economically. To succeed in that effort, you must have a clear sense of your purpose in writing the report.

When your purpose is to inform your reader about how to use a piece of equipment, you will use *description*—description of the equipment and description of the process. When your purpose is to help your reader understand a concept, you will use *definition*. When your purpose is to describe the potential effects of a particular event, you will use *analysis*. Other purposes are best served by other techniques, including classification and division, comparison and contrast, and visuals. Knowing how each technique works by itself and how it works in combination with others will help you decide how to achieve your purpose while fulfilling your reader's needs.

Description

If you want to help your reader visualize a piece of equipment, understand how and why it works, or learn how to operate it, you will probably decide to describe the equipment. When your main purpose is to help your reader build a mental image of the equipment, you will use a *mechanism description*. When your purpose is to help your reader understand a series of events, you will use a *process description*. When you want to help your reader perform a certain act or series of acts in a particular way, you will use *instructions*. Each technique has a different purpose that springs from the reader's needs.

Mechanism Description

In describing a mechanism, you are trying to help the reader visualize it. You may be

> ordering a replacement for the mechanism or for some part of it.
>
> preparing work or repair orders.
>
> writing an instruction manual.
>
> preparing a patent application.
>
> corresponding with customers.
>
> writing specifications.

In any of these cases, an effective way to describe an object is to organize your information in three stages: the overall purpose of the object, the parts that compose it, and its physical characteristics. Here is a useful outline for a report based on description:

I. Overview
   A. Object you are describing (with definitions of any specialized terms)
   B. Reason for describing the object (based on reader's need)
   C. Purpose or use of the object
   D. Your purpose
   E. Major parts of the object

II. Major Part "A"
   A. Physical characteristics
   B. Purpose of the part
   C. Subparts
      1. Physical characteristics
      2. Purpose of subparts

III. Major Part "B"
   A. Physical characteristics
   B. Purpose of the part
   C. Subparts
      1. Physical characteristics
      2. Purpose of subparts

IV. Major Part "C," etc.

V. Closing
    A. How all the parts work together when the object is used for its characteristic purpose
    B. Variations or different physical characteristics of other models
    C. Conclusion (summary based on reader's need and writer's purpose)

You will, of course, adapt this outline to accommodate the points you want to make, the sequence you deem best, the amount of detail you feel the reader needs, and your principal focus. You will be guided by the specific purpose your reader will have in mind when reading the description. It may be to figure out a way to manufacture the mechanism you are describing, to learn how to operate it, or to learn how to repair it. Whatever the reader's purpose, you must describe the physical characteristics of the mechanism, its parts, and its intended use. Knowing the reader's specific purpose will help you decide which elements to emphasize and which to play down. Table 9-1 summarizes the emphases appropriate to various readers' needs.

In presenting information to describe an object, organize it according to the sequence in which the reader will use it. If, for example, you are trying to help the reader identify a screwdriver, begin with a description of the handle. If you are informing the reader of the purpose of word-processing equipment, begin with a description of the keyboard. Ask yourself what the reader is likely to encounter first when approaching the object, what he or she is likely to encounter next, and so on, until you have completed your description. The sequence

Table 9-1. Reader's Need and Appropriate Emphasis

Reader's Need	Elements Emphasized	Notes
To use object	Purpose of object	The reader needs to visualize the object in operation with parts working together
To identify object	Phyical characteristics of object	The reader needs to visualize the object; specifications are important
To repair object	Parts and subparts	The reader needs to know how the parts fit together

should parallel the sequence of the reader's experiences with the object.

The choice of visuals to accompany your description should also be in accord with the reader's needs. Will the reader need a detailed drawing of the object? That depends on the reader's purpose. If the reader wants to learn how to use the object, you might present a simple view with all the controls carefully detailed and labeled. If the reader wants to learn how to repair the object, you might present several views relating to various malfunctions. If the reader wants to know how to identify the object, you might present a comprehensive view showing all its physical characteristics. Other purposes might suggest the inclusion of detailed drawings of subparts and groups of parts. Figure 9-1 shows one way of integrating such visuals into a descriptive report. A flow chart consisting of a series of drawings showing the steps to follow in operating the equipment might also be appropriate for certain readers.

Process Description

A process description describes how something works or how an action is performed. Perhaps you want to tell your reader how the parts of a videotape recorder work together when it is performing its characteristic purpose. Or you want to describe how a plant manufactures a bicycle before you specify how a worker performs a particular step in the process. Or you want to give a repairman some understanding of how a toaster works before listing instructions for repairing and testing it.

Process descriptions are useful for a wide variety of purposes, including

operating manuals.

patent applications.

instructions on how to repair or modify a machine.

letters and reports on procedures.

job descriptions.

Process descriptions are meant to give the reader an understanding of relationships, not to enable the reader to duplicate the process. To provide an understanding of relationships, the writer uses a special verb form called a *gerund*—a form that ends in "-ing" and serves as a noun. Compare the following:

1. Replacing the spark plugs . . .
2. Replace the spark plugs.

DESCRIPTION OF A PAPER PUNCH

This report describes for the general reader the paper punch made
by students in GENT 1222. The paper punch is a single-hole type
and is easily operated by inserting the paper into the slot and
depressing the plunger. The paper punch has an overall length and
height of about 2″ and a width of about 1″. The four major parts of
the paper punch are body, plunger assembly, locking pin, and
spring. The relative position of each part is shown in the exploded
assembly view.

Body

The body is the largest part of the paper punch and is made from
steel. It is about 1″ x 1″ x 2″ with a sloping back side. Opposite the
sloping side is a ⅛″ slot, about ¾″ deep. A ¼″ diameter hole
(plunger guide hole) is drilled through the body perpendicular to
the slot. This hole guides the plunger. The finish of each surface has
been mill filed and looks as if it has been sanded but is very smooth.

Plunger Assembly

The plunger assembly consists of two parts: the thumb button and
the plunger shaft. Both parts are made of steel. The thumb button is
hemispherically shaped approximately ⅝″ in diameter with a small
hole drilled through it. The plunger shaft is cylindrical and has
varying diameters and a length of about 1½″. The plunger assembly
does the actual punching of the hole in a piece of paper. A locking
pin limits the vertical travel of the plunger assembly .

Continued on page 142

Figure 9-1. Mechanism description.

Locking Pin

The locking pin is a small steel shaft that intersects the plunger guide hole (see three-view drawing). The locking pin limits the travel of the plunger, both up and down, because of the location of the smallest diameter of the plunger in relation to the locking pin. It is very difficult to see the locking pin in an assembled paper punch because the ends have been hammered and filed smooth.

Spring

The last part of the paper punch is the spring. The spring returns the plunger to its uppermost position after the punching operation. The spring is made from steel wire that is wound into a coil.

Summary

The assembly of parts provides an easy and efficient way to punch holes in paper. The user inserts the paper to be punched in the slot, aligns the paper so the hole will be punched in the desired location, and depresses the plunger until it penetrates the paper. When the plunger is released, the spring returns the plunger to its uppermost position, and the user is ready to punch another hole.

Written by William Pranger and used with his permission.

Figure 9-1. (continued)

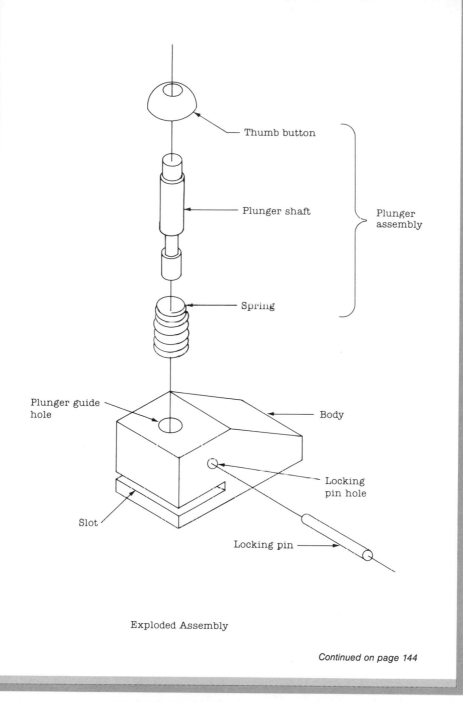

Thumb button

Plunger shaft

Plunger assembly

Spring

Plunger guide hole

Body

Locking pin hole

Slot

Locking pin

Exploded Assembly

Continued on page 144

Figure 9-1. (continued)

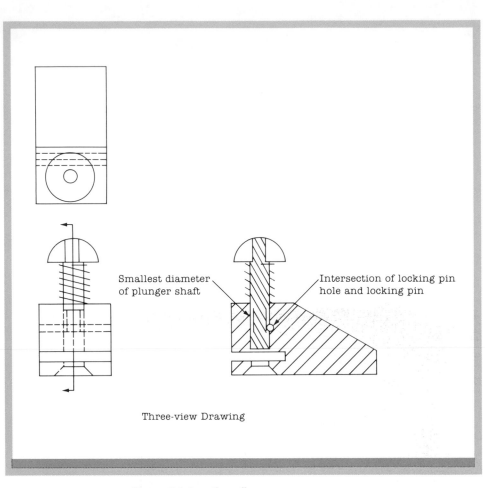

Smallest diameter of plunger shaft

Intersection of locking pin hole and locking pin

Three-view Drawing

Figure 9-1. (continued)

Sentence 1 makes no suggestion that the reader is to do anything, whereas sentence 2 leads to action. The verb in this sentence, "Replace," is the command form, more appropriate to instructions. Process descriptions employ verb forms that do not lead to action. Figure 9-2 provides a sample process description. The sample roughly follows the outline below. Use this outline as a starting point in creating a process description of your own.

    I. Overview
        A. Name of process you are describing (with definitions of any specialized terms)
        B. Reason for describing this process (based on the reader's need)

Audit Procedure

Persons wanting to invest in a company can make a more meaningful decision about that investment if they know the financial condition of the company. One element in that condition is the audit procedures followed by the company. This report outlines those procedures normally followed in an audit of a company's financial condition. That procedure consists of five steps: flowcharting the system, understanding the functions of a cycle, determining the strengths and weaknesses, evaluating the impact of the strengths and weaknesses, and creating tests to determine the importance of the weaknesses.

Flowcharting the System

The first step involves flowcharting the system. A system's flowchart is a diagram representing the organization's documents and their sequential flow through the organization. A well-prepared flowchart helps the auditor identify weaknesses in the system by providing a clearer understanding of how the system works. It is easier to follow a diagram than to read a complicated description. Once the auditor has prepared a flowchart, the next step is developing an audit program.

Developing an Audit Program

The second step, developing an audit program, involves understanding the function of each cycle or department within the organization. The auditor issues questionnaires, conducts interviews of employees, and observes performance of duties. What the auditor wants to learn is how management and other personnel believe the system works. The auditor then can make a preliminary evaluation of controls in the system and define the areas that have significantly weak controls. He evaluates each cycle separately, identifying strengths and weaknesses.

Continued on page 146

Figure 9-2. Sample process description.

Determining Strengths and Weaknesses

The third step the auditor performs is determining the specific strengths and weaknesses in the system. When controls exist that prevent errors, they are strengths in the system. Where controls do not adequately prevent errors, they are weaknesses. Once the auditor knows the specific strengths and weaknesses, he can evaluate their impact.

Evaluating the Impact of Weaknesses

The fourth step involves evaluating the impact the weaknesses have on the system by determining the potential errors. The auditor evaluates the importance of these errors and looks for any offsetting factors. The more important the potential error, the less likely the auditor is to rely on the information included in the financial statements without further testing.

Creating Tests

The fifth and final step in the audit procedure is creating tests to determine the impact of the weaknesses on the information from the audit. The more important the potential error, the more tests need to be done before the auditor can decide on the reliability of the information. The auditor develops these tests to make certain that the duties are being performed and that the mathematics are accurately calculated. Once the auditor develops the tests, he has an audit program.

Armed with the information from the audit, the investor can make an intelligent decision about investing. Knowing the procedures auditors use to develop an audit program gives the investor confidence in the financial statement.

Written by Tana Tobias and used with her permission.

Figure 9-2. (continued)

C. The theory involved in the process (optional, depending on the reader's need)
    D. Your purpose (include limitations)
    E. Major steps in the process (expressed in gerunds)

II. Major Step "A"
    A. Name of step, with appropriate definitions
    B. Any substeps
    C. Details—enough to suit the reader's need

III. Major Step "B"
    A. Name of step, with appropriate definitions
    B. Any substeps
    C. Details

IV. Major Step "C," etc.

V. Closing
    A. Summary of major steps
    B. Reference, if appropriate, to instruction manual
    C. Restatement of how the description relates to the reader's need and the writer's purpose

Once again, the purpose of a process description is to help the reader understand the process, not to duplicate it. Remember that the reader is coming to your description with no prior knowledge of the process you are describing. Avoid using technical terms, and supplement your description with carefully devised visuals. Flow charts are particularly useful in process descriptions, because they isolate the steps of a process and at the same time show *how* these steps are related. As an example, Figure 9-3 presents a flow chart to describe the process you follow in writing a report. You might use other visuals to support your text, such as a drawing to show what happens inside a mechanism as the process you are describing takes place.

Instructions

You will sometimes be asked to write a set of instructions explaining how a certain activity is to be performed. Instructions may be as simple as leaving a message telling someone where to pick up your laundry, or as elaborate as a technical manual telling a mechanic how to install the transmission in a new-model Porsche. Writing instructions, whether simple or complex, depends on the same factors as other kinds of technical writing:

1. What are the reader's needs?
2. What is my purpose?

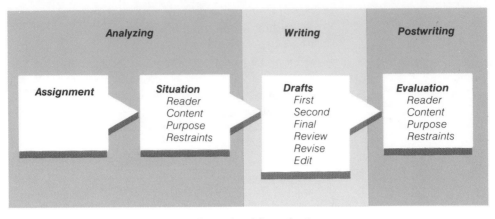

Figure 9-3. Example of flow chart.

Knowing your reader's needs serves as a guide in selecting the details to include in your instructions and suggests the assumptions you can make about what the reader already knows or can understand. When you tell the reader to adjust the gap in a spark plug, for example, can you assume the reader knows how to do so? Or must you include instructions for adjusting the gap? Does the reader even know what a spark-plug gap is?

The test of the effectiveness of your instructions lies in whether the reader performs the act correctly. Can the reader of your instructions adjust the gap properly? Or does someone else have to step in and explain the correct procedure?

Instructions must be failure-proof. If they are not, they are useless. To make them failure-proof, you must ensure that they communicate efficiently and without ambiguity.

INSTRUCTIONS THAT COMMUNICATE Writing instructions that communicate requires that you pay careful attention to the words you use, the way you organize details, and the way you position the instructions on the page.

The words you use tell the reader what to do. The verbs specify the activity, and the nouns specify the objects required for that activity. Compare:

Adjust the spark-plug gap.

The spark-plug gap must be adjusted.

The first sentence instructs the reader to do something. The only response to the second sentence might be, "Really?" The verb gives no indication that the reader is to do something, nor does the sentence even suggest who is supposed to take action. Presumably, someone is meant to make the adjustment, but not necessarily the reader. Although the first sentence does not actually name the person who is to perform the action, the reader has no doubt who it is to be.

The difference between the two sentences lies in the verbs. The first verb is in the command form (the imperative mood), while the second is in the informational form (the indicative mood). Moreover, the second verb is in the passive voice. It says that something needs to be done but does not say by whom. And so the reader responds with "Really?"

The point is clear: When you write instructions, use the imperative mood for all verbs.

The nouns you use in writing instructions must be accurate, concrete, and familiar to the reader. Use nouns that make it easy to visualize the object you are referring to. (A "spark plug" is easy to visualize; a "device for intermittent transmission of electrical current" is not.) Avoid building nouns into phrases when a simple verb will do. For example, "adjust" means the same as "make an adjustment." The nouns in clumsy phrases of this sort usually end in "-ment" or "-ion."

Expecting your reader to translate your language into common terms wastes time and introduces the possibility of error. True, technical terminology allows you to express complex ideas in shortened form, but the reader must know what the terms mean. A common cause of the failure of instructions to communicate is their use of terms the reader does not understand.

Another essential in writing instructions that communicate is the proper handling of *conditionals*. A conditional situation exists when the reader, before taking action, must decide whether or not a certain condition or set of conditions exists. Four types of conditional circumstances are common in instructions:

1. Logical addition, characterized by "and": Condition 1 *and* condition 2.

2. Logical choice, characterized by "or": Condition 1 *or* condition 2.

3. Single conditional, characterized by "if ... then": *If* condition 1, *then* condition 2 also.

4. Dual conditional, characterized by both conditions: *If* condition 1, *then* condition 2; *if* condition 2, *then* condition 1.

Whenever the writer introduces a conditional into instructions, the reader is alerted to the need to think through the situation before taking action. Here are some examples:

> *Addition:* The engine must idle roughly and need a tune-up before you change the spark plugs.
>
> *Choice:* The engine must idle roughly or need a tune-up before you change the spark plugs.
>
> *Single conditional:* If the engine idles roughly, then it must need a tune-up. Change the spark plugs.
>
> *Dual conditional:* If the engine idles roughly, then it must need a tune-up. If the engine needs a tune-up, then it must idle roughly.

Sometimes several conditionals must be specified:

> If the engine idles roughly and if the acceleration is poor, or if gas consumption suddenly increases and the car keeps stalling, then change the spark plugs or clean and regap them.

ORGANIZATION OF INSTRUCTIONS Sound organization is essential when you are writing instructions. Demonstrate to your reader how you have organized the material by using overviews, summaries, and previews of what is to come next. Make sure that the sequence of actions is orderly and is precisely related to the steps followed in actual practice.

The most effective way of organizing instructions is to sequence the actions in chronological order. State what the reader must do first, second, third, and so on. If the reader must perform two steps at or about the same time, make that clear.

The importance of chronological organization was emphasized in an episode of the TV series *M*A*S*H**, in which Hawkeye and Trapper John set about defusing an unexploded bomb. Colonel Blake read the instructions to them (from a safe distance). One step called for them to cut two wires—"But, first . . ." That "But, first" came after they had already cut the wires. (The bomb did explode, but it was only a propaganda bomb.) The writer had assumed that the reader would read all the instructions before proceeding. That was a bad assumption. If you have to include a "But, first" in an instruction, put it at the beginning.

It is always advisable to prepare the reader for the instructions that follow by leading off with an introduction or overview:

I. Overview
   A. Name of the process (with definitions of any technical terms)
   B. Importance of the instructions
   C. The theory involved in the process (optional, depending on the reader's needs)
   D. Equipment and materials needed
   E. Major steps

Always number the steps in instructions. Numbering makes the sequence clear and makes it easy for the reader to follow the steps. Without numbers, the reader may skip a step or become confused about what comes next. Moreover, the very act of numbering the steps helps you to isolate each step and forces you to keep the length and complexity of each step within reasonable limits.

Each instruction should present a single action. If the action entails substeps, list them under the main step. Organizing the instructions in this manner will ensure that the reader performs all the actions the step requires. If you include more than one action in a step, the reader is likely to read the first part ("Cut the blue and red wires") and ignore the rest ("and remove the subassembly before closing the lid").

Limiting each step to a single action will also help you keep your instructions short. If you find that you have written an instruction that contains fifteen words or more, break it into a main step and two or more substeps.

LAYOUT OF INSTRUCTIONS Number each step and substep and position each on a separate line. A three-step instruction containing two substeps would appear like this:

1. Step 1
2. Step 2
      a. Substep 1
      b. Substep 2
3. Step 3

Laying out your instructions this way enables your reader to read a step, perform the action, and read the next step with little chance of becoming confused or skipping a step. It also provides space at the beginning and end of each step and between steps, providing additional clarity.

If you use visuals, position them in a way to help the reader associate the instruction with the appropriate visual. Figure 9-4 shows several ways of positioning visuals.

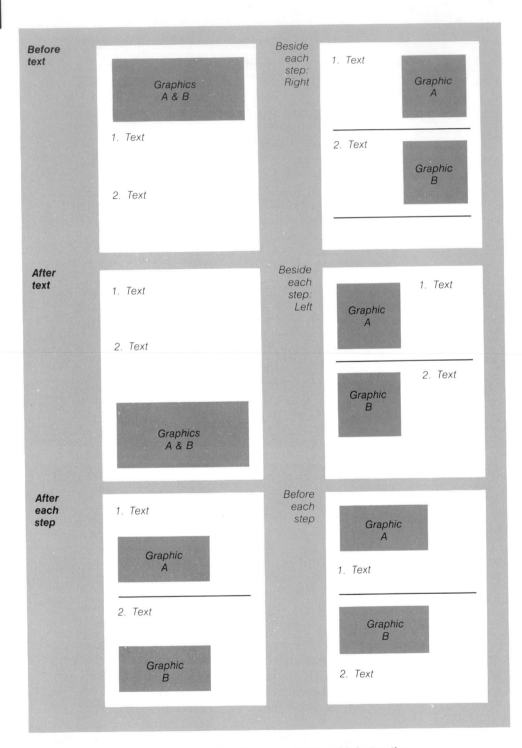

Figure 9-4. Positions of graphics with instructions.

Table 9-2. Checklist for Writing Instructions

Words	1. Use command form of verbs (imperative mood).
	2. Use active voice for verbs.
	3. Use terms your reader can understand.

Organization	1. Use chronological sequence for steps and substeps.
	2. Number each step and substep.
	3. Include only one action in each step and substep.
	4. Use short sentences.

Layout	1. Provide plenty of white space.
	2. Use graphics where appropriate.
	3. Separate steps with a line.

Be sure that each visual you select supports the instruction it accompanies. Deciding whether to use a visual depends in part on your analysis of the reader's knowledge. Will the reader need to see a drawing of the spark plug and the gapping tool? Or will it be enough just to tell the reader to gap the plug?

Notice in Figure 9-5 that the sample page has a line separating the steps from the visuals. The line helps the reader to isolate each step and to concentrate on that step before moving on to the next one.

Table 9-2 presents a checklist to follow when you write instructions.

You will find it useful to conclude instructions by summarizing the major steps and listing the technical details (or specifications). It is also common to provide a troubleshooting guide to major problems. This guide is really a condensed set of conditional instructions. Use headings similar to those in the sample shown in Figure 9-6.

Definitions

In technical writing you are often obliged to use specialized terms that serve as a kind of shorthand for concepts, procedures, and objects. Ordinarily, you can assume that your reader will have enough professional competence to understand such terms. But if there is any doubt in your mind, define all the terms that are crucial to your communication.

Use and Placement of Definitions

The vocabulary you use in a report includes terms, concepts, and contexts. A *term* is the actual word you use; a *concept* is the idea the term represents; a *context* is the setting in which the term appears.

On which of these levels, in your judgment, will your reader need definitions? The meaning a reader perceives is affected

T.O. *XXX-X-XX-X*

3-5. DISASSEMBLY OF CONSTANT SPEED DRIVE

3-6. Disassemble the CSD according to the general disassembly instructions in T.O. XXX-X-XXX and the following steps:

1. *Remove machine plugs (1 and 8) and check valve (29) as follows:*

a. *Remove machine plug (1) from CSD. Remove preformed packing (2) from machine plug (1).*

b. *Remove machine plug (8) from CSD. Remove preformed packing (9) from machine plug (8).*

c. *Remove check valve (29) from CSD. Remove preformed packing (30) from check valve (29).*

A-21748

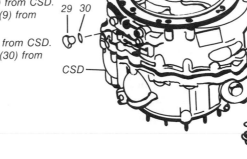

2. *Remove self-closing plug assembly (3) as follows:*

a. *Remove self-closing plug assembly (3) from CSD.*

b. *Separate plug (4) and self-closing valve assembly (5).*

c. *Remove preformed packing (6) from magnetic plug (4) and preformed packing (7) from self-closing valve assembly (5).*

A-21334-1

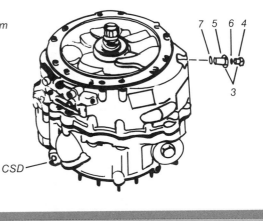

Figure 9-5. Page from a technical manual.
Source: Sundstrand Corporation. Used by permission.

Troubleshooting Demand Apparatus

Symptom	Cause	Cure/Action
Contaminated air entering facepiece on inhalation	Exhalation valve stuck open	Close mainline valve, open bypass valve, and leave immediately for safe area.
	Puncture in low-pressure hose	Close mainline valve, open bypass valve, and leave immediately for safe area.
	Diaphragm punctured or torn	Close mainline valve, open bypass valve, and leave immediately for safe area.
	Inadequate face-piece seal	Preventive cure: Test seal after donning facepiece and before entering toxic area. Check facepiece position, readjust head harness. If incurable in toxic area, close mainline valve, open bypass valve, and leave immediately for safe area.
Exhaling difficult; exhaled air leaving through facepiece seal; facepiece pressurized	Exhalation valve stuck closed	No emergency action necessary; affects only comfort
Air supply to facepiece stops	Pinched low-pressure hose	Straighten low-pressure hose
	Demand valve stuck closed	Close mainline valve, open bypass valve, and leave immediately for safe area

Figure 9-6. Example of a troubleshooting guide.
Source: Reprinted with permission of Fire Protection Publications.
© Board of Regents Oklahoma State University.

at all three levels. Is that meaning likely to correspond to the meaning you have in mind? When you use words with very restricted meanings, you can be reasonably certain that your reader will understand them as you intended. For example, consider the word "ampere." If you look up "ampere" in a desk dictionary and then in a technical dictionary, you will find that the definitions generally agree. But many terms do not have such a common meaning within the area of experience you share with your reader.

Once you have judged that your reader needs a definition, you must decide whether to use a short definition or an extended definition. *Short definitions* rarely exceed one or two sentences. They give the reader only the basic details about the term:

> Writing is a means of transferring ideas from one person to another.
>
> A ballpoint pen is a writing tool that applies quick-drying ink to paper.

Extended definitions provide more details. The definition of "ampere" given in a technical dictionary, though it agrees basically with that given in a desk dictionary, is likely to be far more detailed. We shall examine the uses of these two types of definitions shortly.

You may introduce definitions directly into the text itself, as the need arises, or you may bring them together in a glossary at the beginning of the report or (rarely) in an appendix. Short definitions usually appear either in the text or in a glossary; extended definitions usually appear in a glossary. Table 9-3 summarizes the uses and placement of definitions.

Short Definitions

A short definition provides the most basic meaning of a term. In framing a short definition, you may choose to give the logical, classical definition of the term, you may stipulate the precise meaning you intend in the context, or you may specify what the reader must do to experience the meaning of the term. The classical definition consists of three parts:

1. The term or word itself.
2. The general class into which the term falls.
3. The characteristics that distinguish the term from other terms in the same class.

This type of definition is direct and straightforward. The (term) falls into a (class) that (differs from other terms in that class).

Table 9-3. Uses and Placement of Definitions

Reader Knows	Does Not Know	Define?	Type	Placement
Term, concept, context	—	No	—	—
Term, concept	Context	Yes	Either	Text
Term	Concept Context	Yes Yes	Extended Either	Glossary Text
Concept	Term Context	Yes Yes	Short Extended	Either Glossary
—	Term Concept Context	Yes Yes Yes	Short Extended Either	Either Glossary Text

For example: An *ampere* [the term] is a unit of *measurement of the flow of electrons* [the class] that *indicates the rate of flow of electricity moving at any given moment* [differences]. Notice that the definition is descriptive. It specifies how "ampere" differs from other measurements of the *flow of electrons*. Table 9-4 gives four definitions from different dictionaries. Each definition identifies the class and specifies how "ampere" differs from other terms in the same class.

The *class* a term belongs to consists of a group of terms that share certain characteristics. For example, a slotted screwdriver shares a number of characteristics with other tools and with other screwdrivers. To define a slotted screwdriver, you would show, specifically, how it differs in key respects from those other tools and other screwdrivers. The more characteristics the term you are defining shares with other members of the same class, the more detailed you must make your definition.

When you define a slotted screwdriver by naming its unique characteristics, you assume that your reader understands the characteristics of the class but does not know how to distinguish the term from other members of that class. So you focus your definition on what the reader does not know.

Your reader may be familiar with only certain aspects of the term. For example, your reader may know what an "asset" is and even have some inkling of what a "capital asset" is (the average taxpayer, for example). Starting from the common meaning of the term "capital," you can proceed to the term "capital asset" and define it in a narrow context. Remember

Table 9-4. Definitions of "Ampere"

Source	Class Identified	Definition
The Random House College Dictionary	"the meter-kilogram-second unit of electric current"	Elect, the meter-kilogram-second unit of electric current, equal to the current that passes in a resistance of one ohm when a potential difference of one volt is applied: equivalent to one coulomb per second.
Longman Dictionary of Scientific Usage	"constant current"	A current of one ampere is that constant current which, flowing in two infinitely long, straight, parallel conductors, of negligible circular cross-section, placed 1 metre apart in a vacuum, would produce a force between them of 2×10^{-7} newton per metre length of conductor. This is the basic SI unit in eletricity; all other units are derived through it.
Dictionary of Science	"A unit of electric current"	A unit of electric current approximately equivalent ot the flow of 6×10^{18} electrons per second. The absolute ampere, which is one-tenth of an abampere (see ab-), is equal to 1.000165 International amperes. The International ampere was originally defined as the unvarying current which when passed through a solution of silver nitrate, deposits silver at the rate of 0.00111800 grams per second. Redefined in 1948 as the intensity of a constant current which, if maintained in two parallel, rectilinear conductors of infinite length, of negligible circular section and placed at a distance of one metre from on another in vacuo, will produce between the conductors a force equal to 2×10^{-7} newton per metre of length. The ampere so defined is the basic SI Unit of current.
Modern Dictionary of Electronics	"A unit of electrical current or rate of flow of electrons"	A unit of electrical current or rate of flow of electrons. One volt across 1 ohm of resistance causes a current flow of 1 ampere. A flow of 1 coulomb per second equals 1 ampere. An unvarying current is passed through a solution of silver nitrate of standard concentration at a fixed temperature. A current that deposits silver at the rate of .001118 gram per second is equal to 1 ampere, or 6.25×10^{18} electrons per second passing a given point in a circuit.

that your reader may have an imperfect or even an erroneous understanding of a term that is centrally important to what you are trying to communicate. So when in doubt, define the term.

Extended Definitions

To distinguish a particular term from other terms in the same class, a number of methods are available. You might copy the definition from a desk dictionary or from some specialized dictionary. The problem with that method is that the lexicographer who wrote that definition did not have your specific context and your specific reader in mind. Dictionary definitions are intended for general readers who come across an unfamiliar word. You, on the other hand, are using the term in a particular context, and you must define it to convey the precise meaning you intend.

You may stipulate at the outset the exact meaning you are ascribing to a term: "In this report *capital asset* will mean . . ." Thereafter, the reader will understand precisely what you mean when you use the term. When precise meaning is essential (in legal documents and proposals, for example), this practice saves time and avoids confusion. The reader may not agree with your definition but is obliged to accept it in the sense in which you are using it.

The details in extended definitions may provide description, comparison or contrast, or analysis. Look at Table 9-4 once again. How does each writer present the distinguishing characteristics of "ampere"? The principal means is description. One writer describes the calculation of an ampere, another describes the measurement of an ampere, and a third describes the history of the word. Table 9-5 shows the class and the method of development these writers use to define "ampere."

In each method the extended definition presents additional information about the term. All these methods are closely related. To define a term, you first name it, then place it in a larger grouping of similar words (that is, classify it), and then show how it differs from other words in the same group.

To avoid interrupting the flow of a report, it is best to place extended definitions in a glossary or an appendix. Give the reader a clear indication of where to find a needed definition at the appropriate point in the text.

Some extended definitions require visuals to make them intelligible to the reader. In such cases include a drawing or a photograph. If you want to show a process, include a flow chart. If you want to analyze, compare, or contrast certain facts, include a line graph, a pie chart, a bar chart, or a table. Choose the visual that will best advance your reader's understanding of the definition.

Table 9-5. Methods Used to Develop Definitions of "Ampere"

Source	Class	Method of Development
The Random House College Dictionary	"the meter-kilogram-second unit of electric current"	Process: "passes in a resistance of one ohm when a potential difference of one volt is applied"
Longman Dictionary of Scientific Usage	"constant current"	Process: "flowing in two infinitely long, straight, parallel conductors, of negligible circular cross-section, placed 1 metre apart in a vacuum, would produce a force between them of 2×10^{-7} newton per metre length of conductor"
Dictionary of Science	"A unit of electric current"	Analogy: "equivalent to the flow of 6×10^{18} electrons per second"
Modern Dictionary of Electronics	"A unit of electric current or rate of flow of electrons"	Cause-effect: "One volt across 1 ohm of resistance causes a current flow of 1 ampere"

Reprinted by permission: Random House College Dictionary, rev. ed. Copyright © 1984 by Random House, Inc.; A Godman and E.M.F. Payne. Longman Dictionary of Scientific Usage, Longman Group Limited, Essex, England, 1980; Graf, Rudolph. Modern Dictionary of Electronics, 5th ed., Howard W. Sams & Co., Inc., Indianapolis, 1977.

Analysis

Analysis is a useful organizing technique for presenting the sequence of events in a process or the relationship of components in a mechanism. In explaining the operation of a machine, for example, you might specify how the parts work together when the machine is performing its characteristic operation. Analysis may also come into play when you are reporting the causes of a particular result (such as an increase in profits), when you are demonstrating that one event is part of a sequence of events, or when you are showing that an event consists of a cluster of related events.

The analytical approach to organization helps the reader understand complex relationships among the data you are reporting and enables you to tailor the organization of your report to your reader's needs. In reporting on the manufacture of a new product, for example, you analyze costs for an accountant but you analyze technical aspects for an engineer. Each reader comes to a report with a particular perspective and particular informational needs.

The three types of analysis commonly used in writing reports are cause and effect, classification, and division.

Cause and Effect

The human mind seeks to impose order on data in an effort to determine relationships among them. When we witness an event, we want to know what caused it. In a report on process, a cause-and-effect approach helps the reader to perceive the complex relationships among the data. Such an approach demands rigorous attention to detail to ensure that the complete reasoning process is presented. The writer must never assume that the reader already knows a particular step or that the significance of a step will be self-evident. Include every step in your reasoning process that is essential to the reader's understanding, even at the risk of providing an overabundance of detail.

Cause-and-effect analysis is particularly useful in setting forth the logical relationships among the components of a problem. (Why are there holes in the parking lot? Because standing water freezes and thaws.) Such analysis is also useful in predicting the results of an event or an action. (What will happen if we surface the parking lot with concrete rather than asphalt? The surface may be more permanent and water may not collect in depressions.)

You have probably used cause-and-effect analysis in writing reports for your courses. For example, in a laboratory report you identify the tests you conducted and the results they produced. Mathematical analysis also lends itself to cause-and-effect reasoning. When you use the cause-and-effect approach, your reasoning process must be logical and clearly stated; otherwise, your reader will distrust your conclusions. Your credibility depends on the rigor of your thinking and on the preciseness of the data you present for evidence and support.

In using cause-and-effect analysis, then, make certain that

1. this is the best organizational approach to satisfying your reader's needs.

2. your data support your conclusions.

3. you do not omit steps in the chain of reasoning because you assume that your reader already knows them or because they seem self-evident.

4. the relationships between cause and effect are logical and convincing.

Classification and Division

The manner in which libraries arrange books and periodicals suggests parallels to the manner in which you can organize data in a report. The most common systems of library classification are the Dewey decimal system and the Library of Congress system. Both systems group books and periodicals according to subject matter. They bring discrete groups together into larger and larger groupings that, taken together, constitute the library's complete holdings. Similarly, in organizing data for a report, you can devise progressively more comprehensive groupings. This is the process of *classification*.

The opposite process is *division*, in which you break down larger groupings into less and less inclusive groupings. The table of contents of a book is organized by division. It divides the overall subject of the book into chapters, and the chapters into sections. When you outline a report, you are doing the same thing.

Classification and division are helpful in organizing individual paragraphs as well. When you lead off with a general statement and follow it with supporting statements, you are using a deductive arrangement. When you present the specifics first and conclude with a generalization, you are arranging your material inductively. These arrangements correspond to classification and division.

Consider the following example. You are preparing a report on how to write and publish a textbook. You summarize the steps this way:

Writing a textbook consists of eighteen steps: idea, research, proposal, review, revision, review, approval, contract, draft of book, review of draft, revision, approval of manuscript, copy editing, design and layout, typesetting, proofreading and corrections, printing, and sales.

When you break the process down into steps, you are using division. But you can see that the whole process consists of three major steps: proposal, writing, production. When you group the steps into three larger categories, you are using classification.

In deciding how to present your report, you can start with the generalization ("Writing a textbook ..."), with the three major steps, or with all eighteen steps:

Division: Writing a textbook consists of three major steps: preparing a proposal, writing the manuscript, and producing the book. Each step consists of several substeps.

Classification: Preparing a proposal, writing a manuscript, and producing the book constitute the three major steps in publishing a textbook.

One way of deciding on the best way to organize your information is to use the words "divide" and "group." If "divide" seems more appropriate ("I can divide the core sample from the parking lot into three parts"), organize your sentences and paragraphs according to division:

General concept
1. Subdivision of general concept
2. Subdivision of general concept
   a. Subpart of subdivision
   b. Subpart of subdivision

If "group" seems more appropriate ("I can group the tests we performed into three types"), organize your sentences and paragraphs according to classification:

1. Subpart
2. Subpart
3. Subpart
   General concept

Comparison and Contrast

In deciding on an organizational plan, you may realize that your reader is familiar with other information that is similar to the information you are presenting. You can make use of this familiar information by comparing and contrasting it with the unfamiliar information. When you point out similarities, you are comparing; when you point out differences, you are contrasting.

Comparison

When two pieces of information have several elements in common, you can promote reader understanding by referring to the similarities between them. Make certain, though, that the similarities are significant and will be meaningful to the reader. To compare test procedure A with procedure B, you must know that they are similar and that the reader is familiar with test procedure B.

Comparison is also useful when you are modifying existing procedures or methods. You can follow the main points of the existing procedure and introduce *minor* changes along the way. But be sure the changes are minor; otherwise you will be contrasting the procedures and creating confusion.

Contrast

If two procedures or events have *major* differences, you can use contrast as an organizing principle. You must be certain, of course, that your reader is familiar with the information you are using as the basis for your contrast. By emphasizing major differences between the familiar and the unfamiliar, you can help your reader understand the new information you are presenting.

Before you decide to use contrast, try to determine your reader's attitude toward the information on which you are basing your contrast. If you are contrasting a new procedure with an old one, is it possible that your reader was the person who instituted that old plan? If so, your contrast may provoke an unfavorable response. And be sure you understand all the details of the existing procedure and the organization's attitude toward it. History has a way of influencing people's acceptance of new proposals.

In summary, when using comparison and contrast, keep these pointers in mind:

1. Carefully analyze what the reader already knows.
2. Relate what the reader knows to the new information you are reporting.
3. Identify *major* similarities or differences.
4. Clearly state when you are comparing and when you are contrasting.

Visuals

When we read, our minds process the words on the page by matching them with information stored from past experience. The word "car," for example, summons up a visual image. That image varies from person to person, however, because everyone has had different experiences with cars. If the word "car" is replaced by a group of words—"Aspen, 1985, green, Dodge, station wagon, four-door, limited edition"—the image will be very much the same for all readers. The more specific the words a writer uses, the more alike will be the images created in the minds of readers. Reference to specific details enlarges the field of common experience through which a writer communicates. Visual images enhance understanding.

By providing visuals, you make it unnecessary for the reader to convert your words into a visual representation. If, instead of using the words "Dodge Aspen," you present a photograph or a drawing, your reader perceives the image immediately. Still, for the significance of the image to be perceived, you must place it in a meaningful context: "A Lincoln Continental ran into my 1985 Dodge Aspen station wagon." Through words, you provide context for the visual.

Visuals are images that the reader can understand directly or with a minimum of processing. When the reader sees a drawing of a car, for example, the processing of the image into a perception of reality is immediate and direct. Some visuals, however, must be "translated" before they can be perceived as reality. A pie chart, for example, does not exist in reality. But apple pies do, and the reader can relate the pie chart to slices of pie and recognize that the segments of the chart represent parts of the whole. In other words, the reader processes the visual image and recognizes it as a representation of reality.

Technical Assignments

1. Select an object—a machine, a tool, or some other mechanical device—for use as the subject of a formal report. Prepare a 500-word report, including:
   a. a short definition of the object.
   b. a description of the object.
   c. a description of how it works.

2. Find an extended definition of a technical term in an encyclopedia or dictionary in your field. Analyze the definition and report on how the writer organized and developed it.

3. Prepare a flow chart that describes the work you have done to date on your final report. Indicate the amount of time you have spent on each part.

4. Below are the opening sentences of several extended definitions. Which technique would be most appropriate for expanding each sentence into an expanded definition? Choose from mechanism description, process description, instructions, cause-and-effect, classification, or division.

   Sentence
   a. *Abrasion resistance* is a property of materials that indicates the amount of friction and wear a material can tolerate.
   b. *Water runoff* is the water that drains off and is not absorbed in the ground.
   c. A *D.C. ammeter* is an instrument used to measure the flow of electrical current.
   d. A *fuel pump* is a device that sucks gas from the gas tank, pressurizes it, and sends it to the carburetor.
   e. *Chemistry* is the science of the composition of substances, their properties as related to their composition and structure, and the formation of new materials by interaction with other structures.
   f. An *operating system* is software that schedules the performance of a computer's tasks, performs supporting functions for job programs, and increases the computer system's efficiency.

g. *Gaussian elimination* is a mathematical process for solving systems of linear equations by reducing the matrix (linear equations) to a solution.
h. A *voltmeter* is a measuring instrument used to determine the potential difference between any two points.
i. An *infection* is the presence of microorganisms in an individual; it can be of three types: (1) harmful, (2) beneficial, and (3) harmless.

10

Writing the Report

echnical writing becomes easier with practice. As your understanding of the process deepens, you will discover new ways of organizing, planning, and revising. There are, however, no new ways to get the words down on paper. You must make a choice: pencil or pen, typewriter, word processor, or, perhaps, dictation. Whichever you choose, you have to form the words first in your mind and then transfer them to paper or screen. And because the mind moves faster than the fingers, you sometimes leave gaps without realizing it. That is why revision is so important. This chapter suggests ways to get the first draft written so that you can revise and polish it into a finished report.

Drafting Outlines

The process of drafting an outline is similar to the process of drafting sentences and paragraphs. Since nothing emerges wholly perfect from the mind, be content to list the sections as they occur to you, with little thought to exact ordering or precise wording. If you worry too much about breaking every section down into subheadings and subsubheadings, you may very well omit a whole section that is crucial to your report.

An outline can serve two purposes: (1) it can be a guide to help you write the first draft, and (2) it can serve as a preliminary document for a lengthy report that you will submit to your supervisor for approval. Knowing which is appropriate to the occasion will help you both in drafting and in revising.

The Outline as Guide

An outline used as a guide to writing the first draft lets you decide what topics to cover and enables you to check your draft report to make certain that it covers all the points you planned to cover. It need not be a formal production. Indeed, you may not even need to use numbers or letters to label the sections. You might devise your own system of capital letters, underlining, dashes, and asterisks. Figure 10-1 shows a sample

DRAFT OF AN OUTLINE
FOR CHAPTER 10

Three parts

* Writing drafts

* Revising drafts

* Preparing final copy

Drafts

* How to write the first draft

* The effective use of outlines

* Keeping the reader and the purpose in mind

* The use of format sections and subsections

Revising

* What to look for when revising

* Checking drafts against reader, purpose, and material

* Editing and proofreadings

Final copy

* Reproduction suggestions (typing and text processing)

* Covers

* Distribution of final copy

* Final proofreading

* Checklist before handing in report

Figure 10-1. Sample outline for use as a guide.

page from an outline used as a guide. (Actually, this is from the outline I used for the first draft of this chapter.)

This first outline is not a set document that you have to follow in every detail. As you develop sections of the report, you may change or rearrange the content to suit a new idea or a new approach. So keep the first-draft outline flexible.

Understanding your purpose and the reader's need for information will suggest the main headings and what to include under each. For example, if you are going to report the results of a laboratory test, you might start your outline by writing "Overview" at the top of a sheet of paper and then writing notes under the following headings:

> Type of report
> Purpose of report
> Specifications
> > Length
> > Due date
> > Level of formality
> Assumed reader or readers
> > Name(s) and position(s)
> > Characteristics

You might then label four more sheets, each with a conventional heading:

> Theory
>
> Methods and materials
>
> Results
>
> Discussion

Or you might follow the overview sheet with six additional sheets, each headed with a question you expect the reader will want answered (see Chapter 8). Jot down your ideas on how you plan to answer each question and then arrange the sheets in the sequence the reader's needs suggest. If you are making notes only for your own use, make sure you will understand them when you refer to them again. But if you are to submit the outline to your supervisor for approval, you will need to be more formal.

As you proceed, you might follow this sequence:

Section	**Usual Reader Question**
1. Solution, recommendation, conclusion	1. "Why do you say that?"
2. Data relevant to the solution, recommendation, conclusion	2. "Well, how did you get that?"
3. Methods/procedures, materials	3. "Why those?"
4. Design of problem-solving process, or theory behind design	4 "Why did you choose that approach?"

Now you have a preliminary outline to follow, and you are ready to get on with the first draft. You may refine your outline as you think further about who your reader will be and how you plan to organize your report. (See Chapter 8, Organization, and the six suggestions for beginning an outline.) Another important problem also disappears: "Where do I begin?" You begin with what you know best.

The Outline as Preliminary Document

Often you will submit a major report to several people in the organization. In such a case you could write the report, send it to those people, wait for their comments, and then revise your report. But this is a time-consuming process, and it may result in the rejection of the entire report. The only time you should follow this procedure is when you know all the readers well enough to judge what will and will not elicit their approval.

A better procedure is to develop a detailed outline and send it to one or two key readers for their approval. (Always send a copy to your supervisor, of course.) Ask for written comments or request an appointment to discuss the outline. Although approval of the outline does not guarantee approval of the final report (circumstances do change), at least you will be able to revise the outline to correct major problems or incorporate changes in the draft report. Having your outline reviewed at this stage will reduce the number of drafts and revisions you will have to make. Moreover, when you come up with the final copy of your report, you can assume that it really is the final copy.

Outlines submitted for review and approval must be as formal and as detailed as possible. Number all major and minor points in a consistent fashion. If your organization has a standard procedure for preparing outlines, follow that system. Figure 10-2 shows three numbering systems in common use.

Include as many details as you can, because your readers will need to see what your full plan is in order to make suggestions. They may also comment on the organization of the outline. This preliminary review will guard against frustrating delays later on. If the readers' comments are not clear to you, don't hesitate to ask questions.

If you are to prepare variant reports for different readers, this outline review will indicate how you should organize each version. By shifting your emphasis and by altering the order of sections, you will be able to respond to the needs of several types of reader.

Each reader will come to your report with a need for specific information. Your responsibility as writer is to determine what information each reader needs. Say you have in-

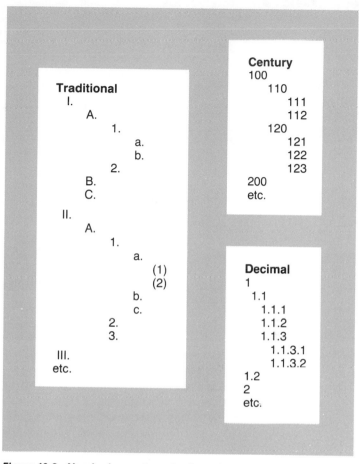

Traditional
I.
    A.
        1.
            a.
            b.
        2.
    B.
    C.

II.
    A.
        1.
            a.
                (1)
                (2)
            b.
            c.
        2.
        3.

III.
etc.

Century
100
    110
        111
        112
    120
        121
        122
        123
200
etc.

Decimal
1
    1.1
        1.1.1
        1.1.2
        1.1.3
            1.1.3.1
            1.1.3.2
    1.2
2
etc.

Figure 10-2. Numbering systems for formal outlines.

formation A B C D E F G H I J K L M N O P Q. Assume that the reader of a particular report needs information in the order A D J C B Q. Knowing what the reader wants means that you can present the relevant information in the main body of the report and discard the nonrelevant information or put it in an appendix. Moreover, within any given sentence, some information will be more important to the reader than other information.

Getting Started

Your specialized training and experience will guide you in deciding what data you need for a particular report. But communicating those data to a reader may be more difficult.

Try to approach writing as a problem-solving process. Actually, the problem that writing presents is easier than most problems, because you need not work it through from beginning to end in a linear sequence. In fact, it is easier not to start at the beginning.

When you sit down to write your rough draft, start with what you are.most familiar with: conclusions/recommendations/solutions. You have already worked through the assignment and you know what you will tell your supervisor. If he or she were to ask about your progress, you would not respond with a lengthy explanation of background, methods/procedures, materials, and theory. You would simply say, "I found out that ..." Begin your draft the same way.

As we have seen, most companies specify the sections that must be included in reports, and in what order. A standard format helps readers to turn quickly to the information they are most interested in. When you consult a reference book, you know immediately where to look for the information you need. The table of contents is always at the beginning and the index at the end. Your company's requirements on format may be very rigid on every detail, or they may specify only certain elements, such as title page, transmittal memo, and summary/abstract, leaving the rest to you. Be sure you are familiar with the format your company requires.

The Draft

Let's assume for the moment that you are free to organize your report as you think best. You have worked up an outline to serve as a guide, and you sit down to do the actual writing. Consider these questions:

1. Do I work best with a pencil or a pen?
2. What kind of paper do I prefer to use?
3. Am I comfortable using a typewriter for a first draft? a word processor or computer?
4. Do I work best in the morning, afternoon, or evening?
5. Do I write best under pressure?
6. Does it help to have music or TV in the background?
7. Am I most comfortable at home or in the library or in the student union?
8. Can I write for long periods of time or do I need frequent breaks?
9. How much can I write at one session?
10. Do I revise my outline as I go along? Do I make notes in the margin?

In short, think about how you work best.

No athlete rushes into a game without training. Nor should a writer. Build endurance through practice. Start slowly. Write for 30 minutes, break for a few minutes, and write for another 30 minutes. But work steadily and pace your efforts. Estimate how much time you have available for each section and work out a schedule accordingly.

How long will it take you to write a rough draft of each section? Some experienced writers can produce 1,000 to 1,500 words an hour. But you should probably count on turning out about 400 to 600 words an hour while writing your first draft. On the second draft, after you have edited and revised, you can probably manage about 700 words an hour. The third draft should get you close to 1,000 words an hour, because you will be recopying the revised report.

Before we discuss these stages, look for a moment at Figure 10-3, which plots degree of perfection against time. Notice that as you strive for greater and greater perfection, you spend more time and achieve smaller and smaller increments of perfection. You never reach 100% perfection, because that would take an infinite amount of time. Some tasks, of course, are worth the greatest effort time permits; others are not. Spending two days revising a two-sentence memo is not a good use of time, effort, and, consequently, money. Spending two days revising a major report might be, however. Ultimately, you must decide, on the basis of your estimate of the value of a

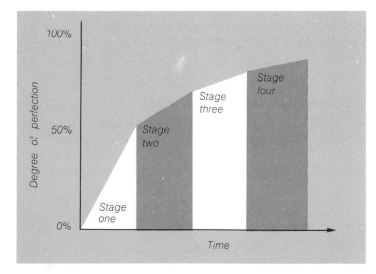

Figure 10-3 Degree of perfection versus expenditure of time.

report to the reader, how much time to spend on gathering data and writing and revising the report.

Gaps in Continuity

You have probably experienced the frustration of listening to a speaker who raced along too swiftly for you to take notes. Everyday speech patterns are rapid, and the mind tends to move at the same rate. You cannot possibly keep up with it as you try to transcribe the words to paper. As a result, your first draft of a report will almost certainly contain gaps in continuity.

You have probably noticed such gaps in your answers to essay questions on examinations. You write under pressure, and you rush to get down everything you want to say. You follow a stream-of-consciousness approach, putting down your thoughts in the order in which they come to mind, without sequential development or conscious organization. But if you work out an outline—even a rough, skeleton outline—before you start to write, you will keep such gaps to a minimum.

In creating the first draft of a report, follow this procedure: Draw up an outline and then put your thoughts down as fully and as quickly as you can. Even with the outline to guide you, there will be gaps in continuity. But you can repair them when you revise the draft. (When you take an essay exam, save five minutes or so at the end to read through your answer and make quick corrections.) In addition to gaps, you will probably discover many poorly constructed sentences. Those, too, can be put right as you revise.

Awkward Sentence Construction

Our ordinary speech is a composite of fragments, grunts, vocalized pauses, and simple sentences. If you tried to transcribe a casual conversation, your transcription would be a long way from a finished report. Since writing is a private act, however, you can adjust both the rate at which your mind speaks and the manner in which it speaks.

When you write, you are the only audience present. And you have been talking to yourself for a long time. If you as writer need you as speaker to slow down, you can control the pace. You can also insist that your mind put subjects and verbs together, along with modifiers, as it delivers ideas. Even so, your sentences will sometimes go wrong and lapse into fragments. Expect that to happen. Do not, however, stop to polish each sentence and paragraph to perfection. Some writers are said to agonize over a sentence for hours, refusing to go on until they have made it perfect. When you are drafting a report, however, you are not after perfection. If you stop to worry about every sentence, you will lose your train of thought and will waste time trying to figure out what you planned to say next. Move quickly, letting the gaps and poorly constructed sentences fall where they may. And spend even less time perfecting the mechanics of your writing (spelling, punctuation, and so forth) and refining your vocabulary.

Lapses of Vocabulary

In speaking and writing we often search for a word and fail to find it. "It's right on the tip of my tongue," we say. When that happens in drafting a report, you might stop and search through your notes for just the right word, or you might settle for a word that is close to what you are after. Or you might just leave a blank and move on. If you stop the flow of words, you destroy the context of your writing. One word triggers another, and the successive words create a context for the ideas you want to communicate. To break that context interrupts the flow. Instead, leave a blank space and put a check mark in the margin to alert yourself to the omission when you revise the draft. Rereading the draft will reestablish the context and probably prompt you to think of the word you want. If not, you can now take the time to search it out without interrupting the flow of your ideas.

In stressing the manner in which your mind "speaks" to you as you write, we may have given the impression that speaking and writing are indistinguishable. Actually, when you write—even when you are writing a draft—you are controlling to some degree the sequence of words and ideas.

Matters of Style

As we read a novel, a textbook, or a report, we tend to suspend our awareness of the individual words on the page. We concentrate on the meaning of the words rather than on the words themselves. But an error in spelling or grammar calls us back to the words on the page and breaks our concentration on meaning. The leisurely reader of a novel may not be overly concerned with such errors, unless they seriously disrupt the meaning of a passage. Readers of technical reports, however, do not have time to cope with such breaks in communication. Stopping to translate and trying to guess the meaning leads to frustration and may cause readers to form a negative view of the recommendations, worthy though they may be. Careless grammar suggests careless mathematics. Recommendations marred by misspellings will cast doubt on your ability to devise a workable solution to the problem.

If you are uncertain about matters of grammar, keep a handbook of grammar or a style guide at your elbow (see Appendix A for a list of style guides). Ask your instructor which guide is best suited to your specialty. Some companies produce their own guides; others use published guides either from commercial publishers or from professional societies. Check your library for such specialized guides.

Just as you must know the principles governing your discipline, so, too, must you know the principles governing acceptable writing. Following are some of the most common trouble spots for technical writers. Watch for them as you revise your report.

Punctuation

Punctuation is a device designed to help the reader understand meaning. Read this sentence:

> Five choices in this area are data communication, software, security of a computer system, minicomputer systems and problems and pitfalls of first time computer users.

What is the fourth item in this series? Is it "minicomputer systems and problems" or "minicomputer systems"? Adding a comma after either "systems" or "problems" would clarify the meaning. The reader could puzzle over the sentence and finally decide that the writer probably meant "problems" to go with "systems," but such a deliberation would break the flow of reading. Notice also the absence of a hyphen between "first" and "time." That means that "time" modifies "computer," creating a special kind of a computer: a "time computer."

Check your punctuation immediately after finishing your first draft. Watch especially for faulty use of the comma and semicolon. Again, keep a style manual or a handbook of grammar handy as you revise. When in doubt about the proper use of a mark of punctuation, look it up.

Spelling

Become conscious of the words you habitually misspell. Work on ways to improve your spelling. Keep a list of troublesome words, memorize the rules for forming plurals, and keep a dictionary or a word list on your desk. Keep a record of the spelling errors your instructors notice in your papers, perhaps with technical words in one list and nontechnical words in another.

Fragments

A fragment is a group of words that does not contain a complete thought, with both subject and verb. Writers of fiction, poetry, or drama may use fragments to stimulate the reader's imagination and to vary the pace of a passage. But in technical reports, every sentence must have a subject and a verb (even though that subject may be understood). Fragments call attention to themselves and break the flow of meaning. Readers of technical reports expect the material to be phrased in complete sentences, and, as we know, pattern recognition is part of the process of comprehension. The use of fragments obscures meaning and makes it difficult for the reader to understand what you are trying to communicate.

Agreement

The subject of a sentence must always be in agreement with the verb that follows. Moreover, any pronoun associated with a noun must agree with the number (singular or plural) of that noun. An associated problem is the use of *this* without a clear antecedent. When *this* occurs by itself in a sentence, the reader must return to the preceding sentence to figure out "this *what?*" The simplest solution is to follow "this" with the noun you are referring to.

Passive Voice

When you use a verb in the passive voice, the subject of the sentence is the person or the object that receives action rather than the person or the object performing the action. Compare these sentences:

> John wrote the check.
>
> The check was written by John.
>
> The check was written.

The verb in the first sentence is in the active voice. Here the person performing the action described by the verb is the subject of the sentence. The verbs in the second and third sentences are in the passive voice. Here the object receiving the action described by the verb is the subject of the sentence.
The passive voice has several legitimate uses:

1. Used sparingly, it provides variety.
2. It emphasizes the receiver of an action rather than the performer.
3. It permits the writer to make complete statements even when the performer is unknown.
4. It permits the writer to make complete statements without naming the performer.

In short, using the passive voice does not mean that the writer is guilty of bad English. But overuse of the passive voice can create serious difficulties:

1. It produces wordiness. In the second sentence above, its use added two words, an increase of 50 percent.

2. It often fails to specify who is taking the action. (Administrators and bureaucrats favor the passive voice for this reason.)

3. It leads to ambiguity. (For example: "Coming into the room, the apparatus had been moved.")

Another reason why the passive voice is a poor choice for reports is that it slows the reader down in recognizing the pattern of a sentence. When the mind perceives an act—writing a check, for example—it visualizes a person in the act of writing the check. It does not visualize "the check being written." To process the passive into the active, the reader must reverse the pattern. This processing action is almost instantaneous, of course, and the occasional use of the passive voice creates no great loss of time. But when it appears over and over in a report, the conversion time begins to build up. And if no performer is ever identified, the reader enters a world where no one does anything: things just happen. That mystification, coupled with wasted time, finally leads to frustration.

The frequency with which the passive voice is used seems to increase in reports that demand a high level of technical information on the part of the reader. Students frequently complain that their assigned readings are hard to understand, especially when they are reading reports of research findings. One reason for the difficulty is the overuse of passive verbs. In revising your writing, change as many verbs from passive to active as you can. Doing so helps your reader. Passive verbs occur in *Time* magazine only about 10 to 12 percent of the time. *The New York Times* editorial and op-ed pages use such verbs with about the same frequency. By contrast, the *Journal of Sedimentary Petrology*, a highly specialized journal, uses the passive voice about 50 percent of the time.

Using active verbs saves both words and time because it is more natural and because it enables readers to recognize sentence patterns swiftly. In your own writing, avoid using the passive voice except in those rare cases where it will create just the effect you desire.

Wordiness

Wordiness slows your reader down. As we have seen, using the passive voice is one form of wordiness. Here are some others:

Using three words where one would do ("in the meantime" instead of "while," for example).

Using prepositional phrases when simple modifiers would do ("the adjustment screw of the machine" instead of "the machine's adjustment screw"; see cautions below on simplifying such constructions).

Overuse of forms of "to be," especially with "there" and "it" ("There are three reasons for failure: A, B, and C, instead of "The three reasons for failure are A, B, and C," or "The reasons for failure, A, B, and C, suggest . . .").

USING MORE WORDS THAN ARE NEEDED When we talk, we present the first and only draft of what we want to say. We cannot edit or revise what we have said except by starting over. Similarly, we tend to use more words than we need when we compose the first draft of a report. But in revision we have a chance to eliminate unnecessary words. As you revise, watch for constructions in which you have elaborated a simple verb into a phrase. For example:

We need *to make an adjustment* in the Jones account.

The italicized portion of this ten-word sentence contains four words, one of which, "adjustment," is a noun made from the verb "adjust." By changing the phrase back to the verb, you can shorten the sentence by 30 percent:

We need *to adjust* the Jones account.

Not only do you save the reader time, you strengthen the sentence. Here are some other examples:

> *Wordy:* Edwards and Company will *make a decision* about the project next week. (12 words)
>
> *Better:* Edwards and Company will *decide* about the project next week. (10 words)
>
> *Wordy:* Our department will *conduct a discussion* on the budget cutbacks Tuesday. (12 words)
>
> *Better:* Our department will *discuss* the budget cutbacks Tuesday. (10 words)

Look for words that end in "-ion" or "-ment" to see whether you can change them into verbs.

A second way to reduce wordiness is to strike out words that will be understood in the context. For example, change "he finished his address to the stockholders" to "he concluded." Here the context makes the two omitted points clear: The reader already knows that the speaker is addressing the stockholders.

Be careful, however, not to create confusion by telescoping several needed words into a single abstraction. You may save words by so doing, but only at the sacrifice of clarity. What does "today" mean in the following sentence?

The computer *today* is a major influence in our accounting procedures.

It might mean any of the following:

> the day the reader reads the sentence
>
> December 17, 1984
>
> December 1984
>
> 1984
>
> 1980s
>
> the second half of the twentieth century
>
> the twentieth century

Here added words will clarify meaning, save the reader time, and keep the communication flowing.

USING PREPOSITIONAL PHRASES INSTEAD OF SIMPLE MODIFIERS Look for places where you have used prepositional phrases as modifiers. See whether you can omit the preposition, adjust the wording, and move the resulting modifier closer to the word it modifies. For example:

The head *of the department* issued the first bulletin *from the vice president.*

This sentence contains two prepositional phrases. You could change the first part of the sentence to "The department head," thereby saving two words. You could change the second phrase, along with the noun associated with it, to "the first vice president's bulletin." But if you did that, you would create an ambiguity (is it the first *bulletin,* or the first *vice president?*) Or you could say "issued the vice president's first bulletin," thus saving two words and creating no ambiguity. Be on the lookout for wordiness as you revise, but do not introduce ambiguity in order to save words.

Be careful too not to string out single-word modifiers before getting to the main subject. The writer who made the following revision may have saved words, but does the revision really help the reader?

Original: The accumulation of data from the procedure of gathering information about the land soil erodibility shows . . .

Revision: The land soil erodibility information gathering procedure data show . . .

Be cautious in changing prepositional phrases to single-word modifiers.

OVERUSE OF FORMS OF "TO BE" Some verbs link the parts of a sentence together while contributing little or no meaning. Others imply an action or state or describe an action. In writing reports, try to use verbs that state action directly. Which of these sentences is more forceful?

John's hat is red and he lost it last week.

John lost his red hat last week.

Another construction that impairs communication begins with "there" or "it" followed by a form of "to be":

There is one reason for adopting this recommendation. It is . . . (10 words)

One reason for adopting this recommendation is . . . (7 words)

It is mandatory that we adopt this plan so that . . . (10 words)

We must adopt this plan so that . . . (7 words)

When you find a sentence beginning with "There is" (or "are"), see whether you can start it with a noun or a pronoun instead. When you find a sentence beginning with "It is," look for a "that" and begin the sentence following it.

Transitions

Transitions provide you with a means of moving from one point to another within sentences, between sentences, and between paragraphs. You tell your reader about the parts of your report by presenting your overall plan, but you must also give the reader guidance in moving from one part to the next. When your transitions are either ambiguous or missing altogether, your reader is obliged to make his or her own way through the report, guessing at the relationships between successive ideas. Figure 10-4 suggests the problem created by inadequate transitions.

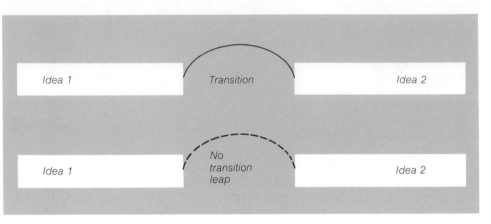

Figure 10-4. Function of a transition.

In writing a short story or a novel, you might use ambiguity to catch your reader's interest and to create tension. Ambiguity is not appropriate in a technical report, however. Consider the following sentence:

Insert the new disc in the disc drive. This provides another 240k of storage.

Does "This" refer to the act of inserting, or to the new disc, or to the disc drive? If this sentence were to appear in a manual, the reader might not stop to figure out what the writer meant. As a technical writer, you cannot take such chances. You must avoid ambiguity at all cost.

Whenever you throw a barrier across your reader's path, you distract his or her attention from what you want to communicate. Whether the barrier is as simple as a misspelled word or as complex as a poorly organized section, the flow of communication is interrupted and the reader is obligated to overcome the difficulty before proceeding.

You will, presumably, see to it that no errors in spelling or punctuation appear in your final draft. These are more or less mechanical matters, and in your role as a professional writer you will guard against such lapses. Devising efficient transitions is somewhat more difficult, and even more indicative of your professional competence.

Table 10-1 lists several transitional expressions, along with the contexts in which they are useful. Notice that some transitions carry little meaning beyond their surface meaning. Numbers, for example, suggest hierarchies of significance or sequences of topics. Other transitions carry richer meaning. The phrase "for example" directs the reader from theory to applica-

Table 10-1. Transitional Expressions

Type	Example
Addition or amplification	moreover, further, furthermore, besides, and, and then, likewise, second, third, finally, last, in the second place, similarly
Contrast, contradiction, or antithesis	but, yet, and yet, however, still, nevertheless, on the other hand, on the contrary, after all, notwithstanding, for all that, in contrast, at the same time, otherwise, despite this fact, although this may be true, whereas, even so
Comparison	similarly, likewise, in like manner, once again, once more, in much the same way
Purpose	to this end, for this purpose, with this object
Consequence or result (see also Restatement)	hence, therefore, accordingly, consequently, and so, then, thus, thereupon, wherefore, as a result, in conclusion, to sum up, for this reason, in other words, and this is why
To introduce an illustration or example	thus, for example, for instance, to illustrate
Time	meanwhile, at length, immediately, soon, after a few days, in the meantime, afterward, later, earlier, formerly, subsequently, so far, until now, this time, hitherto
Place	here, beyond, nearby, opposite to, adjacent to, on the opposite side, elsewhere, there, above, below, farther on
Summary, repetition, exemplification, intensification, recapitulation (see also Consequence)	summing up, to sum up, in brief, on the whole, in sum, in short, as I have said, in other words, to be sure, as has been noted, for example, for instance, in fact, indeed, in any event, all in all, altogether, to summarize

Continued on page 184

Table 10-1. (continued)

Type	Example
Restatement (see also Consequence)	that is, in other words, in simpler terms, to put it differently
Concession	to be sure, granted, of course, it is true, certainly, doubtless, no doubt
Restriction	if provided, provided, in case, unless, last
Qualification	specifically, especially, usually, frequently, occasionally, in particular, in general
Sequence	first, second, finally
Expected, natural, or obviously true	naturally, for that matter, surely, of course, as a matter of fact, it follows (then, that)
Insistence	anyway, indeed, in fact, yes, no, as we have seen

This material was developed by Dr. Sherry G. Southard, Oklahoma State University. Used by permission.

tion, to a means of understanding the theory. The skillful use of transitions will add immeasurably to the impact and effectiveness of your reports.

The Net Effect   The saving of a few words here and there may not seem much at the time, but in a report of 10 or more pages it may be considerable. Conciseness may not always lead to clarity, but most often the one leads to the other.

Figure 10-5 contains the body of a memo that an upper-level manager distributed to middle-level managers in a large organization. The original version comes first, then an edited version. The subject of the memo is the need for budget reductions in response to decreased income. (Unfortunately, the first version is what the writer sent.)

Final Copy   Once you have finished revising your drafts, you are ready to prepare the final copy. You may decide to hire a typist, but that can be expensive, especially if the typist charges by the hour. To keep costs down, always provide your typist with a clean

ORIGINAL MEMO

Since I am sure that rumors are running rampant, I feel that it is incumbent upon me to communicate directly to you about the current budgetary situation. First, however, let me suggest that a calm orderly approach to the problem is called for. Be assured that no precipitous actions will be taken and that I will attempt to maintain the lines of communication with you at all times.

We have been notified by the central administration that a budget reduction is necessary to accommodate to the ... shortfall which affects all ... agencies. I met with all the ... department heads on Friday afternoon to discuss with them the development of departmental plans to meet the ... budgetary shortfall. These plans will be submitted to me on Tuesday morning, and I will meet with Vice-President Smith as soon afterwards as possible. The magnitude of our portion of the cuts will be clearer to me at that time.

I would be less than candid if I did not acknowledge that this is a stressful situation, particularly in view of the need for immediate action at all levels. You may rest assured, however, that I will do the utmost in my power to insure that this temporary perturbation does not harm our ... programs.

REVISED MEMO

Because rumors are circulating about the current budget problems, I wanted to tell you about our responses. We need a calm, orderly approach to the problem. We have taken no hasty actions and will keep you informed as we develop our plans.

The central administration told us to reduce our budgets. I met with the various department heads Friday afternoon to discuss plans to meet the problem. They will submit their plans to me Tuesday morning, and I will meet with Vice-President Smith. We should have an idea of the exact reductions then.

This is a difficult time, particularly because we must act quickly at all levels. You should know that we will do everything we can to insure that this problem does not harm our programs.

Comments: Although this rewrite reduces the number of words and provides added clarity, it still needs a lot of work. The second sentence in paragraph one, for example, does not follow logically from the first sentence, and sentence three relates to neither. Paragraph two is a little better, because it tells the reader what meetings were held and what deadlines were set. Paragraph one is very vague and needs specific detail. The last paragraph tries, not very successfully, to soothe the readers' fears.

Figure 10-5. Body of administrative memo.

copy of your latest revision. You will save time answering questions, and you will save money, especially if the typist charges a premium to handle messy copy. Your final copy will also have fewer errors. Give your typist adequate lead time. Plan on at least five days to get a 20-page report typed, proofread, corrected, and reproduced. When you are working for an organization, the lead time required will depend on the availability of typists.

Give the typist clear instructions on how much space to leave for any visuals you plan to include in the text. If you plan to include a full-page visual, tell the typist how to adjust the page numbers to accommodate it.

When the typist finishes the report, proofread it carefully for errors in spelling, punctuation, and grammar that the typist may have introduced. (Presumably, the copy you provided was error-free.) Avoid adding or deleting sections or moving sections around—unless your typist uses a word processor. The purpose of proofreading is not to introduce additional revisions but to compare the original manuscript with the typed version.

If you spot any errors, indicate your corrections in a manner your typist will understand. The best policy is to ask the typist what system to use. Make corrections neatly and lightly with a pencil, so that you can erase them later. If your typist uses a word processor, ask for a preliminary copy that you can proofread and correct before the final copy is run.

If you plan to type the final copy yourself, schedule your time carefully. A relatively unskilled typist may take 20 to 25 minutes to produce one typed page. That means that a 20-page report may take from 6½ to 8½ hours to type.

Technical Assignments

1. Write to a major corporation and ask which style guide it uses for report writing. Ask how you can secure a copy.
2. Prepare a flow chart showing how you developed a writing assignment for this or some other class.
3. Prepare a short report describing the process you use to write a report; be prepared to share it with your classmates.
4. Rewrite the following sentences to eliminate passive-voice verbs.
   a. Reports should not be sent by engineers if they have not been carefully proofread.
   b. The covering should be removed before beginning operation.
   c. The results of the experiment were reported by the researcher to the group that had control of the contracts that were negotiated by the legal department.

    d. Calcium has been thought to help in the process, but it has not been proved yet.

    e. Each technique is discussed below focusing on why I believe it to be useful in the report.

5. Revise and rewrite the following items. Consider verbs, voice, wordiness, spelling, and any other elements that may impair communication.

    a. The purpose of this study is to determine the feasibility of converting the existing prospective student communication system into a word-processing program.

    b. The first step in cleaning the maintenance area is to distinctly mark off the area to be cleaned with engineering tape.

    c. On December 3, I began my formal report on the feasibility of establishing a variable speed pump for English.

    d. This inaccuracy could lead to the improper investing of people relying on the financial position of a business to make their decisions about purchase.

    e. This section is included to inform the reader of the issues subject to possible future action.

    f. We regret that the parts manufactured by us for your machine malfunctioned. There are several causes for that malfunction, and you should consult your owner's manual for a troubleshooting guide in the appendix. In any case, we stand ready to assist you in any way we can to make certain your machine functions to its full design capacity. When it does, you will find that all of the jobs you had to do by hand can now easily be done on the machine. For example, you can both install new fence posts and remove old ones or ones that you want moved. Likewise, the drill attachment can be used to provide dirt removal in new well operations. Carefully following instructions can make the machine the finest, all around tool on your farm. The accessories add many dimensions you may not have thought about. I have enclosed a catalog of the attachments, and I invite you to call for estimates.

    g. Logical development in the history of the department shows how the problems came to be identified, investigated, a solution suggested and tested, and finally the new department created. Materials handling has always been one of those areas which was assumed to be a necessary evil. Production costs, sales costs, management costs, raw materials costs, and so forth are all easily discovered because attention is constantly focused on them. The receiving, storing, and distribution of raw materials, however, was not that obvious. Consequently, few outside receiving and, perhaps, purchasing, realized what these costs were.

11

Other Reporting Forms

I n this chapter we will describe certain forms of technical writing other than formal reports that you may be asked to prepare on the job. This discussion is intended only to familiarize you with the various forms and to give you some idea of how to produce them. If you want to learn more about these forms, consult Appendix A.

Here we discuss the following forms:

Abstracts

Catalogs, sales literature, advertising copy

Brochures

Technical manuals

Annual reports

Abstracts

In Chapter 7 we discussed the preparation of abstracts to be incorporated into formal reports. Your supervisor may ask you to prepare abstracts for other purposes as well, mainly to provide information in concise form for other members of the organization. Usually the assignment will be to abstract the content of a journal article or a technical report. The reader of an abstract wants answers to these questions:

1. What are the key points of the article?
2. How do they apply to the organization?
3. What is your evaluation of the article?

Since the reader needs specific information for a specific purpose, you can approach the writing of abstracts much as you approached the writing of reports. However, because you know precisely who your reader will be, your analysis of the reader's ability to understand technical information is greatly simplified. You also know why the reader wants the abstract and, consequently, whether you should emphasize key points, applications, or evaluations.

Abstracts commonly follow this pattern:

1. *Source.* State where you found the article or report and how the reader can locate it if the need arises.

2. *Key points.* Present the key points in the order in which they appear in the material. List the points without repeating all the details.

3. *Application.* Indicate how the key points relate to the reader's needs. The assignment will probably suggest why the reader wants the abstract and how it will be used. If it does not, ask about applications before you prepare the abstract.

4. *Evaluation.* What is *your* opinion of the value of this article or report? Does it apply to your supervisor's needs? Should the supervisor read the report in its entirety?

The length of a given abstract depends in part on the length of the original article, but try to limit abstracts to a single typed page. Remember that the purpose of abstracts is to save your reader time.

When you abstract an article or a report, watch for organizational devices that highlight the main points. Read the introduction carefully for clues to the major sections and subsections. Use the headings and subheadings as a preliminary outline of your abstract, and be sure to incorporate the main points under each heading. In short, when you abstract a report written by someone else, apply what you already know about writing an effective report.

A word of caution: Never trust abstracts that come with articles and reports. Always read the original yourself. Such abstracts are usually prepared by editors after a rather superficial reading of the article, and their purpose is likely to be quite different from yours. They may very well shift the emphasis of the article or overlook a key point. You have a specific purpose in mind, and the only way to carry out that purpose is to read the entire article yourself.

Catalogs, Sales Literature, Advertising Copy

Although your primary duties will probably be of a technical nature, your organization may call on you from time to time to help with marketing.

The readers of catalogs and sales literature differ from

the readers of advertising copy in significant ways. When the ABC Company advertises a new razor, it wants to convince readers that its product is superior to that of its competitors. Thus, the advertising copy for a razor may stress some technological innovation without going into specifications or other technical details.

When the ABC Company announces a new machine for the manufacture of plastic molding, however, it is addressing a technically qualified purchasing agent or the members of a committee that decides on major acquisitions. Sales literature for this purpose must contain technical details on the design, use, and cost of the new machine. It must also be comprehensive, because the writer is never sure just what information a particular reader will be looking for. At the same time, the literature must be kept reasonably brief, to keep the costs of printing and distribution under control.

When the ABC Company prepares sales literature for a major product, its intention is to motivate prospective purchasers to invite the company's representatives to demonstrate the product and to point out its distinctive features. The company does not expect the literature to produce a sale directly.

Catalogs, sales literature, and advertising contain varying levels of technical detail based on the needs of different readers. Catalogs aim at technically sophisticated readers. Advertising copy aims at a broad audience with little interest in technical detail. Sales literature aims at an audience somewhere in between: one that is moderately interested in technical detail.

Catalogs

Catalogs contain technical data that describe the specific characteristics of a product or a service. The level of detail depends on the particular group of readers the organization wants to reach. Although catalogs are rarely as detailed as a set of specifications or a technical manual, they do accommodate the anticipated reader's desire for technical information about the products listed.

Catalogs rely heavily on description of both products and processes. The principles governing effective description discussed in Chapter 9 apply equally well to writing catalog copy:

1. Emphasize the reader's needs. Decide what information the reader wants and concentrate on that information—construction of the product, physical characteristics, uses, cost.

2. Match your presentation of technical details to the reader's ability to comprehend.

3. Make sure the reader understands how the product will serve particular applications.

Suit your copy to the range of readers who are likely to consult the catalog and to the amount of space available for each entry. Readers of catalogs vary widely in level of sophistication. You can accommodate that range by organizing your copy so that it moves from the general to the specific. Unless the catalog is clearly intended for a specialized audience, begin with a brief overview of the product and then proceed to specific details. Here is a suggested scheme of organization:

1. Overview
   a. Name of product or process
   b. Purpose of product or process
   c. Photograph or drawing

2. Applications
   a. Range of uses
   b. Benefits to the reader

3. Specifications
   a. Technical details based on readers' needs
   b. Detailed drawings

A good way to familiarize yourself with the ways in which professional writers of catalog copy respond to the needs of different audiences is to compare the descriptions of two products in a general merchandise catalog. Figure 11-1 shows two descriptions of electrical equipment from a Sears catalog. The amount and type of technical detail differ because the writer assumes that the readers will have differing needs.

Figure 11-2 shows a description of a similar product from a catalog intended for readers who want more detail and who are capable of comprehending that detail.

Again, if you are ever called on to write catalog copy, identify your readers' need for information and their ability to comprehend it, and organize your copy accordingly.

Sales Literature

Sales literature ranges from leaflets and brochures to multipage treatments of a single product or a group of products. Whereas a catalog describes the whole range of products an organization offers, sales literature concentrates on a single product or a single group of related products. The copy is targeted to specific readers with identifiable needs and interests. The object is to persuade the reader to request a visit from a sales representative or an opportunity to see the product in operation. Figure 11-3 provides an example of sales literature.

New at Sears! Our finest Electronic Digital Blood Pressure Monitor operates 4 separate functions in one unit and has a printed readout for a permanent record

LCD display Unit measures and displays blood pressure, pulse rate, and body temperature plus functions as a digital alarm clock. Measurements may also be printed with date and time for a permanent record.

OPERATING INFO: Instruction manual must be read carefully. For systolic (maximum) and diastolic (minimum) blood pressure readings, first, set the clock to the correct time and date. Push power switch. The Rubber Bulb mark and WAIT should appear on panel. (See instruction manual.) When READY is displayed, inflate cuff to proper pressure. After inflation, MEASURING will appear. The numbers will begin flashing and descending on display panel. When readings are complete your systolic, diastolic and pulse rate will be displayed. Unit will then automatically release all pressure from cuff. A printed readout can then be obtained by pushing print button. To measure body temperature; connect THERMOPROBE to main unit. Insert probe into disposable sanitary cover and place under tongue or armpit. Obtain reading by following instruction manual. To print out completed reading, push print button.

CONSTRUCTION: Plastic housing. Vinyl zippered case for cuff and thermoprobe. Imported.

ORDER INFO: Step-by-step instruction manual. 2 rolls of print paper and 100 probe covers are included. Uses 4 "C" batteries (included) or optional 6-v adapter sold below. 1-year warranty.

Professional-type Testing Equipment

• Engine Analyzer has large, easy-to-read 8-inch dial • more test functions than our other analyzers

CRAFTSMAN pro-type Analyzer—our best. Performs 30 tests. Pre-set at factory—needs no electrical adjustment. For trouble-shooting conventional and electronic ignition systems. Detects problems with starter, battery, alternator, voltage regulator, electronic ignition modules plus checks rpm, charging and starting amps.

METER: Large 8-inch D'Arsonval meter with color-coded scales; glass lens. Zero-adjusting feature.

SCALES: Color-coded 0-1200, 0-6000 rpm; 0-45°, 0-60°, 0-90° dwell; low 10 ohms center scale, high 10K ohms center scale 0-100 and 0-400 amps; 0-3.2, 0-16, 0-32 v.; good/bad scale for point resistance, alternator tests. Direct readings on 4, 6, 8-cylinder scales.

ELEC INFO: Solid-state integrated circuitry. Detachable 6-foot color coded neoprene-insulated test leads. Ohms test powered by 9-v. transistor radio battery (not incl.). Other tests powered by vehicle's 12-v. battery.

HOUSING: Black-painted steel with high-impact plastic panel. Measures 14x9¼x7⅛ inches. Carrying handle. Accessory storage space.

ACCESSORIES: Inductive pickup clamp with neoprene-insulated leads. Primary coil terminal clip. Delco high-energy ignition adapter, battery post adapter, jumper wire. Detailed illustrated instruction manual included.

Figure 11-1. Technical description for general and professional readers.
Source: Sears Roebuck and Company. Reprinted with permission.

LO-II Flow Totalizer

SPECIFICATIONS:

Power Supply—110 V AC, 230 V AC, 12 V DC or 24 V DC

Temperature Range— – 20° to + 130°F

Totalizer—8-digit non-reset (standard) others available

Totalizer Units—Any desired engineering units (see Table 1 for standard units)

Accuracy— ± 1 count

Input Frequency—0 to 3000 Hz

Input Amplitude—30 to 2000 mv peak to peak

Signal Cable Length—50′ (standard)

Power Cable Length—6′

Pulse Output Option—Normally open contacts, 28 VAC contact rating—1 amp max or 30 V DC max, 50 ms closures at same increments as totalizer

Flow Rate Option—Instantaneous flow rate in desired units displayed on meter located on front of instrument.

Additional Divisor—Extra ÷ 10 or ÷ 100 circuit to increase divisor capabilities

Additional Counter—6-digit manual reset or 8-digit non-reset wired in parallel with standard counter

Halliburton flow totalizers for use with turbine flow meters provide rugged construction and operational economy with minimal maintenance requirements.

The Model LO-II flow totalizer for use where external power supply is available can be equipped for indoor panel mounting or with a weatherproof housing for outdoor service. Variations of this model are available with housings that permit installation in hazardous areas.

Figure 11-2. Technical specifications.
Source: Halliburton Services. Reprinted with permission.

Advertising Copy

Sometimes the writer of advertising copy must create a need that readers have not been aware of. By the skillful presentation of details and suggested applications, the writer can arouse in readers a desire for additional information about a product they had no prior interest in. To create that desire, the writer must be thoroughly familiar with the product and the range of its possible applications.

When you are faced with the task of writing effective advertising copy directed to a diverse audience ranging from accountants to purchasing agents to engineers, you must explore every available source of information about that audience. What kind of information is likely to prompt your readers to initiate the purchasing process? What can the organization's sales representatives tell you about their customers? How do those customers use the product? What problems does it solve

ELEMENTS OF EXCELLENCE • ENGINEERING & MANUFACTURING-WICHITA

NCR ADP-40 DISK CONTROLLER MODULE

The NCR ADP-40 Disk Controller Module is a 52-pin, hybrid integrated circuit designed to be the nucleus of a high-performance, intelligent Winchester disk controller. The controller module consists of five NCR custom VLSI chips mounted and inter-connected on a ceramic substrate.

When controlled by an external microprocessor, the NCR ADP-40 performs virtually all disk interface functions including the following.

- Format, read, and write control
- Disk drive and system buffering
- Error Correction Code generating, checking, and correcting

FEATURES

- Uses standard 8085A-2 microprocessor interface
- Contains internal dual-sector buffers (allows contiguous sector transfers)
- Allows 256- or 512-byte sectors
- Provides 56-bit ECC generating, checking, and correcting
- Allows full Small Computer System Interface (SCSI) implementation
- Provides extensive internal diagnostic testing
- Contains address decoding for external I/O connection
- Supports flex disk usage of internal buffers
- Supports 5 Mb/s data transfer rate (ST506)
- Supports ST506 address mark detection and NRZ data separation
- Provides external control for write precompensation
- Encodes write data in 5 Mb MFM format
- Requires single 5 V dc power supply

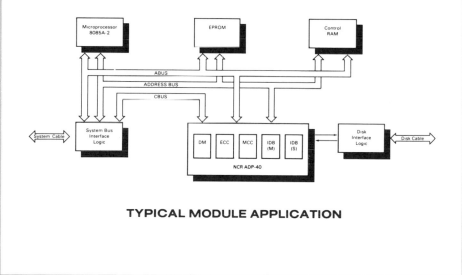

TYPICAL MODULE APPLICATION

Figure 11-3. Example of sales literature.
Source: NCR. Reprinted with permission.

for them? What approach do competing organizations take in marketing similar products?

Decisions to purchase industrial products or services are usually made by highly trained purchasing agents or committees who are well qualified to judge whether your product will suit the needs of their organization. Your job in writing advertising copy is to convince them that your product or service is better suited to their needs than any other. You must anticipate who these readers are and what they are looking for. Will the purchasing decision be made by the committee or by one person? Will your readers need a complete set of specifications? Will they have time to review your material and ask for more information before having to meet some deadline? Are they acting for a local, state, or federal government agency with prescribed procedures for making purchasing decisions?

To summarize, when you write advertising copy, keep in mind

1. the purpose of the piece.
2. your readers' ability to understand technical information.
3. your readers' need for information and how they will use that information.

Brochures

Organizations use brochures for a wide range of advertising and informational purposes. Think of all the brochures you have seen and the many subjects they have covered. Some of them you read with interest, looking for specific information on the subject. Others you glance at and toss away. Reader interest, coupled with effective layout and design, determines whether or not a given brochure will command a second look.

Reader Interest

Most readers have only a casual interest in the brochures that come their way. Thus, when you are writing a brochure you must provide information that will arouse and sustain interest at first glance. What will your assumed readers want to know about the subject? In what order? In how much detail? If you are describing a service, state the service at the outset and then list the steps required to obtain it. If you are describing a product, identify the product and then list specifications, method of operation, and purpose. You may decide to develop two or more separate brochures in order to satisfy the needs of particular readers.

Layout

Once you have settled on the content of a brochure, you must determine how it will appear on the printed page. In a large organization, a graphic artist will probably handle layout and design decisions on the kind of type and visuals to use and their placement on the page. If you have to handle these matters yourself, here are some suggestions:

1. Keep the content to a minimum. Your purpose is to create interest.
2. Use attention-getting visuals, such as photographs or drawings of the product or of people performing or using the service.
3. Draw on the resources of the printing company that will be producing the brochure. Many printers have staff designers to assist their clients.

Technical Manuals

Technical manuals may range from one page to a hundred or more in length. The instruction sheet that came with your popcorn popper is a technical manual in miniature.

Manuals contain a number of sections, depending on their purpose:

1. An *introduction* or *overview*, which provides definitions, suggestions for use, and perhaps the operating principle of the product.
2. A list of *applicable documents* that suggests additional references the reader may need, such as other manuals and service bulletins.
3. A list of *equipment*, which informs the reader of any special tools and equipment, such as test equipment, that may be needed.
4. *Step-by-step procedures.*
5. *Specifications,* which provide the operator with details about performance and indications to insure that the product is functioning properly.
6. A *troubleshooting guide,* which describes malfunctions and methods for correcting them.

Which sections you decide to include will depend on whether the manual is an operating manual, a maintenance manual, or an assembly manual.

Remember that the reader of the manual will take some sort of action in response to your instructions. Ambiguity may be disastrous. The operator may be somewhat familiar with standard procedures for using the equipment, but do not assume absolute familiarity. If you expect the operator to take a reading or to make a measurement in a way that differs from standard procedure, be sure to specify exactly how it is to be done.

Visuals play a more significant role in technical manuals than they do in routine reports. In fact, some operators concentrate all their attention on drawings, photographs, and schematics and pay little or no attention to the accompanying text. Your visuals must therefore be very clear and readily understood.

Plan your visuals to parallel your text:

1. *Overview*. Include a photograph or a drawing of the complete product, or of that part of the product you are describing in a particular section. You might also include a flow chart to show the process the reader is about to perform.

2. *Specific views*. Use specific views to illustrate the steps being described in the text. Make sure that they can be understood at a glance so that the reader does not have to stop and analyze each one. Keep details to a minimum. Try to show a hand or a person performing the step described in the text.

3. *Specifications*. Arrange specifications in tabular form and place them where the reader will need them. Do not relegate them to a separate section that has to be searched out.

Always plan your visuals at the same time you plan your text, to ensure that the two elements will work together.

In positioning visuals on the page, provide sufficient space around them to avoid confusion. Remember that the reader will be reading the text, studying the visuals, and performing the step all at once, turning from manual to equipment and back again. Hunting for that next step on a crowded page may result in skipping a step or in failing to complete a step. So arrange your visuals to enhance comprehension and to avoid confusion.

Annual Reports

Annual reports tell stockholders and the general public how the organization performed over the past year. They usually contain a message from the president or the chairman, statements by the principal corporate officers, and supporting financial information. More elaborate annual reports may include photographs of the organization's facilities, services, or products.

In a very real sense, annual reports are a form of advertising directed mainly at the general public. Readers who want specific details about sales, profits, indebtedness, and assets will consult other reports tailored to their needs. Consequently, technical details should be kept to a minimum in annual reports, and all the information and all the visuals should be readily intelligible to the general public.

If you are ever assigned the task of writing an annual report, use a style that is appropriate to that readership:

1. Use short, simple sentences.

2. Keep the paragraphs short.

3. Use active verbs.

4. Use personal pronouns—you, we, us.

Collecting and Organizing Data

In collecting the data you will need for the various forms we have been discussing, you will follow essentially the same process you follow in collecting data for a formal report. You already possess extensive information on your own specialty. An engineer, an accountant, a technician— each has a store of information about the organization's products and operating procedures. When you are asked to prepare a catalog or a brochure, however, you must assemble data from a variety of sources. By asking the basic questions of the reader's needs and the reader's capacity to comprehend, you can narrow your sources down to those that will serve your purpose best.

Who in the organization is the best source of information on technical details? on cost details? on operating details? Who knows most about the benefits provided by the product or the service? Who is best informed on applications?

As usual, once you have collected the data you need, you must set about organizing them.

The process of organizing data for use in a manual or a catalog parallels the process of organizing data for a report. For these purposes, however, you must be more selective in the details you include. Unlike a formal report, a manual has no appendix into which you can tuck all the details that do not fit into the organizational plan of the main text. Thus, you must select your details with great care and organize them in a manner that will satisfy your reader's needs directly and efficiently.

A Final Word

Approach the writing of abstracts, catalog items, sales literature, advertising copy, brochures, or technical manuals with the same control as you would exercise in writing a report:

1. Know your purpose.
2. Know how the reader will use the written material.
3. Know what information your reader needs.
4. Know your reader's capability to comprehend the communication.
5. Organize the information to suit the purpose, the function, and the reader's needs and abilities.

Technical Assignments

1. Locate examples of the various items discussed in this chapter. Select one or two for analysis.
   a. What evidence is there of the writer's awareness of purpose, function, and reader's needs?
   b. What information would you add? Where and how would you add it?
   c. Who is the assumed reader? How is the reader meant to use the item? How do you think the reader will actually use it?
2. Prepare a rough draft of a brochure designed to encourage high school students to attend your college and to concentrate in your major. Discuss the draft with the head of your department or with one of your major professors.
3. Compare a current catalog with a catalog published by the same company several years ago. (Sears and other companies publish reproductions of earlier catalogs.) What differences do you note in content (technical detail), layout, and visuals? Is the current catalog superior to the earlier one? If so, in what respects?

Making an Oral Presentation

The prospect of speaking to a group can be very unnerving. Most of us are more comfortable listening to a speaker than we are making a speech. Do effective speakers have any special techniques for doing what they do so well? The answer is yes, but what works for one may not work for another. Following are some suggestions that may help you make a better speech.

Reducing Nervousness

When you make a speech you are bound to be somewhat nervous. Try to use your nervousness as a motivation to do your very best. Over time, you will learn how to reduce your nervousness and walk confidently and calmly to the speaker's platform. Two ways to gain confidence are to concentrate on preparation and on presentation.

Preparation

Allow yourself sufficient time to prepare your speech. Be as thorough in analyzing your audience as you are in researching the topic you are going to talk about. Prepare note cards carefully so you can use them with confidence. Plan to speak naturally instead of reading your speech from a prepared script. (Nothing kills audience interest faster than a speaker who approaches the lectern carrying a bulky script.) Plan your visuals so that they will truly support the key points of your speech.

Practice your speech several times and set a different goal for each practice session. Use a tape recorder—or, if possible, a video recorder—and analyze each delivery. Ask someone to join you at your final practice session, and invite constructive criticism. During practice, try to work up a natural mode of delivery, using note cards rather than relying on memory. (Forgetting a single word in a memorized speech may prove disastrous.) Be sure that the notes on your cards are truly promptings rather than a written-out speech. (Many successful speakers use a single note card with the key points and sub-points typed on it.) Keep practicing until you are confident that you have the content of your speech firmly under control. Later in the chapter you will find additional pointers for practice sessions.

Presentation

When at last you face your audience, try to avoid the natural impulse to freeze up and clutch the lectern. Make some physical movement in the first few seconds. After you have been introduced, thank the introducer, greet the audience, and begin your speech:

[To introducer]	Thank you, Mr. Edwards, for that introduction.
[To group]	Good morning, ladies and gentlemen. As you heard Mr. Edwards say, I want to talk to you about whether or not our department should buy a computer. I have organized my remarks around four major points:
[Move to the visual]	1. The background of the problem.
	2. The solution to the problem.
	3. The benefits of that solution.
	4. My recommendations.

If you are using an overhead projector, move to the projector and present your first visual, listing your four major topics. If you are using a slide projector, step aside and trigger the first slide. Simple movements of this sort will relax your body and promote naturalness and ease.

As you move into your speech, the confidence you built up during your practice sessions will return and will help dispel any nervousness you might experience at the outset. Continue to move naturally as you move from point to point. For example:

	"My first major point is . . ."
[Gesture]	Item
[Gesture]	Item
[Major movement]	"My second major point is . . ."

> [Gesture]   Item
> [Gesture]   Item

You might gesture toward the screen, emphasizing the major points and subpoints as you go along. To make a major movement, you might move from one side of the screen to the other.

Talking to the Group

In making your presentation, avoid giving the impression that because you know a great deal about the topic you are somehow superior to your audience. Avoid "talking down" to your listeners, acting as though they have no understanding of the problem and no ideas about how to solve it. If a psycholinguist were speaking to a group of astrophysicists about the cognitive process, he or she would probably need to define a good many terms. But it is possible to define terms without suggesting that one's listeners are second-graders. In short, you should define terms when necessary, and provide examples and analogies, but treat your listeners as intelligent adults.

Make your points in a friendly manner, explaining technical details as though you were discussing them with a friend in another field. Avoid giving a tedious recitation of data and details. Remember that your audience is limited in its capacity to assimilate details as you tick them off.

If you feel you must present a full array of specifications—in comparing two types of microprocessors, for example—present them visually, and have copies of your visual presentation available to give to your audience. You might distribute these handouts only after you have concluded the presentation, or you might pass them out beforehand so that your listeners can follow you point by point and take notes along the way. Providing them with a copy of your visuals enables them to listen to what you are saying and to jot down their thoughts on the spot. This procedure gives you three reinforcing devices:

1. Your listeners hear you make a point.
2. They see the point on the screen.
3. They find the point on their copy and note its relevance to their own interests.

You will find these suggestions helpful regardless of the formality of the speaking situation. Whether you are presenting your data informally to a small group or formally to a large group, your decision on when and how to distribute your handouts will depend on your purpose and on the importance of the material.

Planning and Organizing Your Content

Making an oral presentation calls for the same care in preparation and planning as you would exercise if you were writing a formal report. You must anticipate your listeners' need for information and supply that information in a form they can understand. You must give careful attention to the level and amount of technical detail you include, the complexity of your visuals, and the need for definitions.

Above all, you must organize an oral presentation in full awareness of the demands of the situation. Whereas the other stages of preparation are essentially the same as in preparing a written report, organizing information for oral delivery is markedly different. Remember that your listeners will not be free to glance ahead or refer back to a section the way a reader can. In order to know what to listen for, they must know the precise sequence in which you plan to present information. Thus, the first step is to decide on the order in which you will deliver your points:

1. What major points does your audience need to know?
2. What is the best sequence for presenting those points?

Plan to inform your listeners at the outset what your major points will be and the order in which you will present them. And plan to remind them of that sequence as you proceed, even at the risk of redundancy. Remember the old principle: "Tell them what you are going to tell them, tell them, and then tell them what you've told them." Listeners welcome the guidance of frequent summaries and clues to what lies ahead. Remember that your listeners are responding to all sorts of distractions as you speak; you will therefore need to use every means available to hold their attention.

In planning your presentation, block out the major sections in logical order:

1. Introduction
   a. What topic/problem will you discuss?
   b. What is *your* purpose? What is your *listener's* purpose? How will the information you present function for listeners?
   c. What will be the order of your presentation? What is the first point you plan to cover? the second? the third? Will you make recommendations? When? Will you state a conclusion? Will you summarize your

remarks? Will you provide time for a question-and-answer period?

   d. What background will your listeners need in order to assimilate your main points? Will you need to explain the history of the problem? Will all your listeners be aware of the significance of your topic? What key terms will you be using? Do you need to define them at the outset? Do you need to define them again as you use them in the presentation?
   e. What specific conclusions/recommendations will you make?

2. Body
   a. Follow the order of presentation you outlined in your introduction.
   b. When you move from point to point, make certain that your listeners can follow you. How does each new point relate to earlier points? Give your listeners an indication of when you have finished with one point and are moving on to the next.
   c. Remind your listeners of what each point means to them. Answer their "So what?" questions. Unless they perceive how your remarks relate to them and their jobs—which is, after all, their purpose in coming to hear you—their attention will wander.
   d. Provide enough technical data to support your points. Listeners cannot absorb unlimited quantities of detail—even if they perceive its relevance. Again, make essential details available through visuals and handouts.

3. Conclusion
   a. Make your conclusion with finality. Don't trail off by muttering, "Well, I guess that's about all I have to say."
   b. Summarize your major points and reinforce their applicability to your listeners' needs. Relate your points to your listeners' purpose in coming to hear you.
   c. Summarize your recommendations.
   d. Announce that you are ready to answer questions about your presentation.

Planning your presentation will help you avoid nervousness when you face your audience. Purposeful practice will add to your confidence.

Practice

When you prepare a report, you often write several drafts, revising and refining each draft as you move along toward the final version. Practicing a speech serves the same purpose. Each practice session should represent an advance toward your final presentation, just as each draft represents a step forward. Use your practice sessions to make revisions that reflect your understanding of your audience, their informational needs, and their capacity to comprehend. The following suggestions will help you use practice sessions to the best advantage.

Preparation

When you are ready to practice your speech, gather the materials you will need and find a quiet place where you can work without being interrupted.

MATERIALS Arrange your note cards in the order you plan to follow in your presentation. A good idea is to number each card lightly in pencil in the upper right-hand corner. As you practice, you may decide to alter the sequence and renumber the cards. Keep a pen on hand to make notes on the cards about new ideas that occur to you during the practice session. Assemble the visuals you plan to use and, if possible, set up a projector like the one you will be using for the actual presentation. Familiarity with the equipment will save you the embarrassment of fumbling with it when you face your audience. Most slide projectors are of standard design, especially those with a carousel slide tray. Overhead projectors, however, differ a good bit in design. At the very least, familiarize yourself with the on-off switch and the focusing knob.

A tape recorder is essential for practice sessions. (A video recorder, of course, is ideal if you have access to one.) Such equipment frees you from having to make extensive notes as you practice your presentation. Whenever you discover a weak passage or a comment you want to omit, make a verbal note on the tape and move on. Then, when you replay the tape, you can work out the changes at your leisure. The tape will also help you to spot any speech mannerisms that may detract from your delivery. A common problem is the vocalized pause: "and ah," "ah," "uh."

ENVIRONMENT You must have a quiet, private environment for your practice sessions, even if you have to go out to the garage or down to the basement to practice. Guard yourself from interruptions by friends, family, or phone calls. You may experience unwelcome distractions during your actual presentation before an audience, but you can control the environment during practice.

When you practice, always stand up so that you can get used to standing and talking at the same time. Your nervousness may not vanish completely, but you will gain confidence as you proceed. Standing gives you a different perspective on the room and focuses your attention on the space that your audience will occupy. If possible, arrange some chairs to simulate the actual speaking situation. If you plan to speak at a lectern, set something up that will serve as a substitute. (Actually, you would be wise to avoid using a lectern. It tends to anchor you to one place and impedes natural movement.) In short, create a practice environment that will duplicate the speaking situation as closely as possible.

GOALS Remember that each practice session should be directed toward a specific goal. Decide in advance what your goal will be for each session:

1. To delete extraneous material.
2. To integrate audiovisual elements.
3. To eliminate vocalized pauses.
4. To achieve a conversational, friendly mode of delivery.
5. To get used to handling note cards.

After each session, evaluate your progress toward achieving the goal you set for yourself. Replay your speech on the tape recorder and criticize your delivery. As you grow more confident, invite your supervisor or a colleague to come in and listen to your talk, or ask a fellow student to serve as a proxy audience. Ask for feedback on these points:

1. Introduction
    a. Did I state my topic clearly?
    b. Did I set forth the organization of my speech?
    c. Did I provide adequate background?
2. Body
    a. Did I make my points strongly and intelligibly?
    b. Did I provide effective transitions?
    c. Were my supporting details adequate and relevant?
    d. Was my summary satisfactory?
3. Visuals
    a. Were my visuals appropriate to the topic and the audience?
    b. Were they legible?

    c. Did I introduce and discuss them acceptably?
    d. Did I handle the projector with confidence?

4. Conclusion
    a. Did I conclude with finality?
    b. Did I provide an adequate summary, conclusions, recommendations?

5. Delivery
    a. Did I use good grammar?
    b. Were there any vocalized pauses along the way?
    c. How was my posture?
    d. Did I use appropriate vocabulary?
    e. Did I make good eye contact?
    f. Did I appear relaxed and assured?

Feedback of this sort will prove invaluable in preparing yourself for appearance before an actual audience.

Practicing Your Speech

For each practice session, set a definite routine for starting and stopping. Pace your delivery to the time limitations you will have to observe when you give your talk. Here are some suggestions to keep in mind during practice:

1. *Timing.* Always time your practice presentation. Know exactly how long your talk runs. Be prepared to shorten or lengthen it if you are confronted with unexpected time requirements at the last minute.

2. *Content.* Make the content of your talk as full as time permits. Remember that listeners cannot stop and reflect after you make a point. Since they are more likely to remember main points than details, make every detail directly supportive of your main points. Through effective transitions and an orderly progression, prepare your listeners to accept your conclusion, just as you would in preparing a formal report.

3. *Language.* Use language that is appropriate to your listeners. Remember that listeners have no glossary to refer to for the definition of a key term, so be sure to define—and redefine, if necessary—any technical terms you think your listeners may not be familiar with.

Visuals

Plan your visuals to support, supplement, and reinforce your main points. Only about 3–5 percent of what we learn comes through listening; the rest comes through seeing. So make good use of this channel of communication.

If your speech requires the presentation of technical data, devise some means of conveying numbers and magnitudes to your listeners in an intelligible fashion. If you read the figures from a note card, you will probably confuse your audience and lose the supporting power of your data. A better way is to arrange your data in tabular form and make an overhead transparency or a slide to project as you speak. Be careful, however, in presenting data in this fashion, because dense columns of figures will become illegible to members of the audience sitting beyond the first few rows.

Another approach is to convert the data into some sort of line graph or chart, properly labeled and drawn to an appropriate scale. Here, too, you must ensure legibility. When you use a graphic presentation in a written report, your readers can study it at their leisure and consider precisely how it relates to the accompanying text. But listeners have no such opportunity. Preparing visuals for an oral presentation requires skill in handling line, color, and type. If you lack such skill, try to get help from someone who is experienced in the preparation of visuals. Using a blurred, confusing visual will shift your listeners' attention from listening to what you are saying to trying to figure out what you have projected on the screen.

Listener Needs

Even in the absence of visuals, listeners are trying to convert the words you are speaking into visual images. That effort requires intense concentration and may divert their attention from the successive points you are presenting. In the worst case, your listeners may become fatigued and simply give up trying to follow you. By devising well-designed visuals you can spare them the effort needed to convert words into images and can keep their attention focused on the true content of your speech.

Moreover, effective visuals introduce variety, relieving your listeners of the boredom that often accompanies an uninterrupted flow of words. As they shift their attention back and forth, from speaker to screen and back to speaker, their faculties will remain alert and their interest high.

Design of Visuals

Again, visuals appropriate to an oral presentation differ significantly from visuals appropriate to a written presentation. In designing visuals, remember that they must be legible and intelligible to many viewers at varying distances from the screen. Even if you have copies of a complex visual (a tabular listing of technical data, for example) printed and handed out to your audience, you cannot expect viewers to follow what you are saying, study the image on the screen, and concentrate on the handout all at the same time. So be sure that any visuals you use are expertly designed to convey a single message to viewers, no matter how distant they are from the screen.

THE SCREEN The reader of a written report can manipulate a page and focus on various elements of a visual until its significance becomes apparent. But a screen is fixed in position and cannot be manipulated. Recognize the limitations of the situation and avoid forcing your viewers to twist their necks and squint their eyes trying to make out what you are presenting.

PROGRESSION The use of visuals in an oral presentation gives you a greater opportunity to dramatize the progression of your material than does the use of visuals in a written report. If you are using an overhead projector, for example, you can use a marking pencil or a succession of overlays to build up a sense of movement, especially in presenting the successive stages of a process. With a slide projector, you can get the same effect with a rapid succession of carefully sequenced slides.

COLOR In a printed report, you are usually limited to black and white in presenting your visuals. But in designing visuals for an oral presentation, you can introduce a variety of colors to add variation and to emphasize major points and relationships.

Preparation of Visuals

In preparing visuals, provide plenty of white space, and make sure that the letters and numbers are large enough and clear enough to be read by all your viewers. Cluttered visuals make it difficult for viewers to distinguish what is important, and visuals that work well enough on the printed page may not translate well into projected images. The table shown in Figure 12-1 contains far too much information for presentation on an overhead transparency or on a slide. Instead of presenting the whole table, decide which elements are relevant to the point you want to make and design a visual that will present only those elements. For example, if you want to draw attention to the total of all the damages listed here, run up the totals and present them as shown in Figure 12-2. If, on the other hand, you plan to refer to only three of the items, present them as shown in Figure 12-3.

Avoid presenting graphs that are too complex and detailed to be intelligible when projected on a screen. If you must present a complex graph in its entirety, consider using color to highlight information or curves, or isolate the information most relevant to your presentation.

TABLE 14
FLOOD DAMAGES

STREAM	LOCATION	STORM DATES	DOLLAR DAMAGE (FLOOD YEAR PRICE LEVELS)	DAMAGES IN 1981 DOLLARS
Covington Creek (Adams Creek Tributary)	Wagoner Co.	Jun 19, 1980	$ 168,000	$ 180,000
Arkansas River	Tulsa	June 3, 1908	250,000	8,660,000
	Tulsa	Jun 13, 1923	500,000	7,880,000
	Tulsa (unleveed areas)	Apr–May–Jun 1957	500,000	2,400,000
	Bixby	Apr–May–Jun 1957	500,000	2,400,000
	Tulsa	Oct 1959	595,000	2,520,000
	Bixby Area	Oct 1959	513,000	1,520,000
Berryhill Creek	Berryhill	Jun 1974[a]	100,000	170,000
	Tulsa Co.	Jun 16–17, 1980	100,000	110,000
Bird Creek	N. Tulsa Co.	May 1974[a]	774,000	1,380,000
	N. Tulsa Co.	Apr–May–Jun 1957	1,637,000	7,610,000
Cherry and Red Fork Creeks	Tulsa	Sep 4, 1980	—	130,000
		Oct 1959	26,000	110,000
Childress Creek	Keifer	Jun 8–9, 1974	9,000	50,000
	Keifer	Sep 6–8, 1971[a]	151,000	310,000
Coweta Creek	Coweta	Jun 19, 1980	1,900,000	2,000,000
Dirty Butter Creek	Tulsa	Jun 20, 1979	b	b
Flat Rock Creek	Tulsa	Jul 15, 1961	—	610,000
		Sep 7, 1971	76,500	160,000
Fisher and Anderson Creeks	Sand Springs	Jun 1974[a]	80,000	140,000
Fry Creeks	N. Bixby	Jun 8–9, 1974	b	b
Haikey Creek	S. Tulsa Co.	May 30, 1976[a]	830,000	1,190,000
	S. Tulsa Co.	Jun 8–9, 1974	650,000	1,120,000
	S. Tulsa Co.	1971	b	b
	S. Tulsa Co.	1970	b	b
Hominy Creek	SE Osage Co.	Sep 3–6, 1971	148,000	320,000
	Skastook—damsite	Oct 1959	180,000	750,000
	to mouth	Apr–May–Jun 1957	115,000	530,000
Joe Creek	Tulsa	May 30, 1976[a]	7,587,000[c]	10,850,000
	Tulsa	May 7–9, 1974	3,301,000[c]	5,680,000
	Tulsa	May 10–11, 1970	17,000	40,000
	Tulsa	Oct 1959	1,050,000	4,450,000
Little Joe Creek	Tulsa	May 10–11, 1970	96,000	250,000
	Tulsa	Jun 20, 1979	b	b
Mingo Creek	Tulsa	May 30, 1976[a]	25,707,000	36,760,000
	Tulsa	Jun 7–9, 1974	11,435,000	19,690,000
	Tulsa	May 10–11, 1970	729,000	1,860,000
	Tulsa	Jun 24, 1968	50,000	150,000
	Tulsa	July 15, 1961	b	b
	Tulsa	May 8, 1861	b	b
	Tulsa	Oct 1959	230,000	970,000
Polecat Creek	Jenks	Jun 8–9, 1974	234,000	400,000
	Jenks	May 19, 1949[a]	b	b
	Heyburn to mouth	Apr–May–Jun 1957	43,000	210,000
		Oct 1959	34,000	140,000
Rock Creek	Sapulpa	Jun 8–9, 1974	241,000	420,000
Snake Creek	Bixby	Apr 13, 1957	b	b

[a]Flood of record
[b]No damage survey
[c]Includes Little Joe

Figure 12-1.   Example of a table not suitable for projection.

SUMMARY OF FLOOD DAMAGES
TULSA, OKLAHOMA URBAN AREA:
1908–1980

DOLLAR DAMAGE (FLOOD YEAR PRICE LEVELS)	DAMAGES IN 1981 DOLLARS
$60,556,500	$124,120,000

Figure 12-2. Example of a table suitable for projection.

LAYOUT In preparing a visual for conversion into a slide or an overhead transparency, use sheets of paper printed with light-blue lines that will not show up when they are copied. To provide for the frame—the overhead frame, or the slide frame—allow plenty of space around the image and center it carefully on the page. On most layout paper the center is clearly marked. Affix the labels carefully and make sure they lie smoothly on the paper. If they do not, the copying process will pick up extraneous lines and shadows.

PRODUCTION To make a slide, you will need a 35mm camera, a light, and a stand of some kind. Appendix C lists books on proper procedures.

To prepare an overhead transparency, first make a photocopy and examine it for any stray markings. If you discover any, obscure them with an opaquing solution and then make a second photocopy. The most common methods of producing overhead transparencies are by heat transfer (the 3-M Thermofax process) and by plain-paper copier. You will probably use a commercial source or an on-campus service to have your transparencies produced. Check each transparency for clarity and contrast and for freedom from random marks and lines.

The company you work for may have a graphic arts department that will help you prepare visuals for oral presentations. If so, give the staff artist as much information as you can about the purpose of your speech, the audience, the projector you will be using, and the manner in which you intend to use the visuals. A talented graphic artist can help you transform an adequate presentation into a truly outstanding one.

STREAM	LOCATION	STORM DATES	DOLLAR DAMAGE (FLOOD YEAR PRICE LEVELS)	DAMAGES IN 1981 DOLLARS
Covington Creek	Wagoner Co.	June 19, 1980	$168,000	$180,000
Hominy Creek	SE Osage Co.	Sep 3-6, 1971	148,000	320,000
	Skiatook— damsite to mouth	Oct 1959	180,000	750,000
		Apr-May- Jun 1957	115,000	530,000
Rock Creek	Sapulpa	Jun 8-9, 1974	241,000	420,000

Figure 12-3. Sample table.

Presention of Visuals

Identify each visual as you present it: "This graph illustrates . . ." Then discuss the key point you intend the visual to make.

As soon as you have made the significance of the visual clear to your viewers, switch off the overhead projector or advance a dark slide in the slide projector. If you are using a flip chart, flip a blank page over the page you have just presented. This simple action will redirect the listeners' attention to you and will enable you to move on to the next point. It will also give your audience a chance to digest the information they have just seen.

Practice in the handling of visuals will help you fit them naturally into the flow of information. Treat them as supporting elements for your main points rather than as independent elements in themselves. As you present them, tell your audience what to look for and how they relate to the main point you are making. Instead of saying, "Here is a view of . . ." say, "This view of . . . shows that . . ."

Meetings

During your first months on the job, you will probably be required to attend a great many meetings. Some of them will seem productive; others will seem a waste of time. Whether a meeting is genuinely productive depends on how well the participants and the leader of the meeting have prepared themselves beforehand.

Participants

A meeting begins not when you and the other participants sit down at the meeting table, but at the moment you receive the notice and agenda of the meeting. You begin to prepare for the meeting by noting the time, date, and place and by entering them on your calendar. Determine the purpose of the meeting. What subject is to be discussed? Does the agenda contain any items directly related to you and your job? If not, can you make a connection between the subject and your job? Do you have any information on file that relates to the subject of the meeting? If so, check it against the items on the agenda. Jot down any notes that may prove useful when you participate in the meeting.

Next, think about the role you will be expected to play at the meeting. Will you be making a progress report on a project you are working on? Will you be called on to offer your views on other projects in the department? If so, plan what you will say. Underline any topics on the agenda you may be asked about, and pull together all the pertinent information at your disposal. Information in the bottom drawer of your desk will be of no use if you are called on to report it at the meeting.

Plan your comments in accordance with your expectations of what the meeting will be and how it will be conducted.

1. Who will attend, and what do you think they will want to know about your project?
2. How much time are you likely to have for comments?
3. What main points will you want to make? What supporting materials should you have ready at hand?
4. Who will be leading the meeting?

Even if the agenda carries no direct reference to you or any of your projects, you must assume that you are being asked to attend the meeting for some reason. You might ask your supervisor what that reason is. In any case, set a purpose for yourself. Think about the subject of the meeting and decide what you can learn from the participants that will relate to your job. Look for items on the agenda that you can ask questions about.

People who habitually complain about meetings tend to be those who make no effort to prepare themselves before attending. If a meeting turns out to be a waste of time, make certain that your own lack of preparedness was not the cause.

Conducting a Meeting

When people are given the responsibility of conducting a meeting for the first time, they sometimes forget all the complaining they have done about wasted time and pointless meetings. They blithely stride into the meeting room unprepared and unmindful of what they have learned about the ingredients of productive meetings. Having failed to prepare either themselves or the participants by issuing an informative memo and agenda beforehand, they succeed only in reinforcing the common impression that meetings are a waste of time.

To ensure success, the leader of a meeting must follow four steps:

1. Acknowledge the purpose of meetings in general.
2. Prepare for each meeting carefully and conscientiously.
3. Conduct the meeting with authority and tact.
4. Hold a postmeeting critique.

ACKNOWLEDGING THE PURPOSE OF MEETINGS Meetings within and between departments in any organization are communication forums whose purpose is to satisfy the informational needs of the organization and its employees. They are occasions for the exchange of information that is vital to the success of the enterprise. In keeping with that purpose, the leader must establish an atmosphere in which information flows freely, questions and concerns are openly expressed and honestly addressed, and participants have a sense of genuine accomplishment. The leader must recognize that purposeful communication does not just happen; it must be fostered and sustained by a conducive atmosphere.

PREPARING FOR THE MEETING Beyond preparing for the specific responsibilities of a particular meeting, leaders must prepare themselves to exercise the awareness and sensitivity that mark the role of leader. Whenever you are preparing to conduct a meeting, give serious thought to the following considerations:

1. *Review of previous meetings.* What were the strengths and weaknesses of the last meeting you conducted? Did you get any feedback on the way you handled it? Did you provide an adequate agenda? Or did you have to explain what some of the items meant? Were the participants well prepared? Did they feel that they had had ample warning about the time and place of the meeting? Did everyone receive a copy of the agenda beforehand?

2. *Agenda.* The agenda is a master plan for the meeting that puts the items of business into proper order and perspective and enables the leader to hold the meeting to its announced purpose. It is also a time-management tool that signals the starting and ending points for the meeting.

A well-constructed agenda is one of the best guarantees that participants will come to a meeting properly prepared and that the meeting will be genuinely productive. When compiling the agenda for a regularly scheduled meeting, you should include both routine topics and new items:

State of the organization: Informs the participants about the current state of the organization, new contracts/business, profit/loss if appropriate, any developments that relate to the organization's condition.

Items from last meeting: Brings the participants up to date on any old business. It gives a status report on items discussed, questions and concerns voiced, and unresolved matters. Such a report will build the confidence among the participants and will influence their behavior during the meeting.

New items: Provides details on new developments within the organization and how they relate to the participants. If new contracts are on the horizon, how will they affect the production department, the materials department, the billing department? This section mentions any new rules and regulations that have been put into effect and any information that your supervisor has asked you to pass along.

A sample agenda is provided in Figure 12-4. How much detail should you include in an agenda? Consider: (1) what the participants need to know about the topics in order to prepare themselves for the meeting, and (2) whether the topics are of a sensitive nature. Ordinarily, it is enough just to list the topics with a minimum of detail but with an indication of who will present additional information at the meeting. Information on sensitive matters is best left to the meeting itself. It is always a good idea to check your agenda with your supervisor before you send it out to the participants.

If you set the practice of following a regular agenda at each meeting, participants will soon learn the wisdom of coming to meetings well prepared. Knowing what is expected of them will promote a cooperative attitude and will prompt a free flow of information.

MEETING OF <u>Quality Control Managers: Monthly Meeting</u>

DATE <u>4-25-85</u> LOCATION <u>Managers' Seminar Room, Q Building</u>

TIME <u>3:30-4:30 pm</u>

THOSE TO BE PRESENT <u>Quality Control Managers: All Shifts</u>

AGENDA

NO.	ITEM	NOTES
1	Call to order	
2	Business picture	
	A. April	
	B. May	
3	Renovations	
	A. Plant additions	
	B. New equipment	
4	Improvement of Control Systems	
	A. Previous problems	
	B. Anticipated problems	
	C. New systems proposals	
5	Quality checks	
	A. First shift	
	B. Second shift	
	C. Third shift	
6	QC Feedback from Departmental Meetings	
7	Adjourn	

ACTION I AM TO TAKE

AGENDA REFER.	ACTION	DUE	TO

Figure 12-4. Sample agenda.

3. *Needed materials.* Gather all the materials you will need for the meeting, and screen each item to ensure that it is relevant both to the purpose of the meeting and to the needs of the participants. If some items are couched in language that will be unfamiliar to the participants, render them in more comprehensible form. Make sure that all the materials relate directly to the items on the agenda. Consider whether it would be helpful to have certain items duplicated and distributed at the start of the meeting.

CONDUCTING THE MEETING When you are conducting a meeting, you are not acting as the judge in a court proceeding. Rather, it is your responsibility to establish an atmosphere conducive to the free exchange of information.

One way to create such an atmosphere is to watch the time. How long should the meeting last? If it runs for as long as an hour, you will risk losing the attention of some of the participants. Half an hour or so is an ideal length for a regular meeting, and not more than two hours should be the limit for a meeting of uncommon importance. Participants who are concerned about pressing chores outside the meeting room find it difficult to concentrate on a meeting that seems to run on and on, especially if the discussion wanders far afield from the announced purpose. You can keep the length of the meeting under control by making frequent summaries and by checking progress against the business specified in the agenda.

Be especially careful to observe starting and stopping times. If you announce that the meeting will start at 3:30, start precisely at 3:30—even though only one or two participants have arrived. If the meeting is to end at 4:15, make certain that it ends then. A few minutes before you close the meeting, tick off the key points that have been covered and announce the items that will be discussed at the next meeting.

Your attitude toward the participants will also have a profound influence on the quality of the meeting. Talk *with* the group, not *at* them. Refrain from making speeches and running on about *your* opinions. Give every participant a chance to participate naturally and voluntarily. If certain members become disruptive, immediately restore order. If they persist, take what action you feel you must, even to the point of calling the meeting to an end. Afterward, talk to the offenders and point out that they are only *members* of the group, not the whole group.

Set the tone of the meeting by listening attentively to what people say. If, however, a member tries to turn the meeting into a gripe session, offer to put complaints on the agenda for the next meeting. You may be able to take care of the complaints before that meeting takes place.

Always check your understanding of what is said. Paraphrase occasionally and ask if that is what the speaker had in mind. If you have misunderstood, it is easier to correct your error on the spot than it will be later on.

Encourage general discussion, and try to keep any one participant from dominating the conversation. If certain members seem reluctant to participate, put a direct question to them and give them time to respond. The purpose of the meeting is to exchange information, and every participant has information to contribute.

HOLDING A POSTMEETING CRITIQUE Your responsibilities are not over when you end the meeting and leave the room. You must follow up on those matters that were discussed but that could not be resolved. You may have been unable to answer a question, or you may not have had the authority to make a decision. Investigate such matters and either report what you have learned to the person who raised the question or put it on the agenda for the next meeting. In any case, assure the group that you take its concerns seriously, and accord them the attention they warrant. Providing prompt feedback creates an atmosphere conducive to communication.

If other participants in the group are responsible for looking into certain matters, distribute a list of their responsibilities. And, as soon as possible, inform the group of the time and place of the next meeting.

The Occasional Meeting

Occasional meetings—that is, meetings that are not regularly scheduled—are called when some unanticipated situation arises that demands immediate attention. Such meetings tend to be special-topic meetings. If time permits, an agenda should be circulated beforehand so that participants can prepare to contribute to the discussion.

If you are to conduct such a meeting, be sure to alert the participants as soon as possible and inform them of the special situation that has prompted the meeting. If you want someone to report on the situation, give him or her adequate warning, either by a memo that serves as the agenda or by a phone call.

When you conduct a meeting—either a regularly scheduled meeting or an occasional meeting—never surprise the participants by presenting a topic that you have not announced beforehand. Such "hidden agendas" erode confidence in your leadership and foster an attitude of cynicism and distrust.

The participants themselves may try to impose a hidden agenda on the meeting. Be alert for such diversionary tactics and insist that the group turn its attention back to the items listed on the formal agenda. If you decide that a serious problem lies behind the hidden agenda, announce that you will enter it on the agenda for another meeting.

Technical Assignments

1. Prepare a progress report on a project to present orally to the class. Follow this outline:
   I. Introduction
      a. Name
      b. Class standing (freshman, sophomore, etc.)
      c. Major and minor (if appropriate)
      d. Project
   II. Progress
      a. Statement of the problem
      b. Importance of the problem and the need for solution
      c. Limitations
      d. Breakdown of tasks
         1. Major steps used to collect data and sources of data
         2. Analysis of data
      e. Work accomplished to date
      f. Work to be accomplished
      g. Preliminary findings and their importance
      h. Projected completion date
   III. Evaluation
      a. Problems encountered
      b. Assessment of progress

2. Prepare an agenda for a regular meeting of some organization you belong to. Submit the agenda to your instructor for suggestions.

3. Prepare a memo to your instructor in which you list the visuals you plan to use during the oral presentation of a project report. Describe the audiovisual equipment you will need and ask that it be provided for your presentation.

4. Prepare notes for introducing a fellow student who is to make a formal presentation to the class. Include
   a. your name.
   b. the speaker's name.
   c. the speaker's qualifications (class standing, major and minor, special knowledge).
   d. the title and the topic of the presentation.
   e. an indication of whether there will be a question-and-answer period following the presentation.
   f. a restatement of the student's name and the topic.

5. Prepare a formal presentation summarizing a project for oral delivery to your class. Prepare visuals to support your presentation. Treat the occasion formally and dress accordingly. Limit your presentation to ten minutes, with a five-minute question-and-answer period. Speak from notes.

13

Correspondence

When you need information about something, you ask for it. You pick up the phone and call a friend to ask what yesterday's assignment was and when it is due. You could write a memo or a letter to get the same information, but that would delay matters. The appropriate communication channel is the phone call.

Suppose you need a new tire for your car but you don't have the money. You can either call your parents or write them a note. If your need is urgent, you call them. If you suspect they will give you a lecture on money management, you write them a note.

What would you do if you received a class assignment to evaluate a piece of testing equipment? You could call the local distributor and ask for the price and for information on its operation and availability. Or you could write a letter to the manufacturer asking for the same information.

Two factors influence the decisions you make about the appropriate mode of communication:

1. Time. If you do not have time to wait for a response by mail, you make a phone call.
2. Complexity of the information. If you need answers to several questions, and if the answers are likely to be complex, a letter is more appropriate than a phone call.

Even when time is short, however, a phone call may turn out to be the wrong decision. Suppose all you want to know is the price of the piece of equipment. You call the local distributor and ask the salesperson to give you the price. You are told that the price depends on various discounts, optional equipment, trade-in allowances, special sales prices, and so on. You decide you had better visit the sales office after all, or, if that is impossible, you ask to have a price list sent to you.

If you want to know more than just price, you would probably decide to write a letter specifying what you need and why. And you would be careful to address your letter to a specific person who has the information you need.

Written communications, properly executed, request and deliver specific information to and from the persons who have it at hand or who have access to it. Such written communications take two main forms: the memo and the letter. In this chapter we will discuss memos and letters as forms of communication that you can use to gather information.

Memos

The memo is a communication most commonly used inside an organization. It follows a specific format and usually discusses a single subject. Memos contain two sections: the heading and the message.

The Heading

Most organizations use printed memo forms that provide space for the date, the name of the intended recipient (along with a list of the people who will receive copies), the name of the sender, and the subject. The heading provides essential information and helps readers decide whether to read the memo. Figure 13-1 shows a typical memo format. The arrangement of the items varies from organization to organization, but most memo forms include all these items.

```
                          MEMO


   DATE:
   TO:                         DISTRIBUTION:
   FROM:                       [optional]


   SUBJECT:
```

Figure 13-1. Typical memo format.

The Message   The message states what you want to communicate to or receive from the reader. Are you conveying information? What is it? Do you need information? What information, specifically? In either case, make the message clear and concise. Figure 13-2 shows a sample memo. This memo makes clear what the meeting will cover. The message is specific about when and where the meeting will take place, what topics will be discussed, and what preparation the participants must make. The purpose of the memo is to transfer information from one person to another in comprehensible form.

Checklist for Memos

1. Make clear for whom the memo is intended.
2. State the subject clearly.
3. In the message, state what you want the reader to do and what response you expect.
4. Give specific details.
5. If you include personal opinions, distinguish them from statements of fact.

DATE: June 6, 1984

TO: Technical Writing Instructors

FROM: Dr. Thomas L. Warren, Director, Technical Writing Program

SUBJECT: Staff Meeting

All instructors of technical writing courses are to attend the staff meeting June 10, 1984, at 10:30 AM in M302B to discuss procedures for the fall semester. The agenda is as follows:

1. Call to order
2. Enrollment predictions for upcoming semester
3. Textbooks
4. Syllabus revisions
5. Other information

Come prepared to discuss textbooks and syllabus revisions.

Copies: Mr. Campbell, Administrative Assistant
         Dr. Weaver, Department Head

Figure 13-2. Sample memo.

Letters

Letters also contain blocks of information arranged in a fashion that is more or less common to all letters. Typically, a letter contains:

1. Date
2. Return (company) address
3. Inside address
4. Salutation or subject line
5. Message
6. Closing and signature

The order of these items is consistent from organization to organization, but their placement on the page may vary a good bit. Here are some of the more widely used placements:

1. *Full block.* Each block is placed flush with the left-hand margin (see Figure 13-3).
2. *Modified block.* The inside address, the salutation or subject, and the message are placed flush with the left-hand margin, but the return address, date, closing, and signature are started about halfway across the page (see Figure 13-4).
3. *Modified block with indented paragraphs.* This format is like the modified block, but the start of each new paragraph is indented (see Figure 13-5).

Arranging the parts of memos and letters according to a set pattern serves a very real purpose. It enables readers to find the information they want in a predictable place. You may, on rare occasions, depart from the traditional arrangement if you want to call attention to a particular part of your communication.

Let us look now at various types of letters: the letter of adjustment, the sales letter, the information letter, and the job application letter (including the résumé, the follow-up to the interview, the job acceptance letter, and the job rejection letter).

The Letter of Adjustment

One of the most difficult types of letters to write is a letter asking for some sort of adjustment. The writer is usually angry because something has gone wrong. If the writer expresses his

Return address _____

Date _____

Inside address _____
_____
_____
_____

Salutation or subject _____

_____
_____
_____.

Message _____
_____
_____
_____
_____
_____.

_____
_____
_____.

Closing _____

Signature **Signature**
Typed name

Figure 13-3. Arrangement of the parts of a letter in full block.

or her anger too extravagantly, the reader may grow angry in turn and resist making the adjustment.

When you write a letter of adjustment, keep in mind that the reader may not have been responsible for the error. Write accordingly, even though you are convinced you are right. ("I am right" will produce a different effect from "You are wrong." So will "I believe I am right" instead of "I believe you are wrong.")

Provide as many facts as you can. State the circumstances, specifically and objectively. Remember, you have one point of view and the reader may have another. Minimize the defensive

Return address _____
_____
Date _____

Inside address _____
_____
_____

Salutation _____
or subject _____
_____
_____
_____
_____.

Message _____
_____
_____
_____
_____
_____.

_____
_____.

Closing _____

Signature **Signature**
Typed Name

Figure 13-4. Arrangement of the parts of a letter in modified block.

attitudes such letters automatically raise in the reader. You can do so in a number of ways:

1. Organize your letter carefully. Make sure the sentences and paragraphs follow one another in logical order. Close by stating the adjustment you want made.

2. Convey a thoughtful tone and attitude. You may be absolutely sure as to who is at fault, but show yourself to be open to other possibilities. Avoid overt hostility.

3. Put yourself in the reader's place. How would you react to a letter requesting this adjustment?

Return address	————————————
	————————————
Date	———————
Inside address	———————
	———————
	———————
	———————
Salutation or subject	———————
	————————————————
	————————————————
	———————————.
Message	————————————————
	————————————————
	————————————————
	————————————————
	————————————————
	———————————.
	————————————————
	————————————————
	———————————.
Closing	————————————
Signature	*Signature*
	Typed Name

Figure 13-5. Arrangement of the parts of a letter in modified block with indented paragraphs.

Consider the following letter and the accompanying notations:

Chronological sequence	On June 5, 1984, I purchased a "Mr. Sharpy" pencil sharpener made by your company. According to the instructions, I was to use 4 size AA
Followed instructions	batteries. The instructions did not mention any specific type of battery but because I intended to use the sharpener at my desk at work, I
Specifics about additional purchases	purchased heavy-duty, alkaline batteries. I put the sharpener into service June 6, 1984.
Sharpener did work for a while	The sharpener worked better than I expected for the first week. I followed your instructions about not pressing hard on the pencil as I
Followed instructions	inserted it into the sharpener. Mysteriously, the sharpener would not sharpen pencils beginning the second week. When I put the pencil in
Problem	the sharpener, the motor would turn but the pencil would not be sharpened. The blades seemed not to cut into the wood. I checked the

Attempted solution

batteries, and found they were good. I also inspected the cutting surfaces and they seemed to be all right.

Return of product

Following the warranty in the instructions, I am returning the sharpener to you with a copy of the receipt of purchase and an explanation of the problem. I would prefer that the sharpener be repaired or replaced rather than have a refund.

Action requested

Notice the care with which the writer stated his perception of the situation and the wealth of relevant detail provided. The letter gives the reader a clear idea of the problem the writer experienced and presents the complaint in a fairly neutral tone. A few of the words have negative connotations, but the tone is not hostile or offensive. The reader is likely to respond favorably to such a temperate, well-reasoned letter.

Responding to a letter requesting an adjustment also calls for tact. How would you reply to this letter? The writer firmly believes that he has been wronged and that you have an obligation to put matters right. Whether or not you feel the writer is totally in the right, you must protect the interests of your organization while trying to regain the customer's good will. By careful planning, by using appropriate language, and by putting yourself in the reader's place, you can achieve both objectives:

Acknowledgment
Reader's effort noted

Thank you for your recent letter concerning our "Mr. Sharpy." We appreciate the details you supplied us about the problems you are having.

Action to expect

You will shortly receive a new "Mr. Sharpy" in the mail. We feel confident you will receive many years of service from this sharpener.

The Sales Letter

Most letters are in effect sales letters. In fact, in most of the writing you will be doing on the job, you will be trying to persuade the reader to do something: to give you information, to accept your information, to support your conclusions, or to respond to your recommendations. You will be trying to convince the reader to agree with you to "buy" your proposition. Your goal may be something as simple as wanting to help a friend or as complex as increasing profits for the company. To achieve your goal, you must somehow motivate the reader to do what you are asking. Analyzing your reader's motivations will help you write more effective letters.

Why do people do what they do? Some say that behavior is a product of heredity, that genes dictate what you do (or at least set a range of tendencies), and that you are in a way "following orders" when you act. Others hold that your current behavior is the end product of previous behavior. Still others believe that behavior is a complex product of both heredity and experience, of both internal drives and external influences.

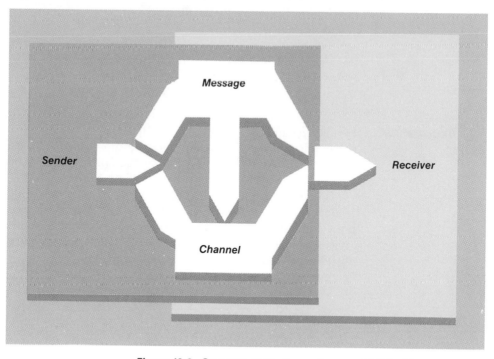

Figure 13-6. Common field of experience established by communication.

When you write a letter or a report, you are exhibiting your own patterns of behavior and are impinging directly on your reader's behavior. Figure 13-6 suggests how the writer's experience and the reader's experience coincide through the agency of the document. Their common experience provides the basis for communication. When you define a word or explain a concept or answer a question you think may be in your reader's mind, you broaden that common field of experience. Because you want to elicit a favorable response, you emphasize the kind of experience that will lead the reader to agree with you.

If you were communicating with a computer, you could provide technical information and some means of processing it. You would have no need to draw conclusions, make recommendations, or ask questions. Unfortunately, many writers of letters, memos, and reports believe that all you have to do is let the facts speak for themselves.

The human reasoning process, however, is highly complex, and to communicate effectively you must take into account many subtle, elusive factors. In writing a sales letter, for example, you might decide to adopt a "you" approach: "Using Wacker's Power Drive will make your frampus more efficient and will bring you hundreds of new sales opportunities." You back up your claim by demonstrating why Wacker's Power Drive will make the reader's frampus more efficient. You enter into a dialogue in which the reader is the "you."

The Information Letter

Most letters and memos speak to a particular situation by providing information. They answer such questions as: When will that new drill press arrive? Why has the shipment been delayed? Why did you send 100 pounds when I ordered 50?

When you are asking for information, remember that the reader needs information from you in order to respond. Suppose you dashed off a letter that consisted of just one question: "What has happened to our shipment?" Think of the questions this letter would raise in the manufacturer's mind:

Shipment of what?

When did you order?

How much did you order?

What is the order number?

What catalog did you order from?

How much better the following inquiry would be:

On June 17, 1982, we ordered 10 gross of insulation wrap for use on our steam lines (our Order No. 25352; Product No. 23-1756). We have not yet received the shipment.

Could there have been a mix-up somewhere? I would appreciate it if you would tell us the status of our order.

This writer anticipates the questions the reader will ask and provides the relevant information. She furnishes specific numbers and dates and closes with a request for action. The informational needs shared by writer and reader form the common ground of experience that makes communication possible. The more extensive that common ground is, the more effective the communication will be.

When someone writes you a letter or a memo asking for information, your response should provide precisely the kind and amount of information the letter writer is requesting. Respond to the request stated in the letter, not to a request you *think* is being made. Consider the following exchange. First, the request:

Since our company is concerned with providing homes that are energy efficient, we are very interested in the water heater insulation kit your company manufactures. Please send us full information on the various sizes the kits come in.

The reply:

Thank you for your inquiry about our Savo Water Insulation Kits. These easy-to-install kits have proven over and over that they will save in heating expense the $29.95 that they cost. Our full instructions allow even the more fumble-fingered do-it-yourselfer to successfully install the kit.

We can ship within ten days after receipt of your order by common carrier or United Parcel. May we have our sales representative contact you at your convenience?

Chances are, the insulation company never got an order, because the reply did not satisfy the request for information. The respondent failed to appreciate that the person requesting the information was not a "fumble-fingered do-it-yourselfer." What that person wanted was information about the sizes of the kits, not a sales pitch. A simple form letter might very well have produced a sale:

Thank you for your inquiry of June 7 about our Savo Water Heater Insulation Kit. You will find a summary of the kit's technical specifications below:

Sizes—5 sizes for 30, 40, 50, 60, and 70 gallon tanks
r value—21
Installation—By a combination of tape (supplied) and contact paper backing (attached).
Price—Retail $29.95 to $49.95 depending on size. On orders of 10 or more kits, 15% discount. We pay shipping on prepaid orders.

Letter of Application

When you apply for a job, the first contact your prospective employer will have with you is through your letter of application. Thus, you want it to represent you, your abilities, and your goals. The letter of application (along with the résumé) should contain the following information:

Paragraph 1
The specific job you are applying for
How you heard about the job
An application for the job
Evidence that your education and experience qualify you for the job

Paragraph 2
>   Three to five sentences focusing on one or two items
>   in your résumé that qualify you for the job

Paragraph 3
>   A reminder that your résumé is enclosed
>   Your availability for an interview
>   Where you may be reached by mail or phone

PARAGRAPH 1: THE OPENING The first paragraph conveys the basic information: it identifies the specific job, states that you are applying for the job, and provides evidence that you are qualified for the job. In a sense, the letter of application is a sales letter. The employer wants a qualified person for a specific job and is probably not interested in training some inexperienced applicant who may or may not work out in time. Don't declare that you are willing and able to take any job that may be available; be specific about the job opening and your experience.

Be sure to mention how and where you learned of the job opening. Was it through a journal or newsletter published by a trade association or through a list of openings published by a professional group as a service to members and hiring organizations? Mentioning such a source suggests that you are a member of a professional organization or at least read its publications. If the employer had to pay for the ad, he or she will be gratified to learn that it is producing results.

Sometimes you will hear of a job opening from a friend who is already working for the organization or from someone who happened to see the job announcement posted on a bulletin board. Mentioning such sources also suggests that you have a level of interest beyond the general, shotgun approach. Someone who is already working for the company may also be able to tell you about the nature of the job, making it possible for you to refer directly to the company's needs. If you name that person in your letter of application, the prospective employer may decide to make some preliminary inquiries about you. Mentioning a professor who is prominent in the field may also add to the appeal of your application. Be sure, however, that you have permission before you mention names in your letter.

Here are some examples of effective opening sentences:

I learned from the November issue of *Publishers Weekly* that you have an opening for a technical editor.

Dr. Marvin Rouse, Director of the Oklahoma State University Accounting Program, has told me of an opening in your audit department for an accountant.

Brian Jones, an engineer in your testing division, told me you have an opening for a junior test engineer.

Next you must declare that you are applying for a position. Don't assume that just because you have sent the letter the prospective employer will know what you have in mind. He or she may never get beyond your opening remarks and may never read your résumé unless you state your purpose. So you add a second sentence to your opening sentence:

An advertisement in the June issue of *Byte* lists an opening in your data processing department. Please consider this letter as an application for the position of programmer.

My major professor, Dr. Paul Campbell, announced that your company had openings for field technicians. Please consider this letter as a formal application for one of those openings.

Finally, in your first paragraph, state that your qualifications are appropriate to the job—that your educational background and perhaps some experience uniquely qualify you for the position.

Express your assurance that you have the capability and the potential to meet the employer's needs. Make certain, however, that you can really do what you say you can. If you overstate your qualifications, you may get the job only to lose it after the first week. Again, some examples:

As you will see from my résumé, my education and experience qualify me for this position.

As my résumé shows, I have the background and experience to do the job.

I believe my education and experience qualify me to make a meaningful contribution to your company.

PARAGRAPH 2: THE PROOF In the second paragraph, present evidence to support your claim. Try, if you can, to learn something about the duties and responsibilities the job entails. What does the employer expect? What do beginning employees usually do when they join an organization in your specialized role? The prospective employer will be interested both in your technical skills and in your ability to communicate. Show that you have both. Make your letter of application serve as evidence of your ability to communicate, and make your résumé serve as evidence that you possess the education (and experience) that the job demands. Expand on one or two items from your résumé that demonstrate your qualifications.

If you are uncertain about what duties go with the job, do some research. Here are some of the sources you can consult:

1. *Professors in your major.* Your professors are a good source of information. Many of them are familiar with the best-known companies in their specialty.

2. *Library.* The library provides many useful publications on what beginning employees do. Remember, though, that these publications tend to describe jobs generally, not specifically.

3. *Placement Bureau.* The placement office at your school may have a file of job descriptions from actual organizations.

4. *Friends and relatives.* If you know someone who works for the organization you are applying to, or for a similar one, ask him or her for information.

5. *The company's personnel office.* You might request information about the job duties from the organization itself, through its personnel office.

6. *Professional organizations.* If there is a professional organization in your major discipline, ask if it can give you information on the type of job you are applying for. If it offers student membership rates, think about joining. Membership in a professional organization is a good item to mention on your résumé.

Knowing something about the job will help you decide which items in your résumé you should emphasize. If you have some experience—even though it is only in an educational setting—it is worth mentioning. For example:

During my senior year I assisted Dr. Lewis in the auditing lab, where I was in charge of internal audits.

In my senior problems class I was part of a team that designed, breadboarded, and tested a circuit suitable for use in a microwave oven program. We produced the prototype for a manufacturing cost of under $50.

I have spent my summers managing my uncle's feedlot, where I was in charge of three helpers and supervised the feeding and scheduling of cattle for shipment. I also had bookkeeping responsibilities for payroll, costs, and income. [Notice that this example mentions supervisory responsibilities. Such experience is an advantage in most job situations, because promotions frequently carry supervisory responsibilities.]

I have taken three courses in computer programming and am confident that I can work with client problems involving computers.

In providing information on your experience, focus on the relevant details. Try to engage your reader's interest so that he or she will go on to read the rest of your letter. You might expand on the above examples as follows:

Dr. Lewis gave me complete responsibility for checking the accuracy of the audits as well as scheduling routine and special audits. The laboratory serves not only the students but also provides limited services to faculty and departments on campus. For example, we handled all internal auditing for the Department of Physics' recent research grant under the sponsorship of the National Science Foundation.

My part in the class project was to coordinate those students designing the circuit and those breadboarding it. I was also part of the test team and had responsibility to calculate the cost of parts and labor for our estimates on how much the circuit would cost when in production. I edited the final report and contributed the "Review of Literature" section.

My uncle inspected the feedlot operation each week, at which time I had to account for all costs and income. I also had to have a plan prepared for the next week's activities as well as a marketing plan. Last summer, my uncle gave me responsibility for hiring. I was not responsible for the purchase and delivery of new stock.

My instructors stressed the importance of computer applications to the management of wildlife refuges, including recreational and commercial facilities.

Each example provides additional information that is likely to catch your reader's interest and lead to an interview—which, after all, is your goal.

PARAGRAPH 3: CLOSING In your closing paragraph, you state forcefully and clearly your sole purpose in submitting your letter of application: to get an interview.

Mention first that you are enclosing your résumé:

> If the enclosed résumé does not answer all the questions you may have . . .

> I have enclosed a résumé that summarizes my education, background, and experience.

> The enclosed résumé gives a fuller description of my qualifications for the job of wildlife ranger.

You might add to this first sentence an indication of when you are available for an interview:

> If the enclosed résumé does not answer all the questions you may have, I will be happy to meet with you any time from March 21 to 28, which is our spring break.

> As the enclosed résumé indicates, I will be graduating in December and will be available for interviews any time after January 1.

If you have already mentioned your résumé earlier in your letter, you might state your availability for an interview:

> I would appreciate an opportunity to discuss this opening with you. Our spring break is from April 2 to 8, and I will be available to come for an interview during that time.

> I will be in Columbus during our Christmas break and would like to meet with you on December 29 to discuss the position. If that is inconvenient, please contact me at the above address or call (605) 555-6935 any time after 4:00 p.m.

Figure 13-7 shows a sample letter of application.

Résumé

The résumé is a summary of your personal background, education, and experience. (The résumé is also called a *curriculum vitae*.) Résumés should be brief, usually no more than one page.

Derek Wheeler
Publications Manager
Barques Co.
1735 South Gray
Guthrie, OK   76192

Dear Mr. Wheeler:

I read in <u>Intercom,</u> newsletter of the Society for Technical
Communication, that you have an opening for a writer-editor.
I am interested in applying for that opening and believe that
my background and experience will make me an asset to your
company.

During my internship, I developed a technical manual for students
in engineering laboratory courses who use the Johnson ATC 100
Testor. Because the original manual was lost, I had to start from
the beginning, interviewing engineering faculty and lab supervisors.
I also worked with a draftsman to produce appropriate drawings.
During that semester, I experienced many of the problems facing
a writer-editor. The enclosed résumé summarizes my other
experiences.

I would appreciate the opportunity to talk with you during our
spring break (April 16-20). If you have any questions, please call
(409) 555-0164.

Sincerely,

Leslie M. Jacobs

ENC: Résumé

Figure 13-7. Sample letter of application.

PERSONAL BACKGROUND This section gives the basic facts:

1. Your full name
2. Your permanent address and phone number
3. Your temporary address and phone number while in school (be sure to indicate how long these will be valid)
4. Career and job objectives
5. Optional information:
   a. Date when available to begin work
   b. Health
   c. Date and place of birth
   d. Marital status

This section should not be overly detailed. Its main purpose is to get the organization interested enough to grant you an interview. When you fill out an application form for employment, you will give a more detailed account of your personal history.

EDUCATION Organize your educational experience in reverse chronological order. Start with data on your higher education. State the degree you expect to earn and when you expect to receive it.

1983 to date   University of Evansville, Indiana. B.S. degree expected May 1987. Major: Accounting. Minor: Computer Science. Grade point average in major 3.72 (A = 4.0); overall grade point average 3.70.

or

1982 to date   Oklahoma State University. B.S. degree expected August 1986. Major: Electrical Engineering. Minor: Physics.

Whether or not you include your grade point average (GPA) depends in part on how impressive you think it is and how important it is likely to be to your prospective employer.
   If you have earned other degrees, mention them next:

1979 to 1981   Tulsa Junior College (Oklahoma). A.S. degree awarded May 1981. Major: Biology; no minor.

   List major courses, minor courses, and support courses to give your reader some perspective on your educational background. Be sure to list courses by short title and subject matter rather than by course number alone.

EXPERIENCE Be selective in describing your experience. Include only those items that relate to your job objectives. If, for example, your stated goal is to achieve a position of responsibility, list those experiences that suggest you are a self-starter, willing to accept responsibility. If you once worked as a sacker in a grocery store, mention that you made suggestions about sacking procedures, or about the design of the work area, or about ways to meet peak demands.

Whatever your part-time or summer job experience, try to analyze it for elements that show your initiative. List your experiences in chronological order:

1983 to date   Summers. Assistant to John Scruggs, owner of Midwidge Company. Duties and responsibilities: supervision of part-time employees (setting schedules and workloads, training and checking quality of work).

1981 to 1983   Kitchen supervisor, Photozetean Society House. Duties: ordering food, managing food preparation and serving, and maintaining kitchen records. Responsible to House Board of Directors, Dr. William Johnson, Chairman.

1980 to 1981   Delivery of *Times*. Suggested reorganization of route system in Southwestern District accepted. Immediate supervisor: Dan Saylor.

OTHER INFORMATION If you believe that certain additional information will help win you an interview, provide it at the end. Such information might include:

Membership in professional organizations

Membership in social and fraternal organizations

Honors, awards, offices held

Salary and travel limitations

Community involvement, service work

Foreign language skills

Hobbies

Physical characteristics

In summary, ensure that your résumé supports your claim that you are capable of making a contribution to the organization.

Process the data so that the résumé will provide the information your reader needs. What does your reader need to know first about you? second? third? Is education more important than experience? What experience relates most directly to your job objective? If you have stated your job objective, is it in vague terms, such as "challenging," "fulfilling," and the like? Or have you used specific terms, such as "responsibility for design development"? The résumé should be as effective a selling tool as the letter of application. Figure 13-8 shows a sample résumé.

Interview

Let's assume that you have submitted a persuasive letter of application and an impressive résumé and that you have been invited to company headquarters for an interview. Now your goal is to be offered a position. You want to make a favorable impression by your appearance and your air of self-confidence. Dress conservatively and neatly. Jeans may be fine for class, but they are not suitable for an interview. Build self-confidence by practicing the interview and by reviewing your qualifications for the job.

In a sense, two interviews will be going on at the same time: The company will be interviewing you, and you will be interviewing the company. The person interviewing you will use your letter of application and résumé as a basis for discussion. You will use your knowledge of the company as a point of departure in your search for additional information about its policies and practices. (You should already have learned how old the company is, what its major products are, and where its main office and branches are located.) This knowledge of the company will suggest that you are seriously interested in the position and that you know how to search out information.

You might take along samples of your course work as concrete evidence of your abilities—a formal report, for example, revised in response to your instructor's comments. Such samples will give the interviewer a chance to see the kind of work you are capable of doing and to judge your ability to communicate. Demonstrating how well you can communicate will help build the interviewer's confidence in you as a prospective employee. And the very act of discussing a project that you have completed will add to your self-confidence during the interview.

A final point: Try to relax during the interview. Careful planning beforehand will reduce the nervousness you are bound to experience. Don't be afraid to ask questions about salary, benefits, transfers, relocation expenses, company programs, and the sort of work you may be doing now and in the future.

Accepting the Job

You made it through your interview with flying colors. Soon you should receive a letter from the company telling you the results. If you have not heard within two to three weeks, you

RÉSUMÉ

Leslie M. Jacobs

Address: (until May 11, 1984)   (permanent)
  201 Bennett Hall   7209 E. Pumpkin Run Road
  Oklahoma State University   Bessel, TX   75123
  Stillwater, OK   74076   (817) 555-5210
  (405) 555-1413

Career Goal: Technical Editor

Education:

1982-Date   Oklahoma State University. B.A., English (Technical
             Writing Option) expected May, 1984.

1980-1982   Oklahoma State University Technical Institute
             (Oklahoma City), A.A., English (Technical Writing),
             May, 1982.

Courses

Major   **Support**

Introduction to Technical Writing   FORTRAN
Intermediate Technical Writing   Personnel Management
Advanced Technical Writing   Engineering Graphics
Internship in Technical Writing   Introduction to Petroleum
Scientific and Technical Editing   Introduction to Electronics

Experience

Summers   Junior technical writer. Simpson Electronics
1982 to date Products, Bessel, Texas. Duties: Proofreading,
              gathering drawings, some work on rough drafts.

Membership

Student member, Society for Technical Communication

References

Upon request from Oklahoma State University Placement Office

Figure 13-8. Sample résumé.

should send a follow-up letter reviewing the situation and asking whether a decision has been reached. Figure 13-9 shows a sample follow-up letter.

Once the company has offered you the position, you must decide whether to accept it. You should consider relocation, salary, benefits, opportunities for advancement, duties, responsibilities, and other relevant matters. If you decide to accept, you will write a letter of acceptance. Figure 13-10 shows a sample letter of acceptance. Notice that the writer reviews the specific details to avoid misunderstanding later on.

Jason Irwin
Director, Technical Services
Irwin Rentals
912 North Plainview
Johnstown, ME 06192

Dear Mr. Irwin:

On January 12, 1984, I sent a letter of application and a résumé to your company applying for the position of computer programmer. You invited me to interview with you during your stay on campus, and we discussed the job on February 10.

I wanted to write to let you know that I am still very much interested in the opening and also to offer to send any additional information you may need. Please do not hesitate to call or write if I can be of further help.

Thank you again for the opportunity to talk with you about the opening, and I am looking forward to hearing from you.

Sincerely,

Figure 13-9. Follow-up letter about interview results.

If you decide not to accept the job, you will send a letter of refusal, such as that in Figure 13-11. Notice that this writer is also specific about the offer, to make sure that there is no misunderstanding about what he or she is turning down. The writer is honest about the reason for rejecting the offer and creates a positive impression. Instead of blaming the company, the product, the offer, or the interviewer, he or she freely admits a limitation in background. The applicant cannot be faulted for not knowing all the details about duties and responsibilities before the interview. Even during the interview, the

Dr. Austin Walker
Senior Test Engineer
Zebco Corporation
8961 West 100th Drive
Rochester, NY   11692

Dear Dr. Walker:

Thank you for your letter of February 12, 1984, offering me the position of engineer in the Testing Department. I am happy to accept your offer.

As I understand it, the salary is $22,500 per year and I am to begin May 17, 1984. I will need to move to Rochester, New York, where your main plant is located. I also understand that your company will pay all reasonable moving expenses in accordance with the company policy explained in the employee handbook.

Again, thank you for inviting me to join Zebco and for the confidence you have placed in me. I am looking forward to coming to Rochester in May and working with Zebco.

Sincerely,

Figure 13-10. Sample letter of acceptance.

interviewer may not describe the job fully (interviewers frequently have only general information about specialized jobs). In any case, this applicant was not comfortable with the offer and refused it in a proper manner.

If the company does not offer you the job, write to thank them for their interest. You may want to apply again, and a letter of appreciation will invite their good will.

Technical Assignments

1. Write a letter of application for a job you are reasonably qualified for. Include a résumé.

Helen Eules
Accounting Department
Werner, Smith, and Weaver
829 Russell Ave.
Tulsa, OK   73172

Dear Ms. Eules:

Thank you for offering me the position of accountant with your Tulsa branch. The salary of $24,000 per year and the fringe benefits package are excellent. I will not, however, be able to accept the position.

I feel that my limited course work in tax accounting would make it difficult for me to be effective. I did not realize how much actual tax work I would be expected to do. Your interviewer was very honest with me in explaining the job. When she described the duties, I realized how little background I had.

Thank you for considering me.

Sincerely,

Figure 13-11. Sample refusal letter.

2. Write a letter to a company requesting information about a specific product or service. Clearly indicate your need for the information. Report the results to the class.

3. You receive a gift item that does not do what it is supposed to do. Write a letter to the company explaining the problem and asking for an adjustment of some kind.

4. Write a memo to your instructor asking for more time to complete an assignment. (Review class procedures for late work *before* you write the memo.)

5. Write a letter to a person or an organization offering your service as a consultant.

6. You receive a letter from a friend who is interested in transferring to your school and majoring in your field. Write a letter containing the information requested.

7. You receive an invitation to interview for a job that you want. Prepare for the interview by making notes about
   a. clothing to wear.
   b. materials to take with you (including your résumé).
   c. questions you want to ask about the organization.
   d. reasons why you would be an asset to the organization.
   e. background information on the organization.

8. Write one of the following letters:
   a. A letter of inquiry about the results of an interview.
   b. A letter of acceptance.
   c. A letter of refusal.

14

Visuals

esearchers estimate that over 90 percent of what we learn comes through visual media, including reading, looking at pictures, studying visuals, and observing our surroundings. Clearly, then, visuals are a significant part of any technical report. In fact, you should begin to plan your visuals as soon as you receive an assignment. As you think about how you will collect your data, think, too, about the kinds of visuals that will best display those data. And as you analyze the data, try to think in visual terms and try to anticipate what treatments will be most appropriate to your reader's needs and ability to understand.

As you rough out your sketches for the visuals you plan to include, ask yourself these questions: How can I position them so that they will reinforce and strengthen the text? How large should they be? Should I place them horizontally or vertically?

Selecting, designing, and preparing appropriate visuals are as much a process as developing and analyzing data, revising successive drafts, and organizing the final draft. As usual, keep the reader's needs and abilities uppermost in your mind throughout the process. Which visuals will best support the text at each point and clarify the information you are conveying?

Communicating information consists of three basic components: the writer, the message channel, and the reader. The channel you select varies with the information you are presenting, the reader's abilities, and your purpose. You can use several channels to communicate the same information, including speaking, writing, and visual presentation. When you communicate information in a report, for example, you often use several channels, the most obvious of which is language. You combine words to form sentences and sentences to form paragraphs. The words carry the basic information, but the sentence structure and the relationship between groups of words enhance the meaning of the words themselves. And the organization of sentences into hierarchical sets within a paragraph enhances the meaning of the sentences.

You also use language in tables, in captions for visuals, and in headings and subheadings. Here you must be especially precise in your choice of words, because you cannot rely on syntax to supplement the meaning of the words themselves.

Another way you can communicate information in a report is through formulas: mathematical, chemical, logical, linguistic, and so forth. When you use these shorthand methods, you must observe strict rules—stricter than the rules of grammar. Your specialized training in college prepares you to use such formulas in a professional manner.

A third channel of communication is the use of visuals. By presenting information in a visual format, you can often make it easier for the reader to comprehend the points you are making. In this chapter we focus on the use of visuals, pulling together the points made in earlier chapters.

Types of Visuals

Visuals are of two basic types: those that present reality directly, such as photographs and representational renderings, and those that use symbols to convey meaning. Symbolic visuals

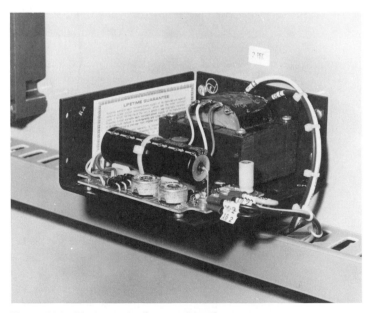

Figure 14-1. Photograph of power transformer.
Source: Jon M. Duff. Industrial Technical Illustration. Brooks/Cole Engineering Division. Copyright © 1982, Wadsworth Inc.

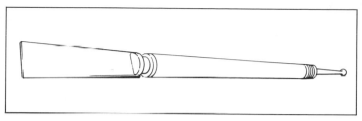

Figure 14-2. Simple drawing.
Source: Jon M. Duff. Industrial Technical Illustration. Brooks/Cole
Engineering Division. Copyright © 1982, Wadsworth Inc.

require the reader to process the message in order to understand it fully.

The image received by the eye registers on the retina before being transmitted to the brain, where it is processed.
There a representation appears in "the mind's eye." The mind
processes a visual image in much the same way as it processes
the written word. The mind needs to do less processing of an
image that bears a close resemblance to reality than it does of a
more symbolic image. A photograph, for example, requires
very little processing (Figure 14-1). Drawings, may require
slightly more mental processing, depending on how representational they are (Figures 14-2 and 14-3). Maps, too, are processed fairly rapidly.

Symbolic representations, on the other hand, require the
reader to make a "translation." Symbols are abstractions that
must be processed before the reader can sense the reality the
writer had in mind. "Vehicle," for example, is a verbal abstrac-

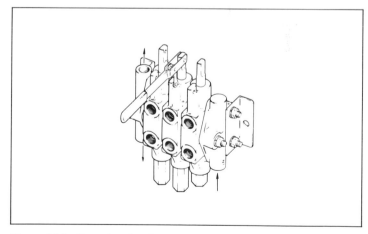

Figure 14-3. Complex drawing.
Source: Jon M. Duff. Industrial Technical Illustration. Brooks/Cole
Engineering Division. Copyright © 1982, Wadsworth Inc.

Figure 14-4. Symbolic drawing.
Source: Adams/Faux. **Printing Technology: A Medium of Visual Communication.** *Duxbury Press. Used with permission of Wadsworth Inc.*

tion that represents a wide variety and great number of objects. Through context and intuition, the reader must sift through various possibilities before settling on the intended meaning. The symbolic visual shown in Figure 14-4 suggests several meanings from which the viewer must infer the one that is most in keeping with the context. Clearly, the fuller the context the writer supplies, the more accurately a symbolic visual will convey information.

The reader extracts information from a visual by matching it with prior knowledge as well as by relating it to its context. If the writer fails to provide adequate context, the reader is obligated to rely exclusively on prior knowledge and may very well misinterpret the meaning of the visual. So, in planning the visuals you intend to incorporate in a report, pay as much attention to context as you do to the preparation of the visuals themselves.

You are undoubtedly familiar with such symbolic visuals as line graphs and tables. And you may have encountered schematics, flow charts, flow sheets, pie charts, and bar charts. In choosing the specific type of visual to use for a particular purpose, it is wise to begin with an analysis of the information you want to communicate and of the reader's ability to comprehend visual representations. Be guided by the same considerations you use when you are deciding on the degree of technical detail to include in the text of the report. Failure to match your visuals to the reader's ability to comprehend them will impair the effectiveness of your report.

Using Visuals in the Text of a Report

The visuals you use in a report are meant to support the text. The adage that a picture is worth a thousand words is not always true. For example, what is the most important piece of information in Figure 14-5? Readers can guess about what is important, but without guidance from the writer, chances are they will guess wrong. Visuals are meant to support the text and are seldom capable of standing alone.

The most valuable use of visuals is to convey concepts that cannot be conveyed as efficiently in any other form. Visuals are a kind of shorthand. We could certainly express in words the information conveyed in Figures 14-4 and 14-5, but we would have to use a great many words, especially for Figure 14-5.

In fact, we can devise visuals to communicate information that we simply could not communicate through words alone. Compare the table in Figure 14-6 and the graph in Figure 14-7. The information conveyed by the graph is less precise than the information conveyed by the table. But notice the dramatic upsweep of the lines. The graph invites the reader to make comparisons, to extend and extrapolate from the information presented.

Designing Visuals

In this section we will suggest ways of creating effective visuals. First, we will make some general comments, then we will discuss tables, graphs, drawings, and charts more specifically. Finally, we will present a problem and suggest some solutions.

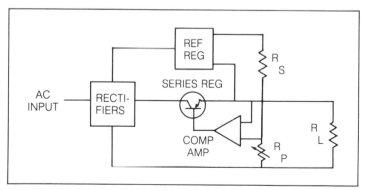

Figure 14-5. Schematic diagram of voltage regulated D.C. power supply.
Source: Rising/Almfeldt/DeJong. Engineering Graphics: Communication Analysis, Creative Design, 5th ed. Copyright © 1977 by Kendall/Hunt Publishing Company.

Year	Total Private	Farm	Nonfarm
1958	99.8	103.0	99.7
1959	103.4	104.8	103.1
1960	105.0	110.7	104.4
1961	108.5	119.4	107.3
1962	113.6	122.2	112.2
1963	117.6	133.1	115.6
1964	122.1	133.7	119.9
1965	125.5	148.8	122.4
1966	129.0	155.8	125.3
Approximate yearly change (compounded) between 1958 and 1966.	2.9%	4.8%	2.5%

Figure 14-6. Table that uses same data as Figure 14-7.
Source: Cecil Meyers. **Handbook of Basic Graphs: A Modern Approach.** © *1970 by Dickenson Publishing Company. Used with permission of Wadsworth Inc.*

Suggestions for Creating Effective Visuals

In addition to supporting the text, visuals may supplement other visuals (graphs, for example, may supplement tables). Their overriding purpose, however, is to present information in a way that is more immediately intelligible to the reader than a straight exposition in words. Consequently, the amount of explanatory material accompanying a visual should be kept to a minimum. These items are usually enough:

1. Labels.
2. Title.
3. Footnotes.
4. Source.

If the visual is unusually complex, a more or less detailed caption may aid reader comprehension. But a better approach might be to revise the visual to make it less complex.

Other ways of making the visual clear to the reader include

1. Identify any symbol or abbreviation that may not be familiar to your reader. Readers who lack a technical background may not, for example, recognize the symbol for sigma (Σ) or the abbreviation of millimeter (mm).
2. Provide a descriptive title for each axis or column of values. On graphs and charts, specify the units of measure. In tables, state the types of data that are being presented and, where appropriate, units of measure. For every visual, provide an overall title that summarizes the

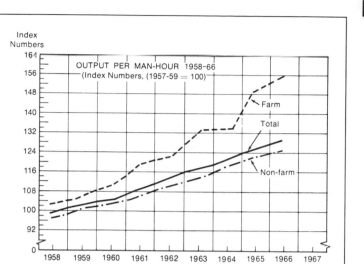

Figure 14-7. Graph based on the data in Figure 14-6.
Source: Cecil Meyers. Handbook of Basic Graphs: A Modern
Approach. © 1970 by Dickenson Publishing Company. Used with
permission of Wadsworth Inc.

data shown. When appropriate, add a subtitle, but make certain that both the title and the subtitle are brief, clear, and descriptive.

3. Provide a footnote if you feel it necessary to explain certain labels or terms, to give a mathematical formula you used in your analysis, or to furnish the reader with information that will make the visual more comprehensible. If you use a footnote, spell out all numbers to avoid confusion with numerals in the visual.

4. Credit the source of any data or visual treatments you draw from other sources. The credit line normally follows the title of the visual.

5. Allow liberal white space both within and around the visual to serve as a visual field. Such space emphasizes the visual and sets it apart from the text. To give the visual a more formal look, you may decide to frame it with straight lines, positioning the title and any notes inside the frame.

Tables

Tables organize data—either verbal or numeric—in vertical and horizontal columns. They may contain only numbers (statistical tables, for example), or only words (such as tables of diseases and symptoms), or a combination of the two.

Table 1. Yearly Enrollments

Year	Enrollments
1977-1978	338
1978-1979	510
1979-1980	630
1980-1981	782
1981-1982	1,037
1982-1983	1,114

Figure 14-8. A simple table. Step 1: Locate item in column 1. Step 2: Locate related item in column 2.

In their simplest form, tables list data in a way that enables the reader to locate an item or a value in one column and a corresponding value in a second column. Figure 14-8 provides an example of such a table. More complex tables contain extensive data arranged in a way that enables the reader to relate a variety of values across several columns. Figure 14-9 is an example of such a table. The form you select depends on the complexity of the data and on your reader's ability to comprehend it.

Table 1. Yearly Enrollments

Year	ENROLLMENTS			
	2333	3323	4523	4533
1977-1978	26	295	7	—
1978-1979	85	411	2	—
1979-1980	142	462	8	12
1980-1981	217	534	7	12
1981-1982	397	604	6	4
1982-1983	403	659	5	0

Figure 14-9. A complex table. Step 1: Locate item in column 1. Step 2: Locate related items in columns 2-5.

Tables provide you with great flexibility in presenting a wide variety of data in a precise manner. You can list fractions, decimals, and whole numbers in whatever sequence you deem most appropriate.

Tables may be either formal or informal, depending on the format you choose. The tables in Figure 14-10 suggest the range of possible formality.

Normally, tables that list extensive data in multiple columns are placed in an appendix. Tables that list selected data are placed in the text.

The following suggestions will help you organize and prepare effective tables:

1. Provide a title above the table that explains the contents.

2. Position the data that you want to emphasize in the first vertical column. If, for example, you are listing the results of ten tests using three different procedures, you can choose to position either the tests or the procedures in column one. The tables in Figure 14-11 show the two treatments.

3. Provide adequate space between columns.

4. Specify units of measure where appropriate (S.I. units, percentages, and so on).

5. Include a footnote below the table if you need to explain an item in the listings.

(a)

Year	Enrollment
1984-1985	958
1985-1986	1,062

(b)

Table 1. Yearly Enrollments	
Year	Enrollment
1984-1985	958
1985-1986	1,062

Figure 14-10. (a) Informal table. (b) Formal table.

(a)   Table A. Results of Three Tests Run on Sample Products

Test	Runs									
	1	2	3	4	5	6	7	8	9	10
A	10	11	8	12	9	11	15	6	8	9
B	12	17	10	19	11	18	6	15	13	17
C	22	12	20	21	16	20	13	23	19	14

(b)   Table A. Results of Ten Runs
                    Using Three Tests of Sample Products

Runs	Tests		
	A	B	C
1	10	12	22
2	11	17	12
3	8	10	20
4	12	19	21
5	9	11	16
6	11	18	20
7	15	6	13
8	6	15	23
9	8	13	19
10	9	17	14

Figure 14-11. (a) Emphasis on the three tests. (b) Emphasis on the ten runs.

6. When you include footnotes, use superscript lower-case letters rather than numerals, to avoid confusion.

7. Credit the source of any data other than your own.

8. Explain where the data came from (see Appendix A for proper form): "Source: Enrollment figures the first day of class."

Graphs

By presenting numerical data visually, graphs enable the reader to make comparisons and recognize trends. The most common type of graph is a two-dimensional line graph enclosed in a rectangle. Various types—frequency polygon, frequency distribution, step charts, log graphs, and semilog graphs—are used for special purposes, but most graphs are used to show relationships between time and distribution.

Line graphs are often accompanied by a table that lists the data displayed in the graph. The table may appear either in the text or in an appendix.

Following are some suggestions for designing a line graph to plot change over time or to show the distribution of two quantities:

1. Draw two lines at a right angle: a horizontal line (the Y axis, or abscissa) and a vertical line (the X axis, or ordinate).

2. Mark the two lines with short marks (ticks) or long marks (grid lines).

3. Indicate the scale values of each line. Usually, independent values (such as time) are shown on the horizontal axis and dependent values (such as number of hamburgers consumed) on the vertical axis.

4. Make all elements of the graph proportional:
   a. Space tick marks equally along the axes. The spacing need not be the same for both axes, however.
   b. Make the vertical axis about three-fourths the length of the horizontal axis.
   c. Draw the ticks and grid lines finer than the axis lines.
   d. Draw the lines on the graph about twice as wide as the axis lines. All graph lines should be of equal width.

5. Use the vertical scale for percentage, rates, or absolute numbers. Use the horizontal scale for time or for some other measure or quantity.

6. Adjust the size of the graph to the amount of data you want to display and to other elements on the page, such as the data table or explanatory comments.

7. Plot all points precisely.

8. Use a straight edge to connect the points on a straight graph. If you are plotting a curved graph, connect the points carefully to avoid distortion.

9. Use horizontal labels, avoiding leader lines and arrows whenever possible. Include a key only when there is not enough space for labels. Position the key in an open area of the graph.

10. Provide a number and title for the graph.

As you set about constructing a graph, consider how you might emphasize and highlight certain elements. By lengthening one of the axis lines, for example, you can emphasize the magnitude of change. By shortening one of the axis lines, you can play down the magnitude of change. And by increasing the increments between tick marks, you can deemphasize change. By decreasing them, you can emphasize change. Figures 14-12 and 14-13 show graphs drawn from the data in the tables in Figure 14-11. Figure 14-14 shows how the scale you select can affect the emphasis of the graph.

The data path on a graph is usually a straight line or a smoothly curving line. Unfortunately, some readers assume that the movement from one data point to another must be regular and consistent, whereas any value is actually possible between two data points. Depending on how accurately you

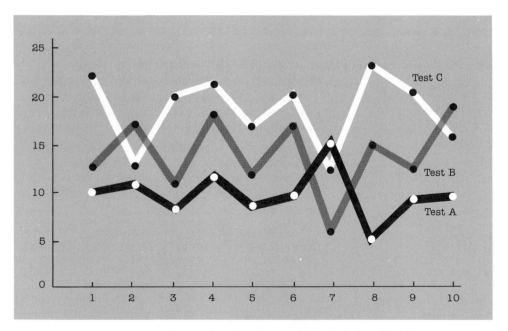

Figure 14-12. Results of ten runs for tests A, B, and C.

want to present your data, you can make the data path straight, curved, or zigzagged. For example, if you wanted to plot the size of a technical writing class over the past few years, you could assemble the data listed in the table in Figure 14-15(a) and render it as a graph, as shown in Figure 14 15(b). But a curious reader might want to ask some questions about this graph:

1. How many semesters or quarters are included in the yearly figures? Are the yearly figures totals or averages?
2. At what point in the term were the enrollment figures recorded: pre-enrollment, the first week of class, before the withdrawal period, or at the end of the term?

Since enrollment fluctuates almost daily early in a term, a line that showed every change along the way would be anything but straight. Line graphs show general trends rather than a series of specific instances. If you decide that your reader needs to know enrollments at various periods during the term, you would use a table like that in Figure 14-16 on page 264.

Drawings

Drawings are a close representation of reality. Unlike photographs, however, they can be designed to be highly selective in what they show. Common types of drawings are cross-sections

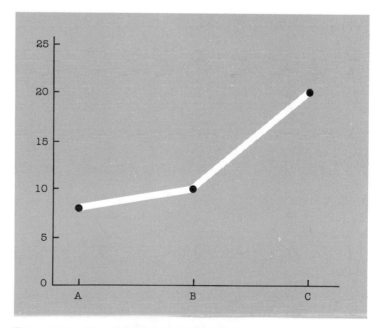

Figure 14-13. Run of three tests A, B, and C.

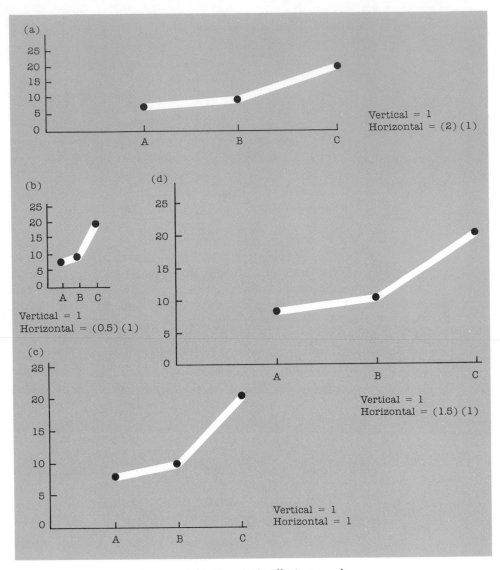

(a)

Vertical = 1
Horizontal = (2) (1)

(b)

Vertical = 1
Horizontal = (0.5) (1)

(c)

Vertical = 1
Horizontal = 1

(d)

Vertical = 1
Horizontal = (1.5) (1)

Figure 14-14. How scale affects a graph.

(Figure 14-17), exploded drawings (Figure 14-18), and detailed drawings (Figure 14-19). (See pages 265–267.)

Drawings can provide the reader with specific information about how an object is repaired, where it is located, or how it is used. In a technical manual, for example, a drawing may show how a pump is to be installed. Since the reader needs only enough information to perform a specific task, all extraneous information should be excluded from technical drawings.

(a)   Table I. Average Class Size of Technical Writing Classes

Year	Number of Sections	Total Enrollment	Average Class Size
1977-1978	10	150	15
1978-1979	17	289	17
1979-1980	20	320	16
1980-1981	23	414	18
1981-1982	25	375	15
Averages	19	309	16.2

(b)

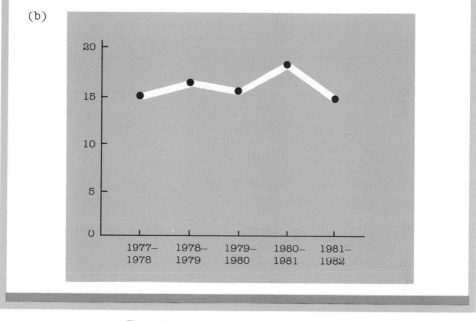

Figure 14-15. (a) A table and (b) a graph based on the table.

When you are preparing a report, especially a report intended for lay readers, you can use a drawing to call attention to the specific point you want to make. You may show an existing object or an object that does not yet exist, such as a proposed building or a piece of equipment. Drawings are particularly valuable when you want to explain the component parts of a piece of equipment, the processes involved in the operation of the equipment, or the specific steps to be followed in using the equipment.

Table II. Enrollments in Technical Writing Classes

Year	Semester	Number of Sections	Pre-Enrollment	Start of Classes	Mid-Term	Final Roll	Average
1977-1978	Summer						
	Fall						
	Spring						
	Total						
1978-1979	Summer						
	Fall						
	Spring						
	Total						
1979-1980	Summer						
	Fall						
	Spring						
	Total						
1980-1981	Summer						
	Fall						
	Spring						
	Total						
1981-1982	Summer						
	Fall						
	Spring						
	Total						
Average							

Figure 14-16. Sometimes tables can convey more information than graphs.

When you plan and design a drawing, keep the following points in mind:

1. Make several drafts to ensure that the drawing will show the exact aspect you want to emphasize. You may need to try several approaches—cross-section, exploded, or detailed.

2. If the drawing is to be of high quality (such as a drawing for a technical manual), have it executed by a technical illustrator. Provide full details and rough drafts. Be sure the illustrator knows the purpose of the drawing and the assumed reader.

3. Position each drawing on a full page, if at all possible. Allow room for labels and any special features.

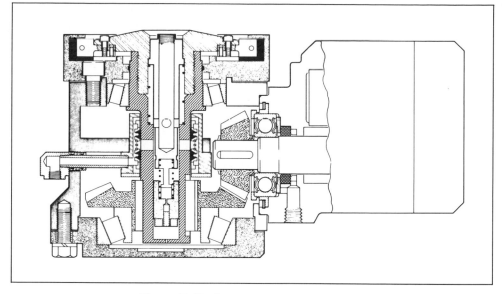

Figure 14-17. Cross-section drawing.
Source: Jon M. Duff. **Industrial Technical Illustration.** *Brooks/Cole*
Engineering Division. Copyright © 1982, Wadsworth Inc.

4. Keep all labels horizontal. Adjust the size of the lettering and the weight of the leader lines to indicate major and minor parts. If you need to show the parts at several levels of detail (major assembly, minor assembly, and subassemblies), use a separate drawing for each.

5. When appropriate, use an existing drawing from a book, journal, or manual. Photocopy it or trace it carefully. Always credit the source.

6. Be careful not to distort perspective. In the text, give your reader an indication of size by listing crucial measurements, for example. And on the drawing itself indicate overall measurements or include an easily recognized object such as a hammer, a screwdriver, or a hand.

7. Provide the reader with proper orientation to the drawing. If you are highlighting one part of a machine, for example, show the whole machine with the part you are concentrating on highlighted by shading, by a circle, or by an arrow.

Charts

Bar charts, column charts, pie charts, and flow charts communicate information through the use of various shapes. The charts you will most often use in reports are bar charts (Figure 14-20),

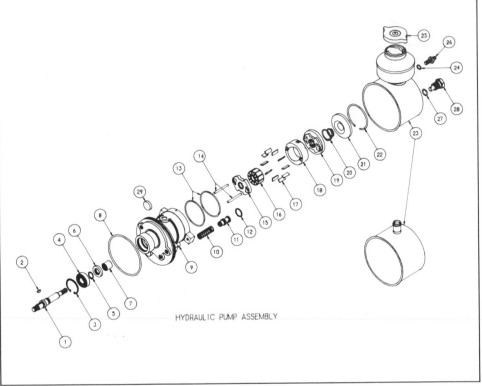

Figure 14-18. Exploded drawing (callouts deleted).
Source: Jon M. Duff. Industrial Technical Illustration. Brooks/Cole
Engineering Division. Copyright © 1982, Wadsworth Inc.

pie charts (Figure 14-21), column charts (Figure 14-22), organization charts (Figure 14-23), flow charts (Figure 14-24), and schematics (refer back to Figure 14-5).

Each type has certain advantages for particular uses. Pie charts, for example, are convenient for presenting data that total 100—as in showing what parts of a dollar are spent for services or products. Bar charts and column charts are useful when you want to show percentages of a whole, changes in time, comparisons between two or more items, and relationships between variables.

BAR AND COLUMN CHARTS A chart with horizontal displays is called a bar chart; a chart with vertical displays is called a column chart. Both types exhibit quantitative data in an easy-to-understand manner.

Here are some suggestions for designing bar charts and column charts:

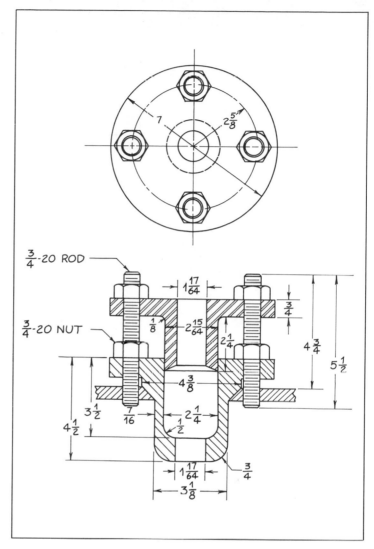

Figure 14-19. Detailed drawing.
Source: Jon M. Duff. Industrial Technical Illustration. *Brooks/Cole*
Engineering Division. Copyright © 1982, Wadsworth Inc.

1. Make each bar or column the same width. Adjust the width to the space you have available. If you want to show from two to five bars or columns, make them about 1" thick. For six to ten, make them about ¼" thick.

2. Use the length of the longest bar or column in deciding how to position the chart on the page. As a general rule, keep the maximum length of a bar to about 4½"; keep

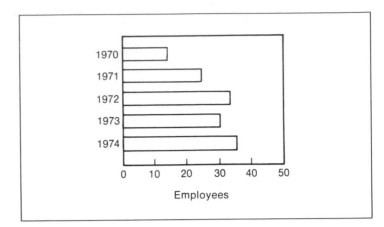

Figure 14-20. Bar chart.
Source: Cecil Meyers. **Handbook of Basic Graphs: A Modern Approach.** *© 1970 by Dickenson Publishing Company. Used with permission of Wadsworth Inc.*

the maximum length of a column to about 6″. These lengths allow for proper labeling.

3. If one bar or column turns out to be twice as long as the next longest bar, you may want to break it. If you find that you have to break more than one, revise your scale. When you break a bar or column, show the break in the axis line as well.

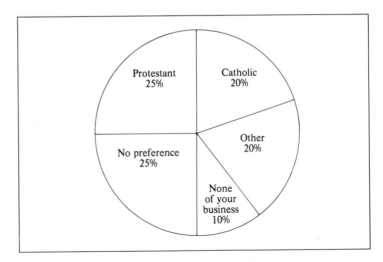

Figure 14-21. Pie chart showing religious preferences.
Source: Coladarci and Coladarci. **Elementary Descriptive Statistics for Those Who Think They Can't.** *Used with permission of Wadsworth Inc.*

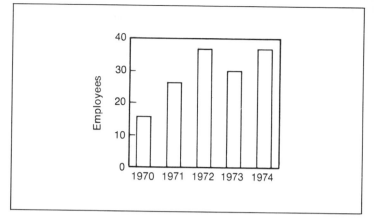

Figure 14-22. Column chart.
Source: Cecil Meyers. Handbook of Basic Graphs: A Modern
Approach. © 1970 by Dickenson Publishing Company. Used with
permission of Wadsworth Inc.

4. Choose a scale appropriate to the information you are presenting.

5. Indicate the scale on the axis lines, using equally spaced tick marks.

6. Enter numbers and units of measurement on both axis lines. Always include a zero marker for the vertical axis.

7. For bar charts, align the labels on the vertical axis by the last letter of each label.

8. Make all the lines sharp and straight.

9. For maximum precision, enter actual figures along the axis lines instead of adjacent to the bars or columns.

PIE CHARTS Pie charts or circle charts are convenient for showing percentages or absolute numbers that constitute a whole. They are especially effective for conveying financial information (often in the shape of a coin) and for comparing proportions. Here are some suggestions for designing pie charts:

1. Draw the circle large enough to make the comparisons immediately apparent. On an 8½ × 11" page, the circle should be no smaller than about 2" across. If you need more than one pie chart, you may use smaller circles placed side by side.

2. Don't try to show more than six segments on a pie chart. Any more than that will make it hard for the reader to grasp the comparisons. Place your labels next

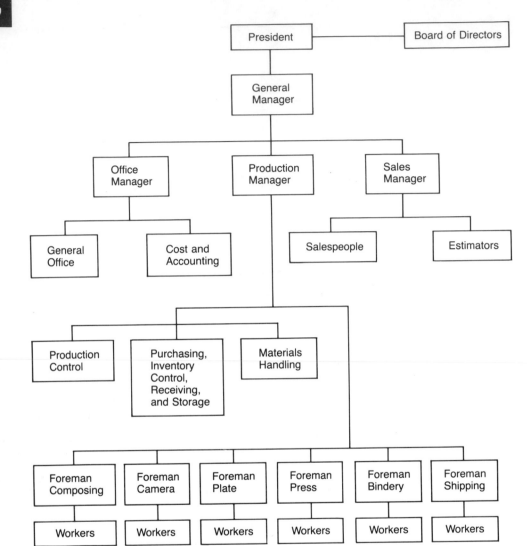

Figure 14-23. *A typical organizational chart showing the structure of a printing company.*
Source: *Adams/Faux.* Printing Technology: A Medium of Visual Communication. *Duxbury Press. Used with permission of Wadsworth Inc.*

to the appropriate segments. Use lines and arrows only if absolutely necessary.

3. Draw a perfect circle, with the center exactly where it should be.

4. When you divide up the circle, pretend you are looking at the face of a clock.
   a. Lightly mark 12:00, 3:00, 6:00, and 9:00.

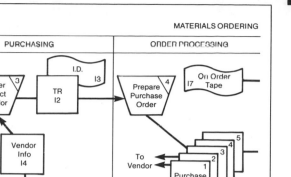

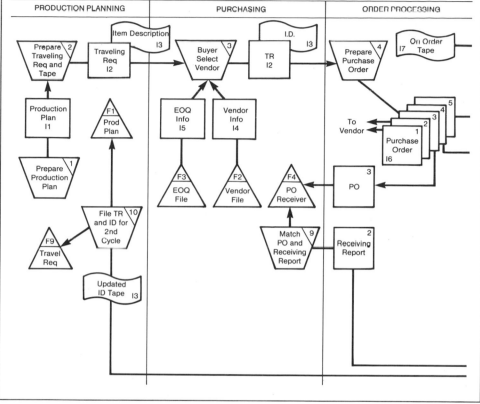

Figure 14-24. System flowchart.
Source: Skees. Writing Handbook for Computer Professionals.
Lifetime Learning Publications. Used with permission of
Wadworth Inc.

        b. Convert your percentages into hours: 25 percent
          equals 3 hours, 50 percent equals 6 hours, and 75
          percent equals 9 hours.
        c. Draw a line from 12:00 to the center and another
          line from the center to your first segment.
        d. Add lines for the other segments.

    5. For greater precision, divide the circle into degrees: 1
      percent equals 3.6 degrees. Draw a line from 0° to the
      center, and then from the center to the first segment.

    6. Arrange the segments so that the largest segment begins
      at the top of the circle, with the other segments in
      descending order of size. For a special effect, start with
      the smallest segment.

7. Label each segment horizontally. Give actual percentages if you believe the reader needs them.

8. To facilitate comparison of entities, place two or more charts side by side. But make sure that they are all the same size.

9. To emphasize one segment of the whole chart, you may want to detach it from the circle. This is a tricky technique that usually requires more than one draft:
   a. Draw the first draft as usual.
   b. Identify the segment you want to emphasize.
   c. Make the lines of that segment heavier.
   d. When you draw the circle for the next draft, place the paper over the first draft and mark the three points of the segment (the center and the two points where the lines touch the arc).
   e. Connect the two points on the arc to the center.
   f. When you draw the rest of the chart, place the center point slightly down and to the left of the center point you used for the emphasized segment.
   g. Complete the arc of the emphasized segment.

10. To emphasize one segment more simply, shade it and leave the other segments unshaded.

OTHER CHARTS Organization charts, flow charts, (Figure 14-3 and 14-4) and schematics (Figure 14-5) present data by means of lines rather than by bars or columns. Organization charts show the lines of responsibility and communication within an organization; flow charts show processes either by a pictorial representation of each step or by rectangles or other shapes, with labels identifying each step in the process; schematics trace the flow of some forie, such as electricity, through various stages. In each case, the visual must be large enough so that your reader can follow the path, simple enough to be readily understood, and complete enough to suggest the whole picture.

An Example

The paragraphs and visuals that follow are all based on the same data. In the first paragraph we assume that no visuals will be included; in the second we assume that visuals will accompany the text.

We have been keeping statistics concerning students who have been referred to the Writing Laboratory, those who have been dropped through poor attendance, and those who completed work in the laboratory (including figures on the final grades in composition classes). Since the 1977–1978 school year, 3,126 students have been referred to the laboratory and 1,772 have completed the work. Of these, 1,366, or 77.1%, have received a grade of "C" or better in their composition class. The remaining 406, or 22.9%, received a "D" or "F," withdrew passing, or withdrew failing. The academic year with the highest referrals was 1980–1981 (770), while the lowest referrals were in 1977–1978 (526). The highest number of students referred and dropped because of poor attendance was 403 (1980–1981) and the lowest 162 (1979–1980). The largest number of students completing work was 507 (1979–1980), and the lowest 257 (1981–1982). The largest number of students making "C" or better was 474 (1979–1980), while the lowest was 199 (1977–1978).

Notice how difficult it is to locate any specific piece of information without reading through the whole paragraph. Now, a paragraph accompanied by visuals (Figure 14-25):

Table A-1 presents the totals of students referred to the Writing Laboratory. It is divided into academic year, total referred, total dropped for poor attendance, and number completing (including those who received a grade of "C" in their composition class and those receiving "D," "F," or withdraw passing or withdraw failing). Better than half of the students referred completed work in the laboratory, and of those, better than three-quarters made a grade of "C" or better in their composition class. We believe that the 77.1% receiving "C" or better indicates that the laboratory is effective.

In the second version, the writer highlights the key points without spelling out all the information contained in the table.

We can render the data in Table A-1 in various ways. Notice that Table A-2 duplicates the data in Table A-1 but emphasizes a different aspect. If you wanted your reader to compare all categories for one year, you would design the table as in Table A-1. If you wanted your reader to compare one category for all years, you would design the table as in Table A-2. In designing visuals, always follow the guidelines set by the style manual for your discipline. (For a summary of page references in selected manuals, see Table 14-1.)

The exact type of visual you choose to use depends on the effect you want to achieve. Tables are very precise; line graphs, pie charts, and bar charts are less precise but more dramatic.

The visuals in Figure 14-26 through 14-32, which are all based on Tables A-1 and A-2, emphasize different aspects of the data. The exact type you select would depend on your estimate of the reader's needs and on your purpose.

Integration of Visuals

Once you have chosen the type of visual that best suits the situation, you must integrate it into the text. Integration consists of three steps: introduction, presentation, and discussion.

Table A-1. Students Referred to Writing Laboratory: 1977-1978 to 1981-1982 Terms

Year*	Number Referred	Number Dropped for Poor Attendance	%	Number Completing				
				Total	"C" or Better**	%	"D," "F," "W," "X"***	%
1977-1978	526	241	46%	285	199	69.8%	86	30.2%
1978-1979	628	272	43%	356	279	78.4%	77	21.6%
1979-1980	669	162	24%	507	474	93.5%	33	6.5%
1980-1981	770	403	52%	367	213	58.0%	154	42.0%
1981-1982	533	276	52%	257	201	78.2%	56	21.8%
Totals	3,126	1,354		1,772	1,366	77.1%	406	22.9%

Notes:
*Includes Fall, Spring, and Summer terms.
**Final grade received in composition class: "A," "B," or "C."
***"D" = poor; "F" = fail; "W" = withdraw passing; "X" = withdraw failing.

Table A-2. Students Referred to Writing Laboratory: 1977-1978 to 1981-1982

	Year*				
	1977-1978	1978-1979	1979-1980	1980-1981	1981-1982
Number referred	526	628	669	770	533
Number dropped for poor attendance	241 (46%)	272 (43%)	162 (24%)	403 (52%)	276 (52%)
Number completing TOTAL	285	356	507	367	257
"C" or better**	199 (69.8%)	279 (78.4%)	474 (93.5%)	213 (58.0%)	201 (78.2%)
"D," "F," "W," "X"***	86 (30.2%)	77 (21.6%)	33 (6.5%)	154 (42.0%)	56 (21.8%)

Notes:
*Includes Fall, Spring, and Summer terms.
**Final grade received in composition class: "A," "B," or "C."
***"D" = poor; "F" = fail; "W" = withdraw passing;
  "X" = withdraw failing.

Figure 14-25. Tables to accompany Writing Laboratory report.

Table 14-1. Summary of References to Visuals in Selected Style Manuals

Style Manual	Illustrations	Captions/ Legends	Tables	Graphs
The Chicago Manual of Style, 13th ed.	303–311	312–318	321–350	
Council of Biology Editors Style Manual, 5th ed.	67–74	72–73	74–80	69–70
U.S. Government Printing Office Style Manual, 1973	1, 14, 15	204–206	187–221	
Handbook and Style Manual for ASA, CSSA, and SSSA Publications	52–56	51–52	56–61	
Handbook for Authors of Papers in American Chemical Society Publications, 1978	65–66, 68–72		55–62	62–65, 66–68
Publication Manual of the American Psychological Association, 3rd ed.	96–100, 102	87–90, 103–104	83–94	94–97, 102
Sugestions to Authors of the Reports of the United States Geological Survey, 6th ed.	48–51, 62–69	52–54	82–90	69–71
Words into Type, 3rd ed.	43–45, 75, 520–524	44–45, 263–266	32–37, 255–263	43
American National Standard Illustrations for Publication and Projection, ANSI Y15.1M-1979	1, 3, 5, 9, 11–12	7, 8, 10	9	2, 4, 8, 10–11

Introduction

In introducing a visual element, you let the reader know that you are about to supplement the text. Introducing visuals is like telling the reader beforehand how you have organized your material. To introduce a visual:

1. Bring the visual to the reader's attention. ("See," "Consult," and so on.)
2. Say whether it is a table or a figure.
3. Mention its number. (Follow the style prescribed by the appropriate style manual, such as those listed in Table 14-1.)
4. Give its title exactly as it appears with the table or figure.
5. Give its location (*below* or *above* if it is on the same page; otherwise give the page number on which it appears).

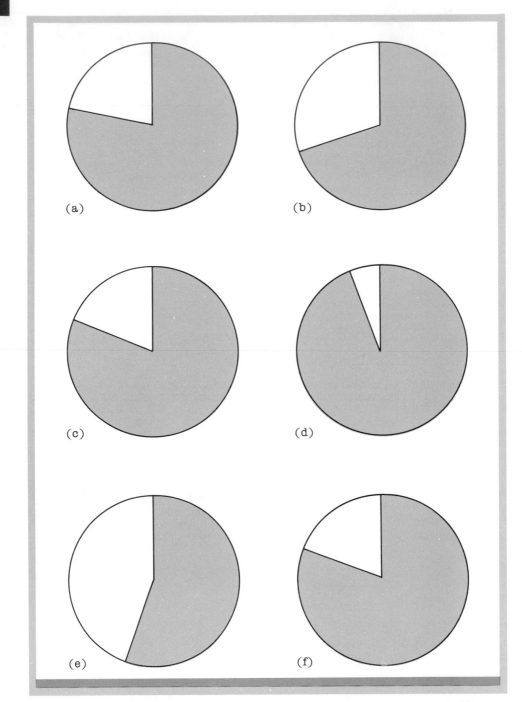

Figure 14-26. Tinted areas represent pecentages for grade "C" or better. (a) Overall: 1977–1978 to 1981–1982. (b) 1977–1978. (c) 1978–1979. (d) 1979–1980. (c) 1980–1981. (f) 1981–1982.

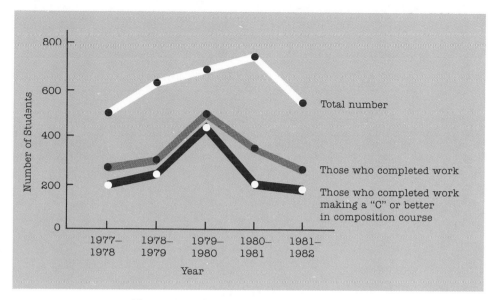

Figure 14-27. Students referred to Writing Laboratory.

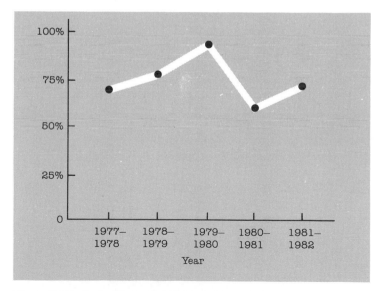

Figure 14-28. Percentage of students making "C" or better in composition classes.

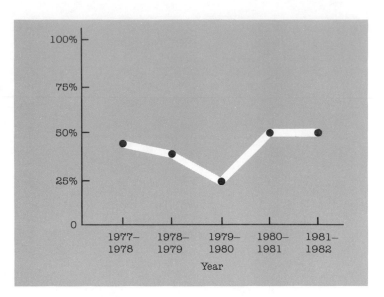

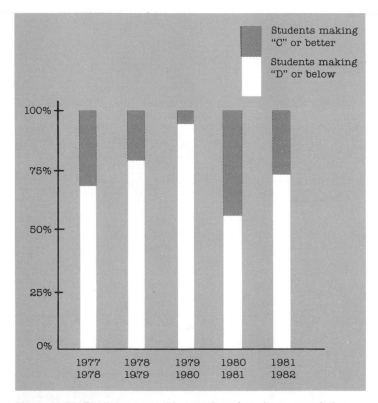

Figure 14-30. English composition grades of students completing Writing Laboratory.

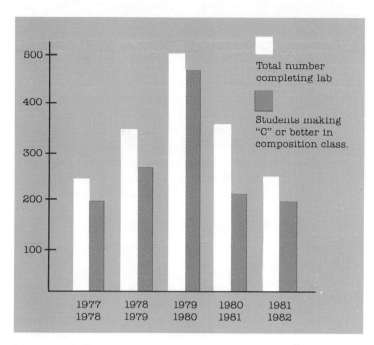

Figure 14-31. English composition grades of students completing Writing Laboratory.

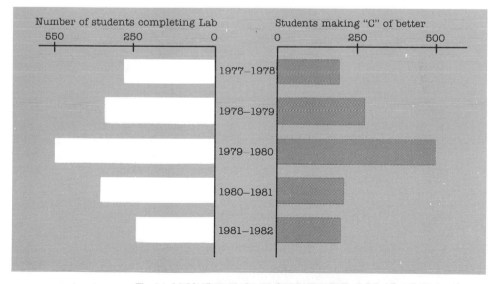

Figure 14-32. Comparison of grades and number of students completing Writing Laboratory.

Presentation

There are several ways of presenting visuals on the page. Figure 14-33 suggests some of them. Again, the placement of a visual depends on what is most appropriate to the context.

Discussion

Once you have presented a visual, direct the reader's attention to its key elements to make certain that the reader will understand its significance. If you are describing an object, refer the reader to certain details of the visual as you discuss them. This practice is especially desirable when you are describing the parts or subparts of an object and their relationships to each other and to the whole object. Label or number the details so the reader can locate them readily.

Technical Assignments

1. Using the data given in the following passages, construct support visuals.* What are some of the possible visuals that you might construct? Consider the various types of readers and indicate which visuals would be appropriate for each of the readers. Then, write a focus or summary sentence—a sentence that summarizes what you are looking for or what you want to show. Write two or three sentences indicating the significance of the data. In other words, interpret the data for the reader. (Of course, the length of this interpretative passage will vary from report to report as well as from support visual to support visual.)

   a. Researchers asked sixth graders at a selected school in Oklahoma how many hours of TV they watched on a normal school day. The girls reported the following: 1.8 percent indicated that they watched no TV; 6.3 percent said 1 hour; 14.9 percent, 2 hours; 18.9 percent, 3 hours; 17.1 percent, 4 hours; 15.8 percent, 5 hours; and 25 percent, 6 or more hours. The boys reported the following: 2 percent indicated that they watched no TV; 8 percent, 1 hour; 11 percent, 2 hours, 18 percent, 3 hours; 11 percent, 4 hours; 20 percent, 5 hours; and 30 percent, 6 or more hours.

   b. Researchers in the above study attempted to account for the way these students were spending their days. First, the researchers assumed that the students spent 6 hours watching TV (since 25 percent of the girls indicated that they watched 6 or more hours of TV on a normal school day and 30 percent of the boys indicated the same). They also assumed that the students had a regular 7-hour school day plus the students slept for at least 8 hours. The students still had to eat, study, play, participate in

---

*This exercise was developed by Dr. Sherry Southard, Oklahoma State University, based on data collected by Dr. Godfrey Ellis, Oklahoma State University, and is used with her permission.

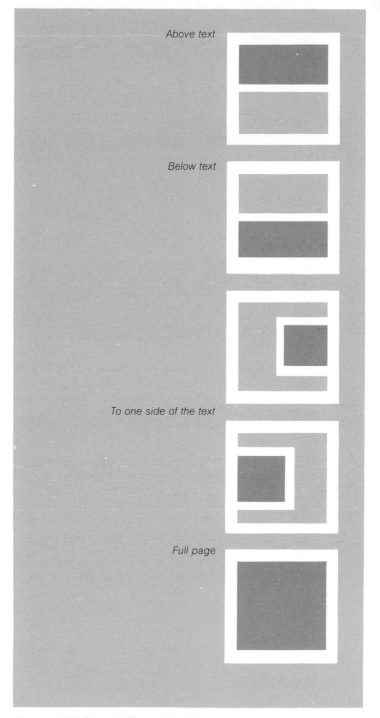

Figure 14-33. Presentation of graphics.

extracurricular activities, and go on outings with their families. Accept these assumptions.

c. The researchers were also concerned with which HBO movies the students were watching. The students reported the following: 73 percent of the girls and 77 percent of the boys had seen *Popeye* (PG rated); 48 percent (girls) and 56 percent (boys) saw *Blue Lagoon* (R rated); 19 percent and 37 percent saw *Altered States* (R rated); 19 percent and 36 percent saw *Hunter's Gold* (PG rated); 28 percent and 47 percent saw *Fort Apache, The Bronx* (R rated); 28 percent and 46 percent saw *Scanners* (R rated); and 58 percent and 80 percent saw *Black Hole* (PG rated).

d. Researchers asked the students if they had rules for watching TV. The students reported the following: 79 percent of the girls had "no" rules and 21 percent had "some"; 77 percent of the boys had "no" rules and 23 percent had "some."

2. Construct a pie chart showing how you spend a typical day during the term. Assign labels or percentages to the segments. Before beginning, decide how you will organize the chart. Will you

a. start the largest segment at 12:00 and move clockwise with decreasing segments?

b. reverse the order and start with the smallest?

c. organize chronologically by activity?

3. Prepare a pie chart showing how you spend your time when you are not in school (between terms, for example). Place this pie chart next to the first one. Write an introductory paragraph for each and another brief paragraph in which you comment on the two charts.

4. Select one of the line charts in this chapter (or from another textbook) and redraw it. Change the scale increments, the spacing, or both. Write a brief paragraph introducing and commenting on both the original graph and the redrawn graph. How have you shifted the emphasis and how have you reflected that changed emphasis in the paragraphs?

Appendix A

Documentation

To someone taking a course in English, "documentation" suggests footnotes and bibliographies. To someone in computer science, documentation suggests manuals of one sort or another. One word, two meanings. In a sense, both refer to the same process.

The *Oxford English Dictionary* tells us that "documentation" is "the action of documenting or fact of being documented." "To document" means "to prove or support (something) by documentary evidence," and "to provide with documents." A formal report is a document. Within the report, you provide verification of your evidence by means of footnotes and bibliographies.

In choosing the proper form for providing verification, consult an appropriate style manual. Style manuals are available for nearly all major disciplines, but despite their diversity, all style manuals have one characteristic in common: They are all collections of arbitrary decisions to ensure uniformity in writing for specialized groups. Each group has decided on a particular form for handling the details of documentation.

When you write a technical report, you must follow the prescriptions of the particular style manual that is preferred in your field. Ask your adviser or a professor in your major which manual you are to follow. (See also Howell, John Bruce. *Style Manuals of the English-Speaking World: A Guide.* Phoenix, Oryx Press, 1983.) If there is no manual specifically designed for your field, consult one of the following:

The Chicago Manual of Style

The Publication Manual of the American Psychological Association

Council of Biology Editors Style Manual

The following sections list various manuals and guides. Table A 1 demonstrates the styles for documentation of references indicated by selected manuals.

Style Manuals

Company Style Manuals

Clements, Wallace, and Robert G. Waite. *Guide for Beginning Technical Editors.* Livermore, CA: Lawrence Livermore Laboratory, 1979.

Information Management Division. *Technical Publication Style Guide.* Bartlesville: Phillips Petroleum Company, 1982. (Shorter version also available.)

Publication Department. *Guide to Style and Format.* Norman, OK: TOTCO, 1982.

Publication Service. *Writing/Editing Style Manual.* Ingalls Shipbuilding, 1981.

Sundstrand Style Guide: How to Use Language Effectively. Rockford, IL: Sundstrand Corporation.

Technical Documentation Department. *Editorial Style Guide*, 3rd ed. Whippany, NJ: Bell Laboratories, 1979.

General Style Manuals

Armed Forces Newspaper Editors' Guide. Washington, DC: Government Printing Office, n.d.

The Chicago Manual of Style, 13th ed. Chicago: University of Chicago Press, 1982.

Gray, Wood, et al. *Historian's Handbook: A Key to the Study and Writing of History*, 2nd ed. Boston: Houghton Mifflin, 1964.

McNaughton, Harry H. *Proofreading and Copyediting: A Practical Guide for the 1970s.* New York: Hastings House, 1973.

Miller, Bobby Ray, comp., ed. *The UPI Stylebook: A Handbook for Writers and Editors.* New York: United Press International, 1977.

Seeber, Edward D. *A Style Manual for Authors.* Bloomington: Indiana University Press, 1965.

Skillin, Marjorie, et al. *Words into Type*, 3rd ed. Englewood Cliffs, NJ: Prentice-Hall, 1974.

Winkler, G. P., comp., ed. *The Associated Press Stylebook*, rev. ed. New York: The Associated Press, 1970.

The York Press Style Manual. Frederickton, N.B., Canada: The York Press, 1978.

Specialized Style Manuals

Blackadar, R. G., et al. *Guide to Authors—A Guide for the Preparation of Geological Maps and Reports.* Ottawa: Geological Survey of Canada, 1980.

Council of Biology Editors Style Manual, 5th ed. Bethesda, MD: American Institute of Biological Sciences, 1983.

Handbook and Style Manual for ASA, CSSA, and SSSA Publications. Madison, WI: American Society of Agronomy, et al., 1976.

Handbook for Authors of Papers in American Chemical Society
 Publications. Washington, DC: American Chemical Society, 1978.

Publications Manual of the American Psychological Association,
 3rd ed. Washington, DC: American Psychological Association,
 1983.

Office Management, Department of the Army. Preparing
 Correspondence. Washington, DC: Headquarters, Department of
 the Army, AR 340-15, 1979.

Bishop, Elna E., et al. Suggestions to Authors of The Reports of
 United States Geological Survey, 6th ed. Washington, DC: U.S.
 Government Printing Office, 1978.

U.S. Government Printing Office Style Manual. Washington, DC: U.S.
 Government Printing Office, 1973.

**Miscellaneous
Style Guides**

The following journals offer style guides or authors' guides:

American Biology Teacher

Adult Education

Publications of the American Chemical Society

Publications of the American Institute of Physics

The American Journal of Clinical Nutrition

Publications of the American Society of Automotive Engineers

The Bulletin of the American Association of Petroleum Geologists

Cereal Chemistry

Chemical Engineering

Community College Review

Engineering Education

Geology

Home Economics Research Journal

IEEE Transactions

Journal of Animal Science

Journal of Chemical Education

Journal of Dairy Science

Journal of Food Science

Journal of Home Economics

Journal of Mammalogy

Journal of Marketing Research

The Journal of Nutrition

Journal of Popular Culture

Journal of Solar Energy Engineering

Journal of Teacher Education

Journal of Wildlife Management

Publications of the Oklahoma Cooperative Wildlife Research Unit

Publications of the Society of Petroleum Engineers of the American
Institute of Mechanical Engineers

Teaching Exceptional Children

Sage Publications

Wildlife Society Bulletin

Supporting Your Data

The very act of putting thoughts into words is a form of documentation. Reporting data that you have collected in the field or in a laboratory or in a library is documentation. In every case, the purpose of documentation is to help your reader to understand the report.

One way to enhance understanding is to inform your reader of the sources of the information you are presenting. Readers are unlikely to accept your recommendations unless you support them with convincing evidence. In demonstrating the evidence on which you base your conclusions, you may use

information developed by logical analysis.

information developed by observation.

information developed by combining analysis with observation.

information derived from authoritative sources.

Each source must be documented:

Source	*Documentation*
Analysis	Notes
Observation	Lab or field notebooks
Analysis plus observation	Notes, outlines, drafts
Authoritative sources	Notes

To enable your reader to evaluate and verify the evidence you present, you may explain the methods you used to gather your data and suggest why those methods are most suitable to the task at hand. Or you may indicate the sources of the data you have collected from authoritative treatments of the subject. The more explicit you are in specifying sources, the more efficiently the reader will be able to evaluate your evidence and understand how you reached your conclusions.

To document methods and procedures, use the approaches we described in our discussion of description (see Chapter 9). Identifying the reader's need for information and

Table A-1. Reference Material in Selected Style Manuals

Style Manual Short Title*	See Pages	Notes in Text (method)	Listing at End	Content Footnotes	Exceptions
ASA, CSSA, SSSA	43–44, 45–50	Numbered (parenthetical) preferred; author/year OK	Number; literature cited (all referenced in text); arrange alphabetically	Avoid; names, addresses only	
CBE (5th ed.)	26–27, 49–65	Author/date; number but list alphabetically; if no system recommended, use author/date	Literature cited; references cited	For explanatory material	
ACS	72–78	Number or author/date	Numerical order or alphabetical	Avoid; names, addresses only, special symbols	See individualized journals (73–74)
Chicago (13th ed.)	399–510	Author/date (400–408); end notes (408–410); footnotes (410–416); unnumbered (416–417), Ch. 17	Reference lists and bibliographies; bibliography form: two styles	See 407–408	See 455
Geology (6th ed.)	45, 71–81	Parenthetical: Author, date, page(s)	"References Cited" or "References" if cited; Selected Bibliography or Selected References if not cited; "Bibliography" if exhaustive	Avoid when possible	See 76–78
GPO (1973 edition)	227–228	Superscript number; start new each page	Varies		

*See the list of style manuals on pp. 284–286 for full titles.

(Continued on page 288)

Table A-1 (continued)

Style Manual Short Title	See Pages	Notes in Text (method)	Listing at End	Content Footnotes	Exceptions
APA (3rd ed.)	105–133	Author/date	Reference list of articles actually used	See 105–106	See Table 17 (118–133)
Words into Type (3rd ed.)	22–32, 37–43	Superscript number	Bibliography of works cited and supplemental works	Special symbols	Special symbols (23)
Bell (style guide for Bell System journals)	102–112	Superscript number; if few, then at bottom; if many, collect under "References"	Bibliography	Special symbols	Books: 103–104; patents, speeches, letters, reports: 108–109
Ingalls	4–1 to 4–8	If few, then bottom of page; if many, collect under "References" at end, number and refer to "Reference number, p. ___" in text	"Bibliography" if not cited in text; "References" if cited in text	Superscript; put at bottom of page	Document references: 4–1 to 4–3; references to material: 4–3; others: 4–4
Livermore	22–26	Either superscript or date	No heading; if superscript, in numerical order and footnote style; if author/date, alphabetical and bibliographic style	Use symbols and not numbers	Use of "(See Ref. 2)": 22

helping the reader to understand that information will help you decide what documentation to include in your methods and procedures section. Remember that your initial reader may not be your primary reader. Use the primary reader's need to know as a guide in deciding how much detail to include.

To document the sources of material taken from other sources, consult an appropriate style manual for guidance on the proper sequence of items and on acceptable punctuation and format.

What to Include

The Chicago Manual of Style (13th ed.) mentions four types of documentation customarily used within the body of a report:

1. Author/date footnotes, used mainly in the sciences.
2. Endnotes (also called backnotes).
3. Traditional footnotes, used mainly in the humanities.
4. Unnumbered notes and notes reflecting line or page numbers.

In preparing reports for course work in college, the style you select depends on your instructor's preferences, the discipline you are working in, and your assumed reader. When you prepare reports on the job, the style you use will depend on the conventions prescribed in the style manual issued by the organization you are working for.

The Chicago Manual lists the following items that are traditionally included in references to books and periodicals:

Books

Author: Name of individual or group of individuals, editor or editors, or institution that wrote the book.

Title: Full title and, if appropriate, subtitle.

Series: If part of a series, the series title and volume or number in the series.

Volume: Volume number or total number of volumes if a multivolume work.

Edition: The number of the edition for editions beyond the first edition.

Publication: City of publication and publisher's name (optional).

Date: Date of publication.

Articles

Author: Name of individual or individuals who wrote the article.

Title: Full title and, if appropriate, subtitle.

Periodical: Name of periodical.

Volume: Volume number and issue number (optional).

Date: Date of publication of periodical.

Pages: Starting and ending page numbers.

Style manuals differ on what should be included in an entry and on how to present the information. The differences are mainly on the use of abbreviations, punctuation marks, capitalization, and italics. Become familiar with the style preferred in your discipline.

Samples of Documentation

The sample entries that follow are based on the most commonly used style manuals: *The Chicago Manual**, 13th ed.; the *Publication Manual of the American Psychological Association,* 3rd ed. (APA); the *Council of Biology Editors Style Manual,* 5th ed. (CBE); and the *Handbook for Authors of Papers in American Chemical Society Publications,* 1978 edition (ACS).

Books

Single author:

Chicago   Bernstein, T. M. 1965. *The careful writer: A modern guide to English usage.* New York: Atheneum.

APA   Bernstein, T. M. (1965). *The careful writer: A modern guide to English usage.* New York: Atheneum.

CBE   Bernstein, T. M. The careful writer: a modern guide to English usage. New York: Atheneum; 1965.

ACS   Bernstein, T. M. "The Careful Writer: A Modern Guide to English Usage"; Atheneum: New York, 1965.

Two authors:

Chicago   Morris, W., and M. Morris. 1975. *Harper dictionary of contemporary usage.* New York: Harper & Row.

APA   Morris, W., & Morris, M. (1975). *Harper dictionary of contemporary usage.* New York: Harper & Row.

For *Chicago Manual* examples, I have used the choice favored for authors in the natural and social sciences (see p. 439).

CBE   Morris, W.; Morris, M. Harper dictionary of
               contemporary usage. New York: Harper & Row;
               1975.

ACS   Morris, W.; Morris, M. "Harper Dictionary of
               Contemporary Usage"; Harper & Row: New
               York, 1975.

More than two authors:

Chicago, APA, CBE, and ACA all require that every
author's name be given.

Editor (no author named on title page):

Chicago   Lewis, Norman, ed. 1961. *The new Roget's
                 thesaurus in dictionary form.* Garden City, NY:
                 Garden City Books.

APA   Lewis, N. (Ed.). (1961). *The new Roget's
                 thesaurus in dictionary form.* Garden City, NY:
                 Garden City Books.

CBE   Lewis, N., editor. The new Roget's thesaurus in
                 dictionary form. Garden City, NY: Garden City
                 Books; 1961.

ACS   Lewis, N., Ed. "The New Roget's Thesaurus in
                 Dictionary Form"; Garden City Books: Garden
                 City, NY, 1961.

Editor (author named on title page):

Chicago   Follett, Wilson. 1966. *Modern American usage:
                 A guide.* Ed. Jacques Barzun. New York: Hill &
                 Wang.

APA   Follett, W. (1966). *Modern American usage: A
                 guide* (J. Barzun, Ed.). New York: Hill & Wang.

CBE   Follett, W. Modern American usage: a guide.
                 Barzun, J., ed. New York: Hill & Wang; 1966.

ACS   Follett, W. "Modern American Usage: A Guide";
                 Barzun, J., Ed.; Hill & Wang: New York, 1966.

Chapter or essay in book or collection:

Chicago   Zuboff, A. 1981. The story of a brain. In *The
                 mind's I: Fantasies and reflections on self and
                 soul*, ed. D. R. Hofstadter and D. C. Dennett,
                 202–212. New York: Basic Books.

APA   Zuboff, A. The story of a brain. Hofstadter,
                 D. R.; Dennett, D. C. eds. The mind's I: fantasies

mind's I: Fantasies and reflections on self and soul (pp. 202–212). New York: Basic Books.

CBE   Zuboff, A. The story of a brain. Hofstadter, D. R.; Dennett, D. C. eds. The mind's I: fantasies and reflections on self and soul. New York: Basic Books; 1981: 202–212.

ACS   Zuboff, A. In "The Mind's I: Fantasies and Reflections on Self and Soul"; Basic Books: New York, 1981; 202–212.

Edition:

Chicago   Fowler, H. W. 1965. *A dictionary of modern English usage.* 2d ed., ed. E. Gowers. New York: Oxford University Press.

APA   Fowler, H. W. (1965). *A dictionary of modern English usage* (2nd ed. E. Gowers, Ed.). New York: Oxford University Press.

CBE   Fowler, H. W. A dictionary of modern English usage. 2d ed. Gowers, E., ed. New York: Oxford University Press; 1965.

ACS   Fowler, H. W. "A dictionary of modern English usage," 2d ed.; Gowers, E., Ed.; Oxford University Press: New York, 1965.

Journal Articles

Normally, journal titles are abbreviated. Some manuals (such as APA) require the full title. Refer to the appropriate style manual and journals for acceptable abbreviations.

Single author:

Chicago   deBeaugrande, Robert. 1982. Cognitive processes and technical writing: Developmental foundations. *Journal of Technical Writing and Communication* 12:121–45.

APA   deBeaugrande, R. (1982). Cognitive processes and technical writing: Developmental foundations. *Journal of Technical Writing and Communication 12*, 121–145.

CBE   deBeaugrande, R. Cognitive processes and technical writing: developmental foundations. J. Tech. Writing and Comm. 12:121–145; 1982.

ACS   DeBeaugrande, R. *J. Tech. Writing and Comm.* **1982,** 12, 121–45.

Two authors:

Chicago   Fodor, J. A., and M. Garrett. 1967. Some syntactic determinants of sentential complexity. *Perception & Psychophysics* 2:289–96.

APA   Fodor, J. A., & Garrett, M. (1967). Some syntactic determinants of sentential complexity. *Perception & Psychophysics, 2,* 289–296.

CBE   Fodor, J. A.; Garrett, M. Some syntactic determinants of sentential complexity. Perception & Psychophysics. 2:289–296; 1967.

ACS   Fodor, J. A.; Garrett, M. *Perception & Psychophysics* **1967,** 2, 289–96.

More than two authors:

Chicago   Burgoon, M., L. Fraedrich, and S. Bachman. 1979. Credibility of communicators and distraction as predictors of change in attitude. *Psychological Reports* 45:479–82.

APA   Burgoon, M., Fraedrich, L., & Bachman, S. (1979). Credibility of communicators and distraction as predictors of change in attitude. *Psychological Reports, 45,* 479–482.

CBE   Burgoon, M.; Fraedrich, L.; Bachman, S. Credibility of communicators and distraction as predictors of change in attitude. Psychological Rpts. 45:479–482; 1979.

ACS   Burgoon, M.; Fraedrich, L.; Bachman, S. *Psychological Reports* **1979,** 45, 479–82.

Other Material

Not all the style manuals give instructions for listing government documents, interviews, letters, and reports. The samples that follow are from those manuals that do give instructions. (See also Tables A-2 and A-3.)

Government documents, Congress:

Chicago   U.S. Congress. Senate. Committee on Foreign Relations. *The Mutual Security Act of 1956.* 84th Cong., 2d sess. 1956. S. Rept. 2273.

NOTES FOR ABOVE ENTRY:

Author: Name of the House or Senate committee.

Title: Full title including any dates within the title.

Table A-2. Additional Forms: Books

Form	Chicago	APA	CBE	ACS
All volumes of multivolume work	449 (see also 399, 437–438)	125, 126, 127 (see also 118–119)	60	
Abstracts		122, 123		77
Audiovisual				
Filmstrips			62	
Motion pictures	482	132	62	
Slides	482		62	
Sound recording	481–482	132		
Video recordings	482		62	
Author as publisher		124, 129	60	
Better known by title			60	
Books in preparation	460, 467	126, 131	60	
Conference proceedings	452	129–130	61–62	
Computer programs	482–483	133		
Corporate author	435	124, 128, 129	59, 61	
Interview	468	(published) 132		
Government	470–475	128	61	
Miscellaneous				
Catalog			64	
Chart			63	
Map			63	
Newspaper articles			63	
Not published but accepted	466	121	60	77
Patents	460	126	63	77

Date: The date is in two parts: (1) Number of Congress (either with or without -th or -d such as 84th or 83d). Congress is abbreviated "Cong." Either 1st or 2nd session. Session is abbreviated "sess." (2) Year of

Table A-3. Additional Forms: Journal Articles

Form	Chicago	APA	CBE	ACS
Abstract	(see also 399, 437–438)	122, 123 (see also 118–119)		76
Article from another journal		123	58	
Article in more than one issue	464		58	76
Article in press		121		77
Article on magnetic tape		133	58–59	
Author affiliation			57	
Corporate author	435	121	56–57	
Foreign-language journals	465–467	123	57	76
No author		121	57	
No page numbers			58	
No title in reference	464	131, 132		
No volume number	465	121		
Nonconsecutive pages		121	58	
Possible confusion of journal	464–465		58	
Published in two places	464			
Single page			57	
Special volume number		(supplement) 122	58	
Title first			57	
Whole issue of journal		121	58	
Reprint	453	127	60	
Reviews		132		

Table A-3 (continued)

Form	Chicago	APA	CBE	ACS
Submitted and not yet accepted		131		77
Technical Reports	454–455	127–129	61	
Translation	465	127	60	
Unpublished				
Dissertation/thesis	467	130–131	64	77
Document/manuscript	469–470	127–129		
	475–476	131	64	
Letters	468	110	64	78
Paper	467	131	64	77
Supplemental material	467–468		65	

publication, which may be different from the date given in the title.

Publisher: The publisher is assumed to be the Government Printing Office. Give the report number rather than name the Government Printing Office. "S." is the abbreviation for Senate, and "Rept." for Report. In the case of a Committee Print or other unnumbered report, giving the type of the report or the document, and the date should be adequate to locate it.

Government documents, author specified:

Chicago   Donnelly, Warren H., and Barbara Rather. *International Proliferation of Nuclear Technology*. Report prepared for the Subcommittee on Energy and the Environment of the House Committee on Interior and Insular Affairs. 94th Cong., 2d sess., 1976. Committee Print 15.

Alternative citation:
U.S. Congress. House Committee on Interior and Insular Affairs. Subcommittee on Energy and the Environment. *International Proliferation of Nuclear Technology*. Report prepared by Warren H. Donnelly and Barbara Rather. 94th Cong., 2d sess., 1976. Committee Print 15.

DOCUMENTATION

APA — Donnelly, W. H., & Rather, B. (1976). *International proliferation of nuclear technology* (Committee Print 15). Washington, DC: Subcommittee on Energy and the Environment of the House Committee on Interior and Insular Affairs.

CBE — Donnelly, W. H.; Rather, B. International proliferation of nuclear technology. Washington, DC: U.S. Congress, House of Representatives, Committee on Interior and Insular Affairs, Subcommittee on Energy and the Environment; 1976; Committee Print No. 15.

ACS — Donnelly, W. H.; Rather, B. Washington, DC, 1976, House Committee on Interior and Insular Affairs, Subcommittee on Energy and the Environment, Committee Print 15.

Department report:

Chicago — National Institute of Mental Health. Center for Studies of Crime and Delinquency. 1971. *Community-based correctional programs.* Public Health Service Publication no. 2130.

APA — National Institute of Mental Health (1971). *Community-based correctional programs.* (Public Health Service Publication No. 2130). Washington, DC: U.S. Government Printing Office.

CBE — National Institute of Mental Health. Community-based correctional programs. Public Health Service Pub. No. 2130; 1971.

ACS — "Community-Based Correctional Programs." *Public Health Ser. Pub.* 1971, No. 2130.

State government document:

Chicago — Illinois Institute for Environmental Quality (IIEQ). 1977. *Review and synopsis of public participation regarding sulfur dioxide and particulate emissions.* By Sidney M. Marder. IIEQ Document No. 71/21. Chicago.

APA — Marder, S. M. (1977). *Review and synopsis of public participation regarding sulfur dioxide and particulate emissions* (IIEQ Document No. 71/21). Chicago: Illinois Institute for Environmental Quality.

| CBE | Marder, S. Review and synopsis of public participation regarding sulfur dioxide and particulate emissions. Chicago: Illinois Institute for Environmental Quality; 1977; IIEQ Document No. 71/21. |
| ACS | Marder, S. Chicago, 1977, Illinois Institute for Environmental Quality (IIEQ) Document No. 71/21. |

Computer programs:

| *Chicago* | International Mathematical Subroutine Library Edition 8 (IMSL 8). Houston, Tex.; International Mathematical Subroutine Library, Inc. NOTE: Use abbreviations only after giving full name for first reference or when using an easily recognized abbreviation or acronym such as FORTRAN, BASIC, COBOL. Always identify by "version, level, or release number, or the date." Identify "the city and name of the person, company, or organization having the proprietary rights to the software" (p. 483). |
| APA | *International Mathematical Subroutine Library* edition 8 (IMSL 8) [Computer program]. Houston, TX: International Mathematical Subroutine Library, Inc. |

Documentation Assignment*

1. Find an appropriate style manual for your field.
   a. Write a bibliographic citation for the style manual using the style recommended by the manual. If the manual recommends use of endnotes or footnotes, rewrite the citation in the footnote style recommended by the manual. Use proper indentation, punctuation, and capitalization. Describe the differences between the footnote or endnote style and the bibliographic citation style if the style manual shows both.
   b. What form is recommended for giving the source of information that is not original? Include the method of citation (footnotes, references, parenthetical citations, and so on), the placement of references (bottom of page, end), and the title given to the reference list (References, Literature Cited, Notes) in your answer. Are footnote numbers or reference numbers to be used? How are they written and where are they placed? Are page numbers to be included in parenthetical citations? Write down any

*This exercise was developed by Elizabeth Schitoskey and is used with her permission.

additional information that you will need to know when documenting sources of information in papers that you write.

c. Photocopy the pages where examples of bibliographic entries (and footnote citations if appropriate) are provided for the following: a book with a single author; a journal article with two or more authors; an interview; any other type of source that you suspect you may be using.

d. Copy the rules for handling numbers within the text of a paper (the rules that tell you when to write out a number and when to use a numeral). You may photocopy these rules or summarize them. Summarize the rules for handling abbreviations.

2. Locate a copy of a professional journal in your field.

a. Select an article in the journal. Write a bibliographic citation for the article using the style recommended by your manual. Does the journal use the same style? If not, rewrite the citation in the style used by the journal.

b. Does the form used to give credit to previously published sources differ from the form recommended by your manual? How?

c. Does the journal provide a page with instructions for authors? Where is it located? Does the journal have its own style manual that you can write for? Is there a charge for this? Does the journal recommend a particular style manual?

d. Is the journal's handling of numbers and abbreviations within the text consistent with the rules in your manual?

Sources About Sources

Bell, Marion V., and Eleanor A. Swidan. *Reference Books: A Brief Guide*, 8th ed. Baltimore, MD: Enoch Pratt Free Library, 1978.

Herner, Saul. *A Brief Guide to Sources of Scientific and Technical Information*, 2nd ed. Arlington, VA: Information Resources Press, 1980.

O'Brien, Robert, and Joanne Soderman, eds. *The Basic Guide to Research Sources*. New York: The New American Library, 1975.

Sheehy, Eugene P. *Guide to Reference Books*, 9th ed. Chicago: American Library Association, 1976.

Todd, Alden. *Finding Facts Fast: How to Find Out What You Want to Know Immediately*. New York: William Morrow & Company, 1972.

Ulrich's International Periodicals Directory, biennial (with quarterly supplement). New York: R. R. Bowker.

Computer Data Bases

Computer-Readable Data Bases

Directory of Data Bases in the Social and Behavioral Sciences

Directory of On-Line Information Sources

Agriculture

Computer Data Bases

AGRICOLA

Bibliographic Retrieval Service

Indexes

Agriculture Index

Agricultural Engineering Index

The American Statistics Index

Bibliography of Agriculture

Biological and Agricultural Index

Current Contents (Agriculture, Biology, and Environmental Science)

Index to Scientific Reviews

Abstracts

Dairy Science Abstracts

Fertilizer Abstracts

Food and Agricultural Chemistry

World Agricultural Economics Abstracts

Biology

Computer Data Bases

ASCATOPICS

Bibliographic Retrieval Service

Biosis

Indexes

Biological and Agricultural Index

Current Contents (Agriculture, Biology, and Environmental Science)

Current Contents (Life Sciences)

Excerpta Medica (Index and Abstracts)

Index to Scientific Reviews

Science Citation Index

Wildlife Review

Abstracts

Bioengineering Abstracts

Biological Abstracts

Biological Abstracts/RRM

Chemical-Biological Activities

International Abstracts of Biological Sciences

Nutrition Abstracts and Reviews

Business

Computer Data Bases

ABT/IMFORM

ASI Accountant's Index

Bibliographic Retrieval Service

DIALOG

International Economic Abstracts and *U.S. Statistical Abstracts*

Indexes

Accounting Index

Accountant's Index

The American Statistics Index

Business Periodicals Index

F. and S. Index

Index to Accounting and Auditing Pronouncements

Index to Economic Articles
Public Affairs Index
Public Affairs Information Service

Abstracts
Accounting and Data Processing Abstracts
Economic Abstracts
Journal of Economic Abstracts
Marketing and Distribution Abstracts
Personnel and Training Abstracts
Top Management Abstracts
Work Study and O & M Abstracts

Chemistry

Computer Data Bases
CA CONDENSATES/CASIA
Bibliographic Retrieval Service

Indexes
ACS Single Article Announcement
Applied Science and Technology Index
ASCATOPICS
CA Search
Central Patents Index
Chemical Abstracts Services Source Index (has quarterly
    supplements)
Chemical Substructure Index
Chemical Titles
Current Contents (Physical and Chemical Sciences)
IFI/Plenum Data Company
Index Chemicus Registry System
Science Citation Index

Abstracts
Analytical Abstracts
Chemical Abstracts
Chemical-Biological Activities
Chemical Industry Notes
Current Abstracts of Chemistry and Index Chemics
Ecology and Environment
Energy
Food and Agricultural Chemistry
Gas Chromatography Literature—Abstracts and Index
Materials

Polymer Science and Technology
PROMT
World Technology: Patent Licensing Gazette

Computer Science

Computer Data Base
Bibliographic Retrieval Service

Indexes
Applied Science and Technology Index
British Technical Index
Computer and Control Index
Current Contents (Engineering, Technology, and Applied Sciences)
Engineering Index
Quarterly Bibliography of Computers and Data Processing

Abstracts
Computer and Information Systems Abstracts Journal
Information Science Abstracts
Science Abstracts (Section C)

Engineering

Computer Data Bases
Bibliographic Retrieval Service
Compendex
DIALOG
ISMEC

Indexes
Alloys Index
Applied Science and Technology Index
ASCATOPICS
British Technology Index
Current Contents (Engineering, Technology, and Applied Sciences)
The Energy Index
The Engineering Index (and *Annual*)
Environment Index
Index of Engineering Mechanics
Index to Scientific Reviews
An Index to U.S. Voluntary Engineering Standards
INIS Automindex
Pandex
Robotics Index
Science Citation Index
NASA/SCAM

Abstracts

Abstracts of Biomedical Engineering
Applied Mechanics Review
ASCO Publications Abstracts
Bioengineering Abstracts
Ceramic Abstracts
Computer and Control Abstracts
Electrical and Electronics Abstracts
Electronics and Communications Abstracts Journal
Energy Abstracts
Energy Information Abstracts
Environment Abstracts
International Aerospace Abstracts
Mechanical Sciences Abstracts
Metals Abstracts
Nuclear Magnetic Resonance Literature—Abstracts and Index
Pollution Abstracts
Safety Science Abstracts Journal
Science Abstracts (Section B)
World Technology: Patent Licensing Gazette

Physics

Computer Data Base
SPIN

Indexes
Current Physics Index
Science Citation Index

Abstracts
Gas Chromatography Literature—Abstracts and Index
Geophysical Abstracts
Physics Abstracts
Science Abstracts (Section A)
Science Research Abstracts Journal
Solid State Abstracts Journal

Science

Computer Data Bases
Current Research Information System
DIALOG
ENVIROLINE
GEO-REF
INSPECT

Pollution
SCISEARCH

Indexes
The American Statistics Index
Applied Science and Technology Index
ASCA
ASCATOPICS
Conference Papers Index
Current Contents
Excerpta Medica
General Science Index
Government Reports Announcements and Index
Index Medicas
Index to Scientific Reviews
Mathematical Reviews
Smithsonian Science Information Exchange

Abstracts
Abstracts of North American Geology
Air Pollution Abstracts
Energy Research Abstracts
Metals Abstracts
Meteorological and Geophysical Abstracts
Minerological Abstracts
NTISEARCH
Oceanic Abstracts
Selected Water Resources Abstracts

Social Science

Computer Data Bases
DIALOG
SCD Search Service

Indexes
Current Contents (Social and Behavioral Science)
The American Statistics Index
ASCATOPICS
Social Sciences Citation Index
Social Sciences Index
Sociological Abstracts

Abstracts
Child Development Abstracts and Bibliography
Psychological Abstracts
Social Science Abstracts

Appendix C

Selected Bibliography

Graphics

Allen, Arby. *Steps Toward Better Scientific Illustrations*, 2nd ed. Lawrence, KS: Allen Press, Inc., 1977.

Enrick, Norbert Lloyd. *Effective Graphics*. Princeton, NJ: Auerbach, 1972.

Fry, Edward B. *Graphical Comprehension: How to Read and Make Graphics*. Providence, RI: Jamestown Publishers, 1981.

Hanks, Kurt, and Larry Belliston. *Rapid Viz: A New Method for the Rapid Visualization of Ideas*. Los Altos, CA: William Kaufmann, Inc., 1980.

Lefferts, Robert. *How to Prepare Charts and Graphs for Effective Reports*. New York: Barnes & Noble Books, 1981.

MacGregor, A. J. *Graphics Simplified: How to Plan and Prepare Effective Charts, Graphs, Illustrations, and Other Visual Aids*. Toronto: University of Toronto Press, 1979.

McKim, Robert H. *Experiences in Visual Thinking*, 2nd ed. Monterey, CA: Brooks/Cole Publishing Company, 1980.

Handbooks

Technical Writing

Bingham, Earl G. *Pockethook for Technical and Professional Writers*. Belmont, CA: Wadsworth Publishing Company, 1982.

Brusaw, Charles T., et al. *Handbook of Technical Writing*, 2nd ed. New York: St. Martin's Press, 1982.

Grammar

Crews, Frederick. *The Random House Handbook*, 3rd ed. New York: Random House, 1980.

Guth, Hans P. *New English Handbook*. Belmont, CA: Wadsworth Publishing Company, 1982.

Hodges, John C., and Mary E. Whitten. *Harbrace College Handbook*, 9th ed. New York: Harcourt Brace Jovanovich, 1983.

Pixton, William H. *Some Conventions of Standard Written English*, 3rd ed. Dubuque, IA: Kendall/Hunt, 1982.

Watkins, Floyd C., William B. Dillingham, and Edwin T. Martin. *Practical English Handbook*, 5th ed. Boston: Houghton Mifflin Company, 1978.

Oral Presentations

Frank, Ted, and David Ray. *Basic Business and Professional Speech Communication.* Englewood Cliffs, NJ: Prentice-Hall, Inc., 1979.

Manko, Howard H. *Effective Technical Speeches and Sessions: A Guide for Speakers and Program Chairmen.* New York: McGraw-Hill Book Company, 1969.

Tacey, William S. *Business and Professional Speaking,* 2nd ed. Dubuque, IA: Wm. C. Brown Company Publishers, 1975.

Timm, Paul R. *Functional Business Presentations: Getting Across.* Englewood Cliffs, NJ: Prentice-Hall, Inc., 1981.

Proposals

Green, Gary. *A Proposal Writing Primer.* Manhattan, KS: Kansas State University, 1978.

Hall, Mary. *Developing Skills in Proposal Writing,* 2nd ed. Portland, OR: Continuing Education Publication, 1977.

Hillman, Howard. *The Art of Winning Government Grants.* New York: The Vanguard Press, Inc., 1978.

Holtz, Herman, and Terry Schmidt. *The Winning Proposal: How to Write It.* New York: McGraw-Hill Book Company, 1981.

Masterman, Louis E. *The Applicant's Guide to Successful Grantsmanship.* Cape Girardeau, MO: Keene Publications, 1978.

Readings

Anderson, W. Steve, and Don Richard Cox, eds. *The Technical Reader: Readings in Technical, Business, and Scientific Communication,* 2nd ed. New York: Holt, Rinehart and Winston, 1984.

Bowen, Mary Elizabeth, and Joseph A. Mazzeo, eds. *Writing About Science.* New York: Oxford University Press, 1979.

Effective Communication for Engineers. New York: McGraw-Hill Book Company, 1974.

Journet, Debra, and Julie Lepick Kling, eds. *Readings for Technical Writers.* Glenview, IL: Scott, Foresman and Company, 1984.

Leonard, David C., and Peter J. McGuire, eds. *Readings in Technical Writing.* New York: Macmillan Publishing Company, Inc., 1983.

Sparrow, W. Keats, and Donald H. Cunningham, eds. *The Practical Craft: Readings for Business and Technical Writing.* Boston: Houghton Mifflin, 1978.

Writing

Barzun, Jacques. *Simple and Direct: A Rhetoric for Writing.* New York: Harper & Row, 1976.

Barzun, Jacques, and Henry F. Graff. *The Modern Researcher,* 3rd ed. New York: Harcourt Brace Jovanovich, 1977.

Bernstein, Theodore M. *The Careful Writer: A Modern Guide to English Usage.* New York: Antheneum, 1965.

Flesch, Rudolf. *The Art of Readable Writing.* New York: Collier Books, 1949.

Gowers, Ernest. *The Complete Plain Words,* rev. by Bruce Fraser. Hammondsworth, Middlesex, England: Penguin Books, Ltd., 1973.

Graves, Robert, and Alan Hodge. *The Reader Over Your Shoulder: A Handbook for Writers of English Prose,* 2nd ed., rev., abridged. New York: Random House, 1971.

Kane, Thomas S. *The Oxford Guide to Writing: A Rhetoric and Handbook for College Students.* New York: Oxford University Press, 1983.

Trimble, John R. *Writing with Style: Conversations on the Art of Writing.* Englewood Cliffs, NJ: Prentice-Hall, Inc., 1975.

Williams, Joseph M. *Style: Ten Lessons in Clarity and Grace.* Glenview, IL: Scott, Foresman and Company, 1981.

Writing for Publication

Day, Robert A. *How to Write and Publish a Scientific Paper,* 2nd ed. Philadelphia: ISI Press, 1983.

DeBakey, Lois, ed. *The Scientific Journal: Editorial Policies and Practices: Guidelines for Editors, Reviewers, and Authors.* St. Louis: The C. V. Mosby Company, 1976.

Gastel, Barbara. *Presenting Science to the Public.* Philadelphia: ISI Press, 1983.

Hill, Mary, and Wendall Cochran. *Into Print: A Practical Guide to Writing, Illustrating, and Publishing.* Los Altos, CA: William Kaufmann, Inc., 1977.

Huth, Edward J. *How to Write and Publish Papers in the Medical Sciences.* Philadelphia: ISI Press, 1982.

Michaelson, Herbert B. *How to Write and Publish Engineering Papers and Reports.* Philadelphia: ISI Press, 1982.

Mitchell, John. *Writing for Professional and Technical Journals.* New York: John Wiley & Sons, Inc., 1968.

Usage

Evans, Bergan, and Cornelia Evans. *A Dictionary of Contemporary American Usage.* New York: Random House, 1957.

Follett, Wilson. *Modern American Usage: A Guide.* New York: Hill & Wang, 1966.

Fowler, H. W. *A Dictionary of Modern English Usage,* 2nd ed., rev. by Sir Ernest Gowers. New York: Oxford University Press, 1965.

Freeman, Morton S. *A Treasury for Word Lovers.* Philadelphia: ISI Press, 1983.

Morris, William, and Mary Morris. *Harper Dictionary of Contemporary Usage.* New York: Harper & Row, 1975.

Nicholson, Margaret. *A Dictionary of American-English Usage: Based on Fowler's Modern English Usage*. New York: Oxford University Press, 1957.

About Language and Usage

Creswell, Thomas J. *Usage in Dictionaries and Dictionaries of Usage*. Birmingham: University of Alabama, Publication of the American Dialect Society, 1975.

Mitchell, Richard. *The Graves of Academe*. Boston: Little, Brown and Company, 1981.

Mitchell, Richard. *Less Than Words Can Say*. Boston: Little, Brown and Company, 1979.

Quinn, Jim. *American Tongue and Cheek: A Populist Guide to Our Language*. New York: Pantheon Books, 1979.

Sample Student Report*

010 East Bennett
Stillwater, OK 74074
May 1, 1985

Dr. Thomas L. Warren
Classroom Building 001
Oklahoma State University
Stillwater, Oklahoma 74078

Dear Dr. Warren:

I submit the accompanying report entitled "Design of a Compound Reverted Gear Train" as the final assignment for English 3323, Technical Writing.

The report develops a method for designing a gear train for the engineer or technician in industry who may have a need for this particular type of gear train. I have discussed the geometrical arrangement of the gears, the calculations for obtaining the number of teeth and pitch radii, and the calculations for determining interference conditions.

I would like to express my gratitude to my consultant, Dr. A. H. Soni, for taking on the responsibility of helping me with this project.

Respectfully yours,

Mark D. Winters

Mark D. Winters

*Sample student report written by Mark Winters. Used by permission.

DESIGN OF A COMPOUND REVERTED GEAR TRAIN

A Technical Report

for

Dr. Thomas L. Warren

English 3323

by

Mark D. Winters

ABSTRACT

This report develops a simple method for designing a compound reverted gear train for various speed ratios. The report covers the geometrical arrangement of the gear train, the calculations for number of teeth and pitch radii, and calculations for interference.

May 1, 1985

Content Approved by:

_____

A. H. Soni

CONTENTS

LIST OF ILLUSTRATIONS

iii

GLOSSARY

Term	Meaning
Addendum (a)	measures radially outward the length of the tooth from the pitch point
Auxiliary angle (γ)	the pressure angle associated with each specific pair of mating gears
Base circle radius (Rb)	the radius of the circle from which the tooth profile begins
Diametral pitch (Pd)	an arbitrary number that relates the diameter of the pitch circle to the number of teeth by the relationship

$$Pd = \frac{N}{D}$$

Term	Meaning
Interval of contact (u)	the length of contact between two mating gears
Pitch radius (Rp)	the radius of the circle for equivalent rolling cylinders
Pressure angle (μ)	the angle between the line of action and the line normal to the center line of the two mated gears

ABOUT THIS REPORT

Engineers and technicians in industry often do not have the time or desire to wade through various methods to find a gear train to fit a given set of speed ratios. This report presents a simple method by which the engineer or technician can easily satisfy any speed ratio by means of a compound reverted gear train.

The report covers the geometrical arrangement of the gears, calculations involving number of teeth and pitch radii, and calculations for interference conditions. It includes a step-by-step procedure for a specific gear train with the speed ratios

$$+1.0, +.75, +.32, -.25, -0.1$$

This report focuses on the kinematic portion of the gear design and does not discuss other areas of the design such as material selection or gear manufacture.

I. GEOMETRICAL ARRANGEMENT OF THE GEAR TRAIN

The first task a designer must contend with in a gear train design is the geometrical arrangement. After deciding on the type of gear train to use, he is limited to the size and shape of the gear train as well as its performance characteristics. These characteristics include the rotation axis of the output relative to the input and the maximum and minimum speed ratios possible.

With the compound reverted gear train, the arrangement provides certain advantages not available using other gear trains. Primarily, a compound reverted gear train allows the output to be along the same axis as the input. This fact is important when considering all the gears, except small idler gears for reverse speeds that are located on two main parallel shafts. The arrangement saves on space and housing requirements.

Geometrical Description

In a compound reverted gear train, the two main parallel shafts support the gear train, and the torque from the driven shaft is the output that turns a cam or driveshaft.

Because these shafts are equidistant the sum of the radii of two mating gears is a constant, and this sum equals the distance between the two shafts. However, this relation does not hold true when an idler gear, mounted on another parallel shaft, is offset from the main shafts. The idler gear serves to reverse the direction of rotation of the output relative to the input. In this case, the gears mounted on the main shafts must not contact each other and the idler gear meshes with both.

1

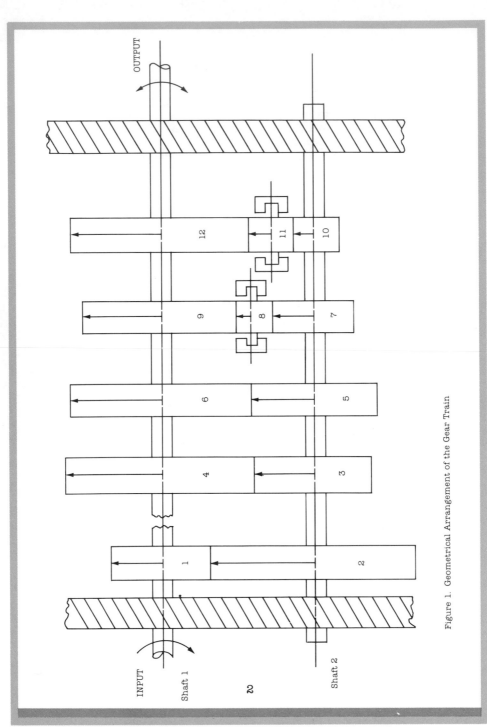

Figure 1. Geometrical Arrangement of the Gear Train

Figure 1, page 2, shows two main shafts. Shaft no. 1 contains the axis for the input and output. The gears on this shaft do not move; they are equally spaced and are wide enough for a gear to rotate between them. Gear 1 is the driver that receives the input torque. A jaw clutch separates it from the other gears on shaft no. 1.

Shaft no. 2 is the countershaft. The gears on this shaft mesh in and out with the gears on shaft no. 1 and the smaller idler gears. The idler gears are offset but parallel to the two main shafts. Because we are dealing with two reverse speeds, we have two idler gears that reverse the direction of the output and hence give us negative speed ratios.

Gear Train Operation

The gear train operates in a simple manner. In the configuration shown in Figure 1, page 2, the input is always through gear 1 and the output is along the same shaft.

A jaw clutch is between gears 1 and 4. The jaw elements comprise an external or internal gear or spline, each element having the same number of teeth. One member slides on a spline connection into and out of mesh with the other. Synchronizing clutches prevents clashing due to speed differences and usually consists of smaller friction clutches that engage through a detent mechanism prior to tooth engagement. In our case, releasing the main friction clutch accomplishes this action.

To obtain a speed ratio of $+1.0$, the jaw clutch is engaged and the input and output are equally matched. This arrangement is direct drive. For the remainder of the required speed ratios, the clutch is disengaged to allow gear reduction through shaft no. 2.

For a speed ratio of $+.75$, the main friction clutch is engaged, and gear 2, along the countershaft, meshes with gear 1. Also, gear 3 meshes with gear 4 so that the input and output are along the same axis. Similarly, for a speed ratio of $+.32$, gears 1, 2, 5, and 6 are in contact.

The reverse speed requires that an idler gear be in mesh with the two gears on the main shafts. This idler gear combines with the other two gears to help in the gear reduction and also reverses the direction of the output. For the $-.25$ speed ratio, gear 8 is the idler and meshes with gears 7 and 9. In a similar fashion, gear 11 is the idler for gears 10 and 12 for the speed ratio of -0.1.

The gear train provides the required speed ratios in the following manner. An angular input, w_1, is applied to gear 1 as shown in Figure 2, Simple Compound Reverted Gear Train, below. Gear 1 then imparts a rotation to gear 2 that is related by the equation $R_1 w_1 = R_2 w_2$, where R_1 and R_2 are the radii of the gears. Because gears 2 and 3 are mounted rigidly on the shafts, we have $w_2 = w_3$. For a

3

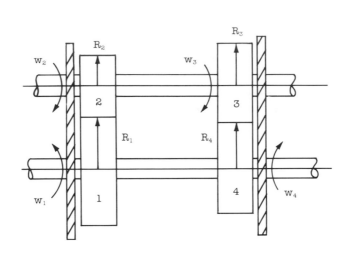

Figure 2. Simple Compound Reverted Gear Train

speed ratio of +.75, gears 3 and 4 are in mesh so that gear 3 drives gear 4. The speed ratio, S.R., is then

$$S.R. = \frac{w_4}{w_1} = \frac{output}{input} = \frac{R_1 R_3}{R_2 R_4}$$

This equation gives the speed of the output, gear 4, in relation to the input, gear 1. For example, in our case, the speed ratio is +.75, which means that gear 4 is rotating ¾ as fast as gear 1 in the same direction.

II. NUMBER OF TEETH AND PITCH RADII CALCULATIONS

In designing a gear train, the designer must have a process to determine the number of teeth for each gear to meet design criterion such as speed ratios and interference conditions. Likewise, determining the pitch radius is important in space and housing considerations and is directly related to the number of teeth.

Calculating Number of Teeth

The procedure for calculating the number of teeth for a compound reverted gear train is a trial-and-error method that results in satisfying all the required speed ratios. While it is easy to meet the criteria for a single speed ratio, the problem is compounded when one tries to meet all the speed ratios in a gear train simultaneously

4

because of the geometrical requirements of the compound reverted gear train, as we shall see later.

The first set of two gears must drive the second set and any gears that follow, so the choice of the first set of gears is critical. The teeth for each set of meshing gears should be relatively close to avoid any interference conditions between the two gears.

Also, the designer needs a tabulated handbook of gear ratios. Any large library should have several of these handbooks.

Procedure. First, choose, at random, a set of two numbers for the teeth of the first set of gears. These numbers should be between 12 and 120 to avoid interference.

As mentioned earlier, the unique geometry of the compound reverted gear train complicates the design process somewhat. As shown in Figure 2, page 4, the gears lie on parallel shafts so that $R_1 + R_2 = R_3 + R_4$, where R is the radius of the gear. Furthermore, the diametral pitches, which relate the number of teeth and the diameter of the gears, are constant for meshing gears. This relation yields $N_1 + N_2 = N_3 + N_4$, where N is the number of teeth per gear.

In our case, suppose we choose the first set of gears to have 46 and 102 teeth for gears 1 and 2, respectively. To obtain the speed ratio of +.75, the number of teeth for the second set of gears, 3 and 4, must equal 148 in addition to providing the required speed ratio.

At this point, the handbook of tabulated speed ratios is helpful. Because we want a speed ratio of +.75, we set up an equation using the ratio of the first set of gears

$$\frac{46}{102} \times M = .75$$

$$M = \frac{.75 \times 102}{46} = 1.66307$$

Next, we look up the nearest ratio to 1.66307 that also has a total number of teeth equal to 148. The book lists a fraction that represents the number of teeth for the second set of gears. In this case, the fraction is

$$R = \frac{92}{56} \text{ where } N_3 = 92 \text{ and } N_4 = 56.$$

Checking these values,

$$\text{S.R.} = \frac{N_1 N_3}{N_2 N_4} = \frac{46 \times 92}{102 \times 56} = .741$$

5

which is a 1.2% error and is acceptable.

The procedure is the same for the other forward speed ratio of +.32. However, we treat the reverse speed ratios in a slightly different manner.

Negative Speed Ratios. The gears on the two main shafts associated with the reverse speed ratios do not mesh. The offset idler gear meshes with these two gears. Therefore, the sum of the radii of these two gears is not a constant. The procedure for finding the number of teeth for these gears and the idler gears, however is generally the same.

The offset idler gear reverses the direction of the output gear so the equation for the speed ratio is the same as that for the forward speeds. In the case of the first negative speed ratio of $-.25$

$$ \text{S.R.} = \frac{N_1 N_7}{N_2 N_9} = .25 $$

We want to find the closest set of two gears that also satisfy the speed ratio and whose teeth numbers, added up, are strictly less than $N_1 + N_2$.

By looking in the handbook, we find these values to be $N_7 = 20$ and $N_9 = 36$. The number of teeth for the idler is arbitrary but should be close to the two gears that mesh with it. A good number for this gear would be $N_8 = 18$, which represents a gear that is smaller than the gear that drives it. We calculate the number of teeth for the other negative speed ratio in a similar manner.

The results of these calculations are listed in Table I, Number of Teeth and Pitch Radii, on page 7.

Calculating Pitch Radii

The pitch radii tell us the relative size of the gears and the distance between the two shafts. By relative size, I mean that the gears can be scaled up or down in any dimensions according to need. The speed ratios are true for any size of gear train.

The calculation for pitch radius is a simple process once we establish the number of teeth for each gear. The equation for the pitch radius is $Rp = \dfrac{N}{2Pd}$, where Pd is the diametral pitch.

Because the diametral pitch is constant for each set of meshing gears, only Rp is unknown. Using Pd = 16 for gears 1-6, Pd = 8 for gears 7-9, and Pd = 10 for gears 10-12, which are standard values, we easily find the pitch radii for the gears. These values are also tabulated in Table I on page 7. Appendix A gives intermediate calculations for number of teeth and pitch radii.

TABLE I. Number of Teeth and Pitch Radii

Gear	Number of Teeth	Pitch Radius
1	46	1.4375
2	102	3.1875
3	92	2.875
4	56	1.75
5	62	1.9375
6	86	2.6875
7	20	1.25
8	18	1.875
9	36	2.25
10	12	0.6
11	30	1.5
12	54	2.7

III. INTERFERENCE CONDITIONS

Preventing interference is a major criterion in designing any gear train. The teeth must mesh properly to prevent locking of the gears, reduce friction and wear, and provide smooth operation. The consequences of a poorly designed gear train with interference may be a burned-out motor or a broken shaft or gear.

Calculation Description

Determining interference conditions involves a somewhat more complicated procedure than teeth calculations.

The calculation for interference conditions is a step-by-step process. Intermediate calculations lead to a final value that determines whether interference exists. This value, called the contact ratio, Gc, should be between 1.5 and 2.0 to avoid interference. This value indicates that between one-and-a-half and two pairs of teeth are in contact at one time. These limits are important to ensure smooth rotary motion.

Obtaining the interference conditions involves the following parameters:

1. Pressure Angle, μ
2. Number of Teeth, N
3. Diametral Pitch, Pd
4. Addendum, a
5. Pitch Radii, Rp
6. Base Circle Radius, Rb
7. Auxiliary Angle, γ

7

8. Interval of Contact, u
9. Normal Pitch, Pn
10. Contact Ratio, Gc

Figure 3, Gear Tooth Geometry, shown below, illustrates how these parameters relate to the gear.

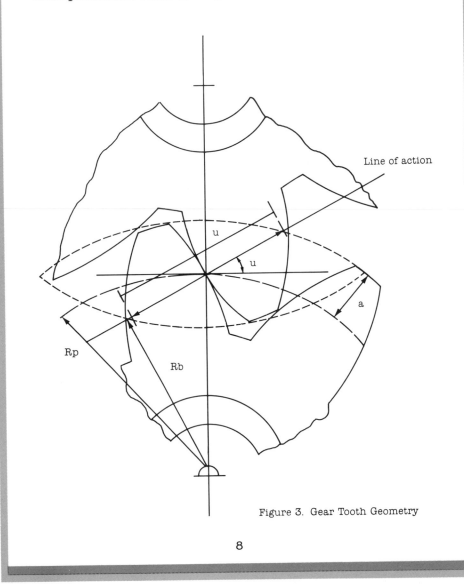

Figure 3. Gear Tooth Geometry

8

Example Calculation. The designer must calculate contact
ratios for all the mating gears, but calculations are similar for all
the gears. As an example, we will look at gears 1 and 2.

For a standard pressure angle of 20 degrees and teeth numbers
of 46 and 102, the calculations proceed as follows. Because we
previously indicated the diametral pitch is equal to 16 for gears 1
and 2, the addendum is easily obtained by,

$$a_1 = a_2 = \frac{1}{Pd} = \frac{1}{16} = .0625.$$

Also, from previous calculations,

$$Rp_1 = 1.4375 \qquad Rp_2 = 3.1875$$

Then, the base circle radius, Rb, is

$$Rb = Rp \cos \varnothing$$

With the pitch radii known and $\varnothing = 20$ degrees,

$$Rb_1 = 1.4375 \cos 20 = 1.351$$

$$Rb_2 = 3.1875 \cos 20 = 2.995$$

Next, we obtain the auxiliary angle, γ, with the equation,

$$\cos \gamma = \frac{Rb}{Rp + a}$$

which yields,

$$\cos \gamma_1 = \frac{1.351}{1.4375 + .0625} = .900667 \quad \gamma_1 = 25.75°$$

$$\cos \gamma_2 = \frac{2.995}{3.1875 + .0625} = .9216308 \quad \gamma_2 = 22.83°$$

Then, the interval of contact, u, is

$$u = (Rp + a)\sin\gamma - Rp \sin \varnothing$$

For gears 1 and 2,

$$u_1 = .160 \qquad u_2 = .171$$

The equation for normal pitch, Pn, is

$$Pn = \frac{\pi}{Pd} \cos \varnothing$$

$$= \frac{\pi}{16} \cos 20 = .1845$$

9

TABLE II. Calculated Values for Interference Conditions

Gear Pair	O	Pd	a	Rb_1	Rb_2	γ_1	γ_2	u_1	u_2	Pn	Gc
1/2	20	16	.0625	1.351	2.995	27.75	22.83	.160	.171	.1845	1.79
3/4	20	16	.0625	2.702	1.644	23.12	24.90	.170	.165	.1845	1.81
5/6	20	16	.0625	1.8207	2.525	24.45	23.34	.165	.170	.1845	1.82
7/8	20	8	.125	1.1746	1.7619	31.32	28.24	.287	.305	.3690	1.61
8/9	20	8	.125	1.7619	2.1143	27.10	27.097	.287	.313	.3690	1.67
10/11	20	10	.1	.5638	1.4095	36.35	28.24	.210	.244	.2952	1.53
11/12	20	10	.1	1.4095	2.537	28.24	25.02	.244	.261	.2952	1.71

Finally, we obtain the contact ratio, Gc, with the equation,

$$Gc = \frac{u_1 + u_2}{Pn}$$

$$= \frac{.160 + .171}{.1845} = 1.79$$

The value is well within the limits for proper meshing and negligible interference.

The remaining gears follow the same procedure. Table II tabulates the contact ratios as well as the intermediate values for all the gear pairs. Appendix B gives individual calculations.

If interference conditions do exist, the designer should look at the closeness between the numbers of teeth, the diametral pitch, and the pressure angle in that order.

SUMMARY

The compound reverted gear train is a special type of gear train in which the input and output are along the same axis. The gear train is useful when space is a factor or the requirements call for more than one speed ratio.

A step-by-step method for designing a compound reverted gear train involves the following:

1. Geometrical arrangement
2. Calculations for the number of teeth and pitch radii
3. Calculations for interference conditions

REFERENCES

Merritt, H. E. 1971. Gear Engineering. London: Pitman.

Page, Ray M. 1961. 14000 Gear Ratios. New York: Industrial Press Inc.

Soni, A. H. 1981. Mechanism Synthesis and Analysis. Malabar, FL: Krieger Publishing Co.

Souders, Mott. 1975. Handbook of Engineering Fundamentals. New York: John Wiley and Sons.

APPENDIX A
INTERMEDIATE CALCULATIONS FOR NUMBER
OF TEETH AND PITCH RADII

Number of teeth
*gears 5 and 6:

$$\frac{46}{102} \times M = .32 \qquad M = .709565$$

*gears 7, 8, and 9:

$$\frac{46}{102} \times M = .25 \qquad M = .55435$$

*gears 10, 11, and 12:

$$\frac{46}{102} \times M = 0.1 \qquad M = .2217$$

Pitch radii

Pd = 16	Pd = 8	Pd = 10
$Rp_1 = 46/32 = 1.4375$	$Rp_7 = 20/16 = 1.25$	$Rp_{10} = 12/20 = .6$
$Rp_2 = 102/32 = 3.1875$	$Rp_8 = 30/16 = 1.875$	$Rp_{11} = 30/20 = 1.5$
$Rp_3 = 92/32 = 2.875$	$Rp_9 = 36/16 = 2.25$	$Rp_{12} = 54/20 = 2.7$
$Rp_4 = 56/32 = 1.75$		
$Rp_5 = 62/32 = 1.9375$		
$Rp_6 = 86/32 = 2.6875$		

A1

APPENDIX B
INTERMEDIATE CALCULATIONS FOR INTERFERENCE CONDITIONS

*gears 3 and 4

$a = 1/16 = .0625$

$Rb_1 = 2.875 \cos 20 = 2.702$

$Rb_2 = 1.75 \cos 20 = 1.644$

$\gamma_1 = \cos^{-1} 2.702/2.9375 = 23.12°$

$\gamma_2 = \cos^{-1} 1.644/1.8125 = 24.90°$

$u_1 = 2.9375 \sin 23.12 - 2.875 \sin 20 = .17013$

$u_2 = 1.8125 \sin 24.90 - 1.750 \sin 20 = .16459$

$Gc = .33472/.1845 = 1.81$

*gears 5 and 6

$a = 1/16 = .0625$

$Rb_1 = 1.9375 \cos 20 = 1.8207$

$Rb_2 = 2.6875 \cos 20 = 2.525$

$\gamma_1 = \cos^{-1} 1.8207/2 = 24.45°$

$\gamma_2 = \cos^{-1} 2.525/2.75 = 23.34°$

$u_1 = 2 \sin 24.45 - 1.9375 \sin 20 = .16513$

$u_2 = 2.75 \sin 23.34 - 2.6875 \sin 20 = .17026$

$Gc = .33539/.1845 = 1.82$

*gears 7 and 8

$a = 1/8 = .125$

$Rb_1 = 1.25 \cos 20 = 1.1746$

$Rb_2 = 1.875 \cos 20 = 1.7619$

$\gamma_1 = \cos^{-1} 1.1746/1.375 = 31.32°$

$\gamma_2 = \cos^{-1} 1.7619/2 = 28.24°$

$u_1 = 1.375 \sin 31.32 - 1.25 \sin 20 = .2872$

$u_2 = 2 \sin 28.24 - 1.875 \sin 20 = .3051$

$Gc = .5923/.3690 = 1.61$

B1

*gears 8 and 9

$a = 1/8 = .125$

$Rb_1 = 1.7619$ from last calculation

$Rb_2 = 2.25 \cos 20 = 2.1143$

$\gamma_1 = 28.24$ from last calculation

$\gamma_2 = \cos^{-1} 2.1143/2.375 = 27.097°$

$u_1 = .3051$ from last calculation

$u_2 = 2.375 \sin 27.097 - 2.25 \sin 20 = .31227$

$Gc = .61737/.3690 = 1.67$

*gears 10 and 11

$a = 1/10 = .1$

$Rb_1 = .6 \cos 20 = .5638$

$Rb_2 = 1.5 \cos 20 = 1.4095$

$\gamma_1 = \cos^{-1} .5638/.7 = 36.35°$

$\gamma_2 = \cos^{-1} 1.4095/1.6 = 28.24°$

$u_1 = .7 \sin 36.35 - .6 \sin 20 = .20965$

$u_2 = 1.6 \sin 28.24 - 1.5 \sin 20 = .24404$

$Gc = .45369/.2952 = 1.53$

*gears 11 and 12

$a = 1/10 = .1$

$Rb_1 = 1.4095$ from last calculation

$Rb_2 = 2.7 \cos 20 = 2.537$

$\gamma_1 = 28.24°$ from last calculation

$\gamma_2 = \cos^{-1} 2.537/2.8 = 25.02°$

$u_1 = .24404$ from last calculation

$u_2 = 2.8 \sin 25.02 - 2.7 \sin 20 = .2609$

$Gc = .50497/.2952 = 1.71$

B2

Grammar and Mechanics

Throughout this book, I have urged you to help the reader read with understanding and comprehension. You may be clear, unambiguous, and succinct, and you may employ all the appropriate analytical and organizing techniques, and yet you may still produce a report, proposal, or letter that goes unread. Discordant elements in your writing will jolt your reader from the subconscious level of reading to the conscious level. I have already discussed the various ways to help your reader read on that subconscious level, but one element remains: the grammar and mechanics of your writing.

Readers generally expect a subject-verb-object sentence pattern, agreement between subjects and verbs, and unambiguous modifiers. They expect words to be spelled correctly and sentences to be punctuated according to standard practice. To disappoint those expectations will force your readers to guess at your meaning. A revised budget that contains errors in grammar or mechanics may erode your reader's confidence in your technical expertise. Effective communication ultimately rests on the credibility of your material.

Following is a brief discussion of the elements of grammar and mechanics. Where different style manuals suggest different practices, I have noted the variants. Always refer to the appropriate style manual on questions of grammar, usage, and mechanics. And always keep an up-to-date handbook of grammar, usage, and mechanics at hand, along with a dictionary and a thesaurus. Appendix C lists several recommended grammar and usage handbooks.

The Parts of Speech

Nouns are words that name persons, places, objects, or feelings. A noun functions as the subject or the object of a verb, as the object of a preposition, or as the modifier of other nouns. Most nouns fall into one of three classes: proper nouns, concrete nouns, and collective nouns.

Verbs are words that show or describe action or relationships, commenting, as it were, on the subject of the sentence. Some verbs require an object to complete their meaning (*transitive verbs*), some do not (*intransitive verbs*), and some simply link the subject to a complement (*linking verbs*).

Adjectives are words that qualify, describe, or limit nouns and pronouns. An adjective may consist of one word or a group of words (a phrase or a clause). Participles are verb forms that describe or limit. Adding *-er, -est, more*, or *most* to an adjective forms the comparative or the superlative.

Adverbs are words that qualify, describe, or limit verbs, adjectives, other adverbs, whole clauses, and even sentences. Adverbs may also join sentences or the independent clauses of a compound sentence (conjunctive adverbs). Many adverbs are formed by adding *-ly* to adjectives or participles.

Pronouns are words that replace nouns or word groups used as nouns and that convey the same meaning as the nouns they replace (their antecedents). Pronouns function in the same way as nouns. Most pronouns fall into one of eight groups: personal pronouns, possessive pronouns, relative pronouns, demonstrative pronouns, indefinite pronouns, reflexive pronouns, reciprocal pronouns, and interrogative pronouns.

Conjunctions are words that join word groups and establish relationships between them. Conjunctions are of several types: coordinating conjunctions, conjunctive adverbs, correlative conjunctions, and subordinating conjunctions.

Prepositions are words that introduce noun phrases, pronouns, or clauses and connect them to another part of the word group. The preposition plus its object (a word, phrase, or clause) usually functions as either an adjective or an adverb.

Interjections are words that convey emotion and usually have no grammatical function in a word group.

Sentences

The *subject* of a sentence is the word or words that normally stand before the verb and name the concept the sentence discusses (usually the actor/agent of the actions described by the active-voice verb). The *complete subject* of a sentence includes modifiers and any other words associated with the subject.

The *verb* in a sentence is the word or words that show action or events. Verbs indicate to the reader a point of view and time. An independent clause includes at least one stated or understood subject and one verb.

The *predicate* comprises the verb and its modifiers, including objects and complements. Each predicate contains at least one verb.

The *object* in a sentence is the word or words that receive the action described by the active-voice verb and that follow the verb. Objects follow transitive verbs. The object of an active-voice verb becomes the subject of a passive-voice verb. The object of a verb may be either indirect or direct, depending on whether it receives the action of the verb directly or indirectly. The *indirect object* normally precedes the *direct object*. Prepositions also take objects. Objects frequently answer "what" or "when" questions, whether they are direct objects, indirect objects, or the objects of prepositions.

A *complement* is the word or words in a sentence that follow a linking verb and that rename the subject (*predicate nominative*) or describe it (*predicate adjective*).

Modifiers are the word or words in a sentence that describe or limit the subject, the verb, the object/complement, or other modifiers. Modifiers function as adjectives or adverbs.

Types of Sentence

A *simple sentence* is a group of words that express a complete thought by means of a subject and a predicate. Either or both may contain more than one item:

> Frank received the assignment.
>
> Frank and Susan wrote the proposal.
>
> Frank and Susan wrote and proofread the proposal.
>
> Susan identified and drew the visuals.

A *compound sentence* is two groups of words (*independent clauses*), each of which contains a complete thought and can stand alone:

> Frank was responsible for writing the proposal, and Susan was responsible for collecting the data.

A *complex sentence* is a group of words containing at least two subgroups: (1) A group that cannot stand alone (the *dependent clause)* because its meaning depends on the second group, and (2) a group that can stand alone (the *independent clause*):

> While Frank wrote the proposal, Susan selected the visuals.

A *compound-complex sentence* is a group of words that combines a complex sentence and a compound sentence:

> While Frank wrote the proposal, Susan selected the visuals and Mary arranged for the typing.

Punctuation

Punctuation marks are visual elements that help the reader understand the meaning of a phrase, clause, sentence, or paragraph. There are four groups of punctuation marks:

1. *Ending marks:* period, question mark, exclamation point.
2. *Joining marks:* comma, semicolon, colon.
3. *Insertion marks:* dash, parentheses, brackets.
4. *Other marks:* quotation marks (double and single), hyphen, apostrophe, italics.

Ending Punctuation

Ending marks indicate the end of a word group that stands alone. They also tell the reader something about the meaning the word group is meant to convey.

The *period* ends a word group that asserts or declares something. In technical writing, most word groups end with a period. Periods are also used with abbreviations and as decimal points.

The *question mark* indicates that the word group raises an issue. Word groups ending in a question mark may raise questions the writer expects the reader to answer, or they may raise questions that the reader is not expected to answer (rhetorical questions).

The *exclamation point* gives a word group special emphasis. The exclamation point is rarely used in technical reports. Overuse of exclamation marks weakens the effect of a statement.

Joining Punctuation

Marks of joining punctuation indicate a continuation of relationships.

The *comma* signals that what follows continues what has come before. It indicates relationships by grouping or dividing word groups. The comma also indicates relationships between numbers (in thousands and millions, for example). As a general rule, use a comma when it will clarify meaning. Some uses of the comma are optional, however. Always consult an appropriate style manual or handbook when in doubt. Generally, commas are used to separate independent clauses and to set off such introductory word groups as dependent clauses and phrases that modify some part of the sentence. Commas are also used to set off a group of words within a sentence that is not essential to the meaning of the sentence.

The *semicolon* indicates the completeness of one word group that is associated with another word group. It may join two word groups that can stand alone but whose meanings are closely related. The semicolon may also separate word groups that have internal punctuation. In a compound sentence, the semicolon precedes the conjunctive adverb.

The *colon* indicates that what follows will provide additional information about what came before. That information is usually presented in list format. The colon indicates a lesser level of completeness than does a mark of ending punctuation. When used to introduce new material, the colon follows an independent clause. A colon follows the salutation in formal letters and separates hours from minutes when time is expressed in numerals.

Insertion Punctuation

Insertion marks are used to summarize information or to provide additional information about what came before. They are usually used in pairs.

The *dash* makes a dramatic interruption in the flow of the word group.

Parentheses set off explanatory material in a less dramatic way than dashes, but they are more formal than dashes. If the explanatory material set off by parentheses occurs within a sentence, it takes no ending punctuation. If it stands independently, however, it begins with a capital letter and takes appropriate ending punctuation.

Square *brackets* enclose material added by the writer in direct quotes or in documentation. They are also used to set off material inserted in a word group already set off by parentheses.

Other Marks of Punctuation

Certain other marks of punctuation group information and convey added meaning to a word group.

Quotation marks (both single and double) set off words that the writer is quoting from another source. Single quotation marks are used for a quotation within a quotation. Do not use quotation marks to indicate that you are using slang or nonstandard language. Using quotation marks for such purposes suggests that you are apologizing to the reader. In any case, avoid such usages in technical writing. Some style manuals recommend the use of quotation marks to indicate article titles and book titles. Punctuation normally goes inside the ending quotation mark (with the exception of colons and semicolons).

Hyphens join a group of words that, taken together, modify another word. They also indicate a break in a word at the end of a line, with the rest of the word carried over to the next line.

Refer to an appropriate style manual for other uses. For the use of hyphens in spelling, consult a current dictionary.

The *apostrophe* is used for the contracted form of two words or to show possession (exceptions are the possessive pronouns *his, hers, yours, its*, and *theirs*). Apostrophes also indicate the plural of a number, letter, or word referred to as such (such as "two l's," "three a's," and "five that's").

Italics (indicated in typing by underlining) indicate that a word or a word group has special meaning or significance. Letters or words referred to as such are italicized, as are the titles of magazines, journals, and books, according to some style manuals. Italics may be used to provide emphasis, but their overuse detracts from the effect.

Constructing Sentences

Sentences are word groups that stand alone. The construction of sentences follows certain well-defined rules. For example, a sentence must contain a subject (either stated or implied) and a verb. Hence, a sentence may be as short as one word ("Go!") or as long as several pages (see, for example, the final chapter of James Joyce's *Ulysses*). Adjust the length of your sentences to fit your reader's ability to comprehend the information you are presenting.

Subject-Verb Agreement

Subject and verb must agree in number and person. If the sentence has only one subject, the verb must reflect that single number. Ordinarily, an *-s* at the end of a verb means that it is singular, and the absence of the *-s* means that it is plural. Some subjects may seem to be singular but must be considered as plural because of the action suggested by the verb. *Audience*, for example, may be either singular (when the verb suggests that the audience is acting as a body) or plural (when the verb suggests that the members of the audience are acting individually):

The audience refuses to applaud.

Will the audience please return to their seats!

When the subject is separated from its verb by a modifier or modifiers, it may seem to be plural when it is really singular. Always refer to the number of the subject itself and ignore the modifiers:

The vice-president of the combined departments arrives tomorrow.

When the subject is a pronoun, the verb must conform to the person and the number of the pronoun.

Verb Tense

Verb tense presents a special problem in technical writing. How do you refer to work that was done in the past but that continues to be valid? Style manuals give different answers, but the traditional approach is suggested by the *Publication Manual of the American Psychological Association* (see Appendix A):

> *Literature review:* Past tense or present perfect tense.
>> *Example:* Researchers showed.
>>> Researchers have shown.
>
> *Procedure description:* Past tense or present perfect tense. (Note: Discussion must be of a past event.)
>> *Example:* The T-test was performed.
>>> The T-test has been performed.
>
> *Results:* Past tense to describe; present tense to discuss and draw a conclusion.
>> *Example:* The researchers performed the test.
>>> The data indicate success.

Always consult the appropriate style manual for your discipline. (Other discussions of verb tense appear in Edward J. Huth, *How to Write and Publish Papers in the Medical Sciences,* Philadelphia: I.S.I. Press, 1982, pp. 94–95, 98–99; and in Robert A. Day, *How to Write and Publish a Scientific Paper,* 2nd ed. Philadelphia: I.S.I. Press, 1983, pp. 142–143.)

Pronoun Antecedent

Because a pronoun substitutes for a noun (its *antecedent*), it must reflect the person and number of that noun. For person, you typically use some form of the third person (singular: *he, she,* or *it;* plural: *they*). When the antecedent is ambiguous, the reader must infer the meaning and may very well come up with the wrong meaning.

An especially troublesome pronoun antecedent problem arises when a sentence begins with *this.* The pronoun *this* may refer either to the last noun in the preceding sentence or to some action expressed by a verb in the preceding sentence.

> *Example:* Our loan officer met with the clients to discuss the default of their loans. This was difficult.
>
> *Revised:* . . . This meeting was difficult.

Whenever you begin a sentence with *this* (or *these*), follow it with a noun that answers "*This* what?" Follow the same rule when you use *this* or *these* within a sentence.

Two problems arise when you start a sentence with *there* followed by some form of the verb *to be:*

1. What number should you use for the verb *to be?* Should it be singular or plural?
2. To what does the *There* refer? Pronouns work by referring to something that came before—an antecedent. What is the antecedent for an initial *There?*

> *Example:* There is ample time to remove the dangerous part.
>
> *Revised:* We have ample time to remove the dangerous part.

Other Problems

Other errors in sentence construction include fragments, fused sentences, and dangling modifiers.

A *fragment* is a word group that lacks either a subject or a complete verb. In some forms of writing, the use of sentence fragments can be very effective. In technical writing, however, the writer uses complete sentences:

> *Error:* The results relating to the test patterns.
>
> *Corrected:* The results relate to the test patterns. *Or* The results relating to the test patterns were conclusive.

Fused sentences are word groups that can stand alone but have been improperly joined together. They throw the reader into utter confusion:

> *Error:* The results relate to the test patterns, they were conclusive.
>
> *Corrected:* The results relate to the test patterns; they were conclusive.

Dangling modifiers occur when the modifier (a single word or a word group) is attached to the wrong noun or pronoun. They often result from efforts to avoid using the active voice:

> *Error:* Showing how current moves, the flux flow is represented by arrows.
>
> *Corrected:* Showing how current moves, arrows represent the flux flow.

Linking Word Groups

There are several ways of joining two word groups that might otherwise stand alone:

1. Use a semicolon:
   The sales team sold all the items; the division made its quota.

2. Choose a coordinating conjunction that suggests the exact meaning you want to convey. Compare the different meanings of the following examples (note the punctuation):

   The sales team sold all the items, and the division made its quota.

   The sales team sold all the items, for the division made its quota.

   The sales team sold all the items, so the division made its quota.

3. Choose a conjunctive adverb that suggests the exact meaning you want to convey. Compare the different meanings of the following examples (note the punctuation):

   The sales team sold all the items; nevertheless, the division made its quota.

   The sales team sold all the items; however, the division made its quota.

   The sales team sold all the items; therefore, the division made its quota.

Joining Sentences

The reader derives meaning both from individual words and from groups of words. When a word appears in one place in a sentence, it means one thing; in another place, it may mean something else. The same is true of word groups. To indicate that one group is *more important* than another, you can give the reader a signal of that relationship. One way of doing so is to use a subordinating conjunction.

To show that two word groups are of *equal importance*, you can use a coordinating conjunction and make the structure of the second group parallel the structure of the first. Coordinating conjunctions indicate contrast, contradiction, antithesis, or purpose.

To make word groups parallel, structure them according to the same pattern. If the first group follows a subject-verb-object pattern, make the second group follow a subject-verb-object pattern:

John hit the ball. The outfielder caught the ball.

The ball was hit by John. The ball was caught by the outfielder.

The verbs in parallel structures should agree in tense, mood, and voice. In the first example, the verb *hit* is past tense, indicative mood, and active voice. So is the verb *caught*. In the second example both verbs are in the passive voice.

The content of the two groups in a parallel structure should be compatible. Ordinarily, the action suggested by the verb in the first word group will dictate the action suggested by the verb in the second group. For example, if a form of the verb *to be* is used in the first group, a form of *to be* should be used in the second group as well.